Glencoe

Literature

The Reader's Choice

Selection and Unit Assessments

British Literature

New York, New York   Columbus, Ohio   Chicago, Illinois   Peoria, Illinois   Woodland Hills, California

Grateful acknowledgment is given authors, publishers, photographers, museums, and agents for permission to reprint the following copyrighted material. Every effort has been made to determine copyright owners. In case of any omissions, the Publisher will be pleased to make suitable acknowledgment in future editions.

From *The Canterbury Tales*, by Geoffrey Chaucer, translated by Nevill Coghill. Reproduced with permission of Curtis Brown Ltd., London, on behalf of the Estate of Nevill Coghill. Copyright Nevill Coghill.

The McGraw-Hill Companies

Send all inquiries to:
Glencoe/McGraw-Hill
8787 Orion Place
Columbus, OH 43240-4027

ISBN-13: 978-0-07-876525-4
ISBN-10: 0-07-876525-0

Printed in the United States of America.

2 3 4 5 6 7 8 9 021 12 11 10 09 08 07

Table of Contents

Unit One The Anglo-Saxon Period and the Middle Ages (449-1485)

Part 1: The Epic Warrior

Part 2: The Power of Faith

Part 3: The World of Romance

Unit Two The English Renaissance (1485-1650)

Part 1: Humanists and Courtiers

Part 2: A Bard for the Ages

Name ______________________ Date ______________ Class __________

Open-Book Selection Test

Score

from *Beowulf* (page 24)

Recall and Interpret (66 points total; 6 points each)
Write the letter of the best answer.

_____ **1.** Before Beowulf arrives, the survivors of Grendel's attacks are those who
- **a.** feign sleep.
- **b.** show no fear.
- **c.** fight as a united group.
- **d.** leave the hall before nightfall.

_____ **2.** Lines 90–100 suggest that Beowulf is motivated to go to Denmark by
- **a.** love of adventure.
- **b.** the offer of a reward.
- **c.** hope of achieving fame.
- **d.** a desire to help the helpless.

_____ **3.** The watchman who sees Geatland is, at first,
- **a.** fearful.
- **b.** furious.
- **c.** suspicious.
- **d.** welcoming.

_____ **4.** When Grendel realizes Beowulf's strength, he tries to
- **a.** flee.
- **b.** find a weapon.
- **c.** plead for his life.
- **d.** call for assistance.

_____ **5.** Beowulf's men are of no help to him because
- **a.** they are asleep.
- **b.** they are bewitched.
- **c.** they are too frightened.
- **d.** their weapons are useless.

_____ **6.** Which of the following does Beowulf use to kill Grendel?
- **a.** magic
- **b.** his hands
- **c.** his sword
- **d.** Grendel's own claws

_____ **7.** During the battle with Grendel's mother, Beowulf is driven on mainly by a desire for
- **a.** glory.
- **b.** wealth.
- **c.** justice.
- **d.** revenge.

_____ **8.** Of the following, which is most responsible for saving Beowulf's life in the battle against Grendel's mother?
- **a.** his mail shirt
- **b.** his sword
- **c.** his strength
- **d.** his cunning

_____ **9.** Which of the following is the main reason that Beowulf cuts off Grendel's head?
- **a.** a desire for revenge
- **b.** a desire to have a trophy
- **c.** the need to prove his victory
- **d.** the need to guarantee Grendel's death

Open-Book Selection Test

(continued)

_____ **10.** The poem suggests that Beowulf's superiority or greatness is apparent to
a. only the Geats.
b. only the Danes.
c. only human beings.
d. all those who come into contact with him.

_____ **11.** Which of the following lines best foreshadow the outcome of the battle between Beowulf and Grendel?
a. lines 314–316 **c.** lines 364–367
b. lines 324–325 **d.** lines 374–377

Analyze and Evaluate (14 points)

12. Identify which scene (Beowulf vs. Grendel, Beowulf vs. Grendel's mother, Beowulf and his men vs. the Dragon) involves both internal and external conflict, and explain how both elements of conflict are present.

____

____

____

____

____

____

BIG IDEA Connect (20 points)
Use a separate sheet of paper to answer the following essay question.

13. Think about what Beowulf's words and deeds suggest about traditional Anglo-Saxon values. Then, in a paragraph or two, identify three of these values. Quote lines that support your choices, or explain what Beowulf says or does to demonstrate these values or to suggest their importance to the Anglo-Saxons.

Name ______________________ Date ______________ Class ________

Selection Test

Score

from *Beowulf* (page 24); from *Gilgamesh: The Death of Humbaba* (page 56); "The Battle of the Pelennor Fields" from *The Lord of the Rings: The Return of the King* (page 59); from *The Collected Beowulf* (page 62)

Recall and Interpret (50 points total; 5 points each)
Write the letter of the best answer.

_____ **1.** Which of the following prevents Gilgamesh from coming immediately to Enkidu's aid?
- **a.** horror
- **b.** pride
- **c.** magic
- **d.** injury

_____ **2.** Gilgamesh's advantage in the battle with Humbaba is due to Gilgamesh's
- **a.** intellect.
- **b.** weapon.
- **c.** greater strength.
- **d.** greater courage.

_____ **3.** At the end of the tale the mood is one of
- **a.** sorrow.
- **b.** suspense.
- **c.** celebration.
- **d.** contentment.

_____ **4.** In "The Battle of the Pelennor Fields," what is the Dark Lord's steed?
- **a.** a white horse
- **b.** a horse named Windfola
- **c.** a mysterious shadow
- **d.** a winged creature

_____ **5.** What happens to Merry when the Dark Lord appears?
- **a.** He is thrown from Windfola.
- **b.** He crouches down behind Théoden.
- **c.** He recognizes Éowyn.
- **d.** He tries to find his horse.

_____ **6.** How does Merry help Éowyn?
- **a.** He kills the Black Rider.
- **b.** He stabs the Black Rider.
- **c.** He gives Éowyn his shield.
- **d.** He brings reinforcements.

_____ **7.** Which of the following is the best example of the supernatural in the "The Battle of the Pelennor Fields"?
- **a.** Éowyn's physical strength
- **b.** Théoden's age
- **c.** Merry's behavior on the field
- **d.** the Dark Lord's disappearance

Name ______________________ Date ______________ Class ________

Selection Test (continued)

_____**8.** In *The Collected Beowulf*, which of the following does most to establish the setting?
- **a.** the 1910 translation of Beowulf
- **b.** the illustrations
- **c.** the colorful language
- **d.** the lack of modern superhero conventions

_____**9.** Which of the following illustrates "weeds of the warrior worthy"?
- **a.** a beard and mustache
- **b.** a suit of chain mail
- **c.** a strong handshake
- **d.** strength-giving plants

_____**10.** Why does Beowulf say, "no further for me need'st food prepare!"?
- **a.** He is setting off to kill Grendel.
- **b.** He won't need food if Grendel kills him
- **c.** He will not eat until he kills Grendel.
- **d.** Grendel has taken his appetite away.

Analyze and Evaluate (30 points total; 10 points each)
Indicate whether you think each character below is a major or a minor one. Then, in each box on the right, give two reasons that support your belief.

11. Théoden Major Character Minor Character	
12. the Dark Lord Major Character Minor Character	
13. Dernhelm Major Character Minor Character	

BIG IDEA Connect (20 points)
Use a separate sheet of paper to answer the following essay question.

14. Basing your answer on *Beowulf*, "The Death of Humbaba," "The Battle of the Pelennor Fields," and *The Collected Beowulf*, how do the authors' descriptions of the settings serve to distinguish the epic hero? Support your answer with examples from the selections.

Name ______________________ Date ______________ Class __________

Selection Test

Score

A Brief History of Heroes (page 69)

Recall and Interpret (40 points total; 4 points each)
Write the letter of the best answer.

_____ **1.** What is the main idea of "A Brief History of Heroes"?
- **a.** All heroes share certain qualities that make them heroic.
- **b.** Most of us have our own definition of heroism.
- **c.** Throughout history, heroes have stood out from the crowd.
- **d.** The idea of the hero has changed with the times.

_____ **2.** Which of these writers is credited with ushering in the new humanism in the fourteenth century?
- **a.** religious scholars
- **b.** Voltaire
- **c.** Petrarch
- **d.** Machiavelli

_____ **3.** Which of the following best describes the hero of the Renaissance?
- **a.** proficient in warfare, scholarship, government, and love
- **b.** skilled at sword-handling, hunting, riding, and politics
- **c.** learned in literature, history, religion, and art
- **d.** strong, handsome, larger than life, and noble

_____ **4.** What was the principal value of the eighteenth-century European Enlightenment?
- **a.** reason
- **b.** political astuteness
- **c.** virtue
- **d.** exploration

_____ **5.** What did the nineteenth-century age of Romanticism celebrate above all?
- **a.** creative development of the human spirit
- **b.** development of the human intellect
- **c.** military glory and national pride
- **d.** a sense of shared community and justice

_____ **6.** In Victorian times, what did Thomas Carlyle react against in defining a hero?
- **a.** the role of individual great men in history
- **b.** the growth of large British corporations
- **c.** the values of the middle class
- **d.** the Industrial Revolution

Name ______________________ Date ______________ Class __________

Selection Test *(continued)*

_____ **7.** Which of the following writers is NOT associated with the idea that every human being is intrinsically heroic?
- **a.** Samuel Smiles
- **b.** Thomas Carlyle
- **c.** Virginia Woolf
- **d.** Alexander Herzen

_____ **8.** Who was primarily responsible for the twentieth-century need to reject heroism?
- **a.** E. M. Forster
- **b.** Charles de Gaulle
- **c.** Winston Churchill
- **d.** Adolf Hitler

_____ **9.** What aspect of modern life often threatens to undermine true heroism, according to the author?
- **a.** national pride
- **b.** multiculturalism
- **c.** the cult of celebrity
- **d.** lack of moral values

_____ **10.** Which of the following does the author suggest is closest to the twenty-first-century hero?
- **a.** the Romantic hero
- **b.** the Renaissance man
- **c.** the Great Man
- **d.** the Quiet Hero

Analyze and Evaluate (40 points total; 2 points each)

11. Fill in the lettered boxes with the appropriate response. In some cases, the correct answer may be "Unimportant."

The Hero	Required Skill	Likely Occupation	Important Quality	Place in Society
Middle Ages	a.	b.	Physical Strength	c.
d.	e.	Soldier, lover, poet, etc.	f.	g.
Enlightenment	h.	i.	j.	Professional
Victorian	k.	Statesman	l.	m.
20th Century	Unimportant	n.	o.	p.
21st Century	q.	r.	s.	t.

BIG IDEA Connect (20 points)

Use a separate sheet of paper to answer the following essay question.

12. Compare either Beowulf or Éowyn to one of the heroes described in "A Brief History of Heroes." Describe their similarities and differences.

Name ______________________ Date ______________ Class __________

Open-Book Selection Test

Score

The Seafarer (page 75)

Recall and Interpret (60 points total; 6 points each)
Write the letter of the best answer.

_____ **1.** What is the main subject of the first 38 lines of the poem?
- **a.** the challenges and difficulties of life at sea
- **b.** the advantages of living the life of a seafarer
- **c.** the differences between seafarers and other people
- **d.** why God calls certain people to lead lives on the sea

_____ **2.** The speaker goes to sea because he
- **a.** fears life on land.
- **b.** must earn a living.
- **c.** finds the sea irresistible.
- **d.** sees no value in life on land.

_____ **3.** The speaker suggests that it is natural for seafarers who are about to embark on a journey to feel
- **a.** bold.
- **b.** afraid.
- **c.** wretched.
- **d.** rejected by God.

_____ **4.** Lines 65–68 make the point that earthly life is
- **a.** hard.
- **b.** pointless.
- **c.** temporary.
- **d.** challenging.

_____ **5.** What practice does the speaker mock in lines 96–102?
- **a.** mourning the dead
- **b.** praying for the dead
- **c.** burying the dead underground
- **d.** burying treasure with the dead

_____ **6.** Lines 102–110 emphasize God's
- **a.** love.
- **b.** power.
- **c.** mercy.
- **d.** forgiveness.

_____ **7.** Lines 109–117 could be summarized as being
- **a.** advice on how to live.
- **b.** a warning about death.
- **c.** a celebration of God's power.
- **d.** an account of the speaker's life.

_____ **8.** In line 119, the word home refers to
- **a.** a ship.
- **b.** heaven.
- **c.** family.
- **d.** an earthly shelter.

Name ______________________ Date ______________ Class __________

Open-Book Selection Test (continued)

_____ **9.** What does the speaker conclude is enduring and valuable?
- **a.** life itself
- **b.** the quest for glory
- **c.** the turning of the seasons
- **d.** the love of God and hope of heaven

_____ **10.** The rhythm in this poem involves four stressed syllables per line and
- **a.** half as many unstressed syllables.
- **b.** twice as many unstressed syllables.
- **c.** an equal number of unstressed syllables.
- **d.** a varying number of unstressed syllables.

Analyze and Evaluate (21 points total; 7 points each)

Select three details (phrase, image, word choice) from the poem that contribute to its somber, mournful mood, and explain what contribution each makes.

11.
12.
13.

BIG IDEA Connect (19 points)

Use a separate sheet of paper to answer the following essay question.

14. Summarize what you think the message of this poem is. Support your answer with details from the poem.

Name ______________________ Date ______________ Class ________

Selection Test

Score

from *The Ecclesiastical History of the English People* (page 85)

Recall and Interpret (56 points total; 7 points each)
Write the letter of the best answer.

_____**1.** The attitude of Edwin toward the opinions of his advisors is one of
- **a.** scorn.
- **b.** respect.
- **c.** boredom.
- **d.** wariness.

_____**2.** At first, Coifi, the chief of the priests, responds to the idea of adopting a new religion with
- **a.** sorrow.
- **c.** defiance.
- **c.** enthusiasm.
- **d.** astonishment.

_____**3.** The main problem that Coifi has with the old religion is that it
- **a.** isn't effective.
- **b.** isn't spiritually satisfying.
- **c.** isn't popular with the people.
- **d.** requires too much sacrifice of its followers.

_____**4.** In the analogy drawn by one of Edwin's men, the sparrow's flight represents
- **a.** Christians.
- **b.** Christianity.
- **c.** human life.
- **d.** human history.

_____**5.** What is the main reason that Edwin's advisors approve of the adoption of Christianity?
- **a.** It makes sense to them.
- **b.** It is what Edwin wants.
- **c.** It is something new and exciting.
- **d.** Their hearts have been filled with love for Jesus Christ.

_____**6.** Bede believes that Caedmon never wrote nonreligious verses because
- **a.** he had never heard any.
- **b.** he wasn't able to do so.
- **c.** he thought it would be a sin.
- **d.** there was no general interest in such verse.

_____**7.** Which of the following convinces the abbess and the learned men that Caedmon's gift truly is from God?
- **a.** Caedmon's word of honor
- **b.** the degree of Caedmon's faith
- **c.** the word of Caedmon's friends
- **d.** the poetry that Caedmon recites

Name ______________________ Date ______________ Class __________

Selection Test

(continued)

_____ **8.** According to Bede, how does the abbess feel upon discovering that God has given great ability to such a simple, uneducated man as Caedmon?

a. jealous
b. suspicious
c. outraged
d. delighted

Vocabulary Practice (12 points total; 3 points each)
Write the letter of the best answer.

_____ **9.** Something that you **aspire** to is a

a. goal. **b.** speech. **c.** stimulus.

_____ **10.** If you do something **diligently,** you

a. mess up. **b.** keep at it. **c.** finish quickly.

_____ **11.** Although **frivolous** activities may be fun, they are essentially

a. immoral. **b.** dangerous. **c.** unimportant.

_____ **12.** A teacher is likely to **expound** a

a. roll call.
b. difficult assignment.
c. disruptive student.

Analyze and Evaluate (12 points)
Given that "The Ecclesiastical History of the English People" is an historical narrative, what sort of details about the "miraculous changes" King Edwin and Caedmon undergo, details that might make these changes more accessible to the reader, are absent from the text?

13.

BIG IDEA Connect (20 points)
Use a separate sheet of paper to answer the following essay question.

14. Choose either of these excerpts and discuss how it qualifies as a history, whether it succeeds as a history, and why or why not.

Name ______________________ Date ______________ Class __________

Selection Test

Score

from *The Canterbury Tales:* from *The Prologue* (page 94)

Recall and Interpret (49 points total; 7 points each)
Write the letter of the best answer.

_____**1.** Near the beginning of "The Prologue," the narrator reveals that his main motivation for making the pilgrimage is
a. guilt.
b. loneliness.
c. religious devotion.
d. the desire for adventure.

_____**2.** In general, the attitude of the characters toward the pilgrimage is one of
a. dread.
b. boredom.
c. resentment.
d. enthusiasm.

_____**3.** When the narrator says of the Summoner, "You'd meet none better if you went to find one" (line 664), he is
a. being sarcastic.
b. exaggerating the truth.
c. trying to mislead the reader.
d. trying to be fair to the Summoner.

_____**4.** Which of the following pairs of characters does the narrator admire most?
a. the Prioress and the Cook
b. the Parson and the Knight
c. the Plowman and the Wife of Bath
d. the Merchant and the Sergeant at the Law

_____**5.** Of the following characters, which is portrayed as being dainty?
a. the Monk
b. the Pardoner
c. the Wife of Bath
d. the Oxford Cleric

_____**6.** To win the contest proposed by the host, a pilgrim must tell the story that is judged to be the
a. funniest.
b. most unusual.
c. most thrilling.
d. most pleasing and uplifting.

_____**7.** What does the host suggest as a prize for the best story?
a. a new horse for the ride home
b. a free night's lodging at the inn
c. a semi-cope made of worsted wool
d. a supper paid for by all the pilgrims

Name ______________________ Date ______________ Class __________

Selection Test

(continued)

Analyze and Evaluate (36 points total; 4 points each)
For each listed character, note a flaw, weakness, or vice and the line number or numbers where this information is revealed. Then check the appropriate column to show whether the narrator characterized each by giving a direct statement about them, by describing the character's actions, or by describing his or her appearance.

	Flaw, weakness, or vice	Line number(s)	Direct Statement	Character's actions	Character's appearance
8. Nun (Prioress)					
9. Monk					
10. Friar					
11. Franklin					
12. Skipper					
13. Doctor					
14. Miller					
15. Summoner					
16. Pardoner					

(Characterization technique(s) used)

BIG IDEA Connect (15 points)
Use a separate sheet of paper to answer the following essay question.

17. What do you think "The Prologue" reveals about Chaucer's attitude toward the clergy? Explain your answer.

Name ______________________ Date ______________ Class __________

Open-Book Selection Test

Score

from *The Canterbury Tales:* from *The Pardoner's Tale* (page 117)

Recall and Interpret (54 points total; 6 points each)
Write the letter of the best answer.

_____ **1.** The attitude of the tavern-knave toward Death is one of
- **a.** respect.
- **b.** loathing.
- **c.** superiority.
- **d.** unconcern.

_____ **2.** The tavern-knave claims that the best attitude to take toward Death is to
- **a.** scorn him.
- **b.** flee from him.
- **c.** search for him.
- **d.** be careful of him.

_____ **3.** At first, the attitude of the three rioters toward Death is one of
- **a.** respect.
- **b.** loathing.
- **c.** superiority.
- **d.** amusement.

_____ **4.** As the rioters go out on their search, their language is all of the following EXCEPT
- **a.** bold.
- **b.** profane.
- **c.** clever.
- **d.** boastful.

_____ **5.** Which of the following reflects the old man's attitude toward dying?
- **a.** terror
- **b.** hatred
- **c.** affection
- **d.** yearning

_____ **6.** The old man scolds the three rioters for their
- **a.** cruelty.
- **b.** disrespect.
- **c.** drunkenness.
- **d.** attitude toward Death.

_____ **7.** The three rioters believe that the old man is
- **a.** Death's spy.
- **b.** Death's enemy.
- **c.** Death in disguise.
- **d.** the ghost of a dead man.

_____ **8.** Which of the three rioters commit(s) murder?
- **a.** all of them
- **b.** none of them
- **c.** only the two who stay behind
- **d.** only the one who goes into town

_____ **9.** Death defeats the three rioters by appealing to their
- **a.** pride.
- **b.** greed.
- **c.** vanity.
- **d.** worst fears.

Name ______________________ Date ______________ Class __________

Open-Book Selection Test *(continued)*

Anzlyze and Evaluate (24 points total; 8 points each)
For each quotation, check one or more small boxes to identify the irony used in that passage. In each large box, explain why the passage is ironic.

10. They made their bargain, swore with appetite,
These three, to live and die for one another
As brother-born might swear to his born brother.
(lines 42–44)

☐ Verbal
☐ Situational
☐ Dramatic

11. It's clear that Fortune has bestowed this treasure
To let us live in jollity and pleasure.
Light come, light go! We'll spend it as we ought.
God's precious dignity! Who would have thought
This morning was to be our lucky day?
(lines 121–125)

☐ Verbal
☐ Situational
☐ Dramatic

12. "Now for a drink. Sit down and let's be merry,
For later on there'll be the corpse to bury."
(lines 227–228)

☐ Verbal
☐ Situational
☐ Dramatic

BIG IDEA Connect (22 points)
Use a separate sheet of paper to answer the following essay question.

13. Identify two morals of this tale and, in a paragraph or two, explain how these morals are conveyed to the reader.

Name ______________________ Date ______________ Class __________

Open-Book Selection Test

Score

from *The Wife of Bath's Tale* (page 125)

Recall and Interpret (35 points total; 5 points each)
Write the letter of the best answer.

_____**1.** After listening to the Wife of Bath, what does the Pardoner plan to do?
- **a.** wed a younger woman
- **b.** put off his marriage
- **c.** marry within the year
- **d.** cancel his marriage plans

_____**2.** What is the Wife of Bath's attitude toward the tale she is about to tell?
- **a.** grave
- **b.** moral
- **c.** pretentious
- **d.** humorous

_____**3.** Who does the Wife of Bath say has purged the fairies that lived in the time of King Arthur?
- **a.** the knights
- **b.** the friars
- **c.** women
- **d.** King Arthur

_____**4.** What is one of the Wife of Bath's opinions about women?
- **a.** Women cannot keep a secret.
- **b.** Women are easily led astray.
- **c.** Old women are ugly and rude.
- **d.** Women want wealth and treasure.

_____**5.** On their wedding night, the old woman questions the knight about
- **a.** his beliefs and values.
- **b.** his family background.
- **c.** why he married her.
- **d.** the cause of his unrest.

_____**6.** The old woman offers the knight a choice between
- **a.** poverty and wealth.
- **b.** learning and ignorance.
- **c.** beauty and faithfulness.
- **d.** good manners and good deeds.

_____**7.** In order to win his bride, what does the knight finally do?
- **a.** He vows to love the old woman despite everything.
- **b.** He chooses to make a pilgrimage to Canterbury.
- **c.** He cannot make a decision, so he asks the Queen to decide.
- **d.** He remembers the advice that saved his life and heeds it.

Name ______________________ Date ______________ Class __________

Open-Book Selection Test *(continued)*

Vocabulary Practice (25 points total; 5 points each)
Write the letter of the best answer.

_____ **8.** An adult might **reprove** you for
- **a.** making too much noise.
- **b.** doing your homework.
- **c.** playing a new game.

_____ **9.** A candidate who loses an election should **concede**
- **a.** plenty.
- **b.** office.
- **c.** defeat.

_____ **10.** Usually, a football crowd will **disperse**
- **a.** to find food.
- **b.** in the stadium.
- **c.** after a game.

_____ **11.** **Arrogance** is a quality demonstrated by the
- a. Pardoner.
- **b.** Wife of Bath.
- **c.** knight.

_____ **12.** Something that would **suffice** for lunch would be
- **a.** too much for dinner.
- **b.** enough to fill you up.
- **c.** too little for a snack.

Analyze and Evaluate (20 points)
Select several comic lines from "The Wife of Bath's Tale" and explain how they exemplify her sense of humor.

13.

BIG IDEA Connect (20 points)
Use a separate sheet of paper to answer the following essay question.

14. How does "The Wife of Bath's Tale" show her commitment to the church, despite her earthy view of marriage and life?

Name ____________________ Date ______________ Class __________

Selection Test

Score

The Roads Now Taken (page 142)

Recall and Interpret (50 points total; 5 points each)
Write the letter of the best answer.

_____ **1.** What is the main idea of "The Roads Now Taken"?
- **a.** Since the mid-1400s, pilgrimages have been in decline worldwide.
- **b.** Faith in Europe is nearly extinct; the Continent is post-Christian.
- **c.** People still make pilgrimages, but they take many forms.
- **d.** People in the 21st century no longer travel in groups.

_____ **2.** Why did the Benedictines build a tunnel in Canterbury Cathedral?
- **a.** to encourage pilgrims to visit the site
- **b.** to allow people to photograph the cathedral
- **c.** to reduce traffic in the rest of the church
- **d.** to expand the storage facilities in the church

_____ **3.** Which of the following does Chu use as an example of the companionship of a pilgrimage?
- **a.** the pilgrimage to Mecca
- **b.** contemplation of an English garden
- **c.** cycling trips
- **d.** Volksmarches

_____ **4.** In a secular age, how is the spiritual impulse likely to show itself, according to Chu?
- **a.** in a pilgrimage to a religious shrine
- **b.** in a mountain-climbing adventure
- **c.** in a trip to the supermarket
- **d.** in the desire to do well in school

_____ **5.** What does the author cite as an example of modern-day mass worship?
- **a.** television viewing
- **b.** a football game
- **c.** a bicycling trip
- **d.** driving an automobile

_____ **6.** The dean of Canterbury Cathedral sees a pilgrimage as something that
- **a.** contributes to self-understanding.
- **b.** helps others who are less fortunate.
- **c.** takes people to unfamiliar places.
- **d.** calls together people of different faiths.

_____ **7.** Which of the following would Chu NOT consider a pilgrimage?
- **a.** an afternoon nap
- **b.** an afternoon in a garden
- **c.** a trip to Gettysburg
- **d.** a shopping trip to Prada

Name ______________________ Date ______________ Class ________

Selection Test *(continued)*

_____ **8.** What does Chu use as an example of a pilgrimage that preserves generational bonds?
- **a.** shopping at an outlet mall in Montevarchi
- **b.** seeing Shakespeare at Stratford-upon-Avon
- **c.** visiting the battlefields of Europe
- **d.** taking a traditional summer vacation

_____ **9.** Chu concludes that most of today's pilgrimages are
- **a.** secular.
- **b.** motivational.
- **c.** commercial.
- **d.** communal.

_____ **10.** How does Chu support his conclusions about modern-day pilgrimages?
- **a.** by statistics from population surveys
- **b.** by quotations from other authors
- **c.** by citing Web sites of pilgrimage destinations
- **d.** by reviewing literature on the history of pilgrimages

Analyze and Evaluate (32 points total; 8 points each)

Shade in the bar graphs below to show how important you think each purpose was to the author in writing this article. Then give two reasons to explain why you rated each purpose as you did.

11. To inform	**12.** To explain	**13.** To persuade	**14.** To entertain
not important — very important	not important — very important	not important — very important	not important — very important

BIG IDEA Connect (18 points)

Use a separate sheet of paper to answer the following essay question.

15. According to Phil Cousineau, author of *The Art of Pilgrimage*, a pilgrimage holds up a mirror to what is sacred for the times. Using what you read in the selection, describe a pilgrimage of today, including at least three of the attributes that the author used to define a pilgrimage.

Name ______________________ Date ______________ Class __________

Selection Test

Score

from *The Book of Margery Kempe* (page 147)

Recall and Interpret (56 points total; 8 points each)
Write the letter of the best answer.

_____ **1.** Which of the following is the main reason that Kempe decides to confess her secret sin?
- **a.** She fears damnation as an unforgiven sinner.
- **b.** Her husband believes that doing so is for the best.
- **c.** She believes that doing so will return her to sanity.
- **d.** She believes that doing so will keep her infant safe.

_____ **2.** When Kempe tries to confess her secret sin to her priest, he
- **a.** ignores her.
- **b.** criticizes her.
- **c.** doesn't believe her.
- **d.** is too quick to forgive her.

_____ **3.** The devils that Kempe believes she saw during her illness gained power over her by
- **a.** abusing and scaring her.
- **b.** coaxing and begging her.
- **c.** tempting her with rewards.
- **d.** threatening the lives of her loved ones.

_____ **4.** Kempe reacts to her vision of Jesus Christ with
- **a.** fear.
- **b.** relief.
- **c.** disbelief.
- **d.** puzzlement.

_____ **5.** Kempe's attendants fear that she wants keys in order to
- **a.** escape from confinement.
- **b.** return to her household duties.
- **c.** give away food and other goods.
- **d.** obtain something harmful to her.

_____ **6.** When Kempe shows signs of recovering, her husband reacts to her with
- **a.** trust.
- **b.** disinterest.
- **c.** suspicion.
- **d.** deep worry.

_____ **7.** By the end of the selection, Kempe's secret sin is known only to
- **a.** herself.
- **b.** herself and the reader.
- **c.** herself and her priest.
- **d.** herself and her husband.

Name ______________________ Date ______________ Class ________

Selection Test

(continued)

Vocabulary Practice (15 points total; 3 points each)
Write the letter of the best answer.

_____ **8.** A person who **divulges** what he or she should not might be called a
a. thief. **b.** chicken. **c.** blabbermouth.

_____ **9.** Something that can be used to **restrain** a dog is a
a. leash. **b.** brush. **c.** ball.

_____ **10.** A person who exhibits **composure** seems to be
a. scared. **b.** relaxed. **c.** bewildered.

_____ **11.** If someone **slanders** you, the person makes a statement about you that is both harmful and
a. true. **b.** untrue. **c.** embarrassing.

_____ **12.** The **instigation** of a crime involves helping to
a. solve it. **b.** punish it. **c.** set it in motion.

Anzlyze and Evaluate (14 points total; 7 points each)
In each box on the left, identify one of Kempe's character traits. In each box on the right, explain how this excerpt from her autobiography reveals that character trait.

13. Character trait	
14. Character trait	

BIG IDEA Connect (15 points)
Use a separate sheet of paper to answer the following essay question.

15. In what ways does Kempe believe she, her priest, and the devil each contributed to her insanity? Support your answer.

Name ______________________ Date ______________ Class __________

Open-Book Selection Test

Score

from *Everyman* (page 155)

Recall and Interpret (56 points total; 7 points each)
Write the letter of the best answer.

_____ **1.** Which of the following lines from the play best states its main theme?
- **a.** "We have in the world so many a day / Be good friends in sport and play."
- **b.** "For it is said ever among / That money maketh all right that is wrong."
- **c.** "For he that will say, and nothing do, / Is not worthy with good company to go;"
- **d.** "For after death, amends may no man make / For then mercy and pity doth him forsake."

_____ **2.** In lines 22–37, what is established as God's main rival for Everyman's attention?
- **a.** Goods
- **b.** Beauty
- **c.** Fellowship
- **d.** Knowledge

_____ **3.** When Death first encounters Everyman, Everyman's response to him is one of
- **a.** relief.
- **b.** horror.
- **c.** surprise.
- **d.** acceptance.

_____ **4.** At first, Everyman tries to avoid doing as Death orders by
- **a.** running away.
- **b.** buying his way out.
- **c.** lying about who he is.
- **d.** seeking help from others.

_____ **5.** What does Death reveal in lines 118–120?
- **a.** the dangers of sin
- **b.** the finality of death
- **c.** the unpredictability of death
- **d.** the importance of good works

_____ **6.** Who argues that his or her presence on the journey would practically ensure Everyman's damnation?
- **a.** Goods
- **b.** Fellowship
- **c.** Knowledge
- **d.** Good Deeds

_____ **7.** What effect has Everyman's neglect had on Good Deeds?
- **a.** She is dead.
- **b.** She is confused.
- **c.** She has forgotten him.
- **d.** She has become weak.

_____ **8.** At Everyman's grave, what does Good Deeds seek for him?
- **a.** happiness
- **b.** forgiveness
- **c.** a quick death
- **d.** time to improve his record

Name ______________________ Date ______________ Class ________

Open-Book Selection Test

(continued)

Anzlyze and Evaluate (24 points total; 8 points each)
Think about what this allegory communicates about people and their lives. In the boxes below, note two lessons the play teaches about each concept listed.

What people should realize about . . .

9. Friends and Friendship	**10.** Possessions	**11.** Good Deeds

BIG IDEA Connect (20 points)
Use a separate sheet of paper to answer the following essay question.

12. Identify two moral lessons of this allegory—one lesson about death and the other about life. How are these lessons communicated to the audience?

Name ______________________ Date ______________ Class ________

Open-Book Selection Test

Score

from *Sir Gawain and the Green Knight* (page 174)

Recall and Interpret (40 points total; 5 points each)
Write the letter of the best answer.

_____ **1.** The initial reaction of Arthur and his knights to the Green Knight is one of
a. awe. **c.** fascination.
b. disgust. **d.** amusement.

_____ **2.** When Gawain explains why he, not Arthur, should be allowed to meet the Green Knight's challenge, his tone is one of
a. awe. **c.** affection.
b. modesty. **d.** amusement.

_____ **3.** Which of the following is demonstrated by both Gawain and the Green Knight during the feast in Arthur's castle?
a. daring **c.** cleverness
b. loyalty **d.** horsemanship

_____ **4.** Which of the following is Gawain's main motivation to seek out the Green Knight a year after their first meeting?
a. honor **c.** curiosity
b. revenge **d.** adventurousness

_____ **5.** The lady gives Gawain the green girdle in the hope that it will
a. give him courage.
b. keep him from harm.
c. tempt him to do wrong.
d. cause him to fall in love with her.

_____ **6.** Which of the following leads Gawain to lie about the green girdle?
a. love **c.** honor
b. guilt **d.** fearfulness

_____ **7.** Which of the following is the Green Knight most interested in testing?
a. his wife's virtue
b. his own physical abilities
c. the virtue of a knight of the Round Table
d. the physical abilities of a knight of the Round Table

_____ **8.** All of the following letter sounds help to create alliteration in lines 515–518 EXCEPT
a. c **c.** l
b. f **d.** t

Name ______________________ Date ______________ Class __________

Open-Book Selection Test *(continued)*

Vocabulary Practice (10 points total; 5 points each)

_____ **9.** A knight who is **intrepid** in battle is
a. sick. **b.** brave. **c.** reluctant.

_____ **10.** When the grieving people wept **copiously**, they wept
a. heavily. **b.** publicly. **c.** shamelessly.

Analyze and Evaluate (30 points total; 10 points each)
How does Sir Gawain demonstrate the archetypal knightly qualities below in his conflict with the Green Knight?

11. Courage
12. Humility
13. Loyalty

BIG IDEA Connect (20 points)
Use a separate sheet of paper to answer the following essay question.

14. How does Gawain feel about himself at the end of the selection, and why? How does the Green Knight feel about Gawain at the end of the selection, and why?

Name ______________________ Date ______________ Class __________

Selection Test

Score

from *A Distant Mirror* (page 193)

Recall and Interpret (50 points total; 5 points each)
Write the letter of the best answer.

_____ **1.** In contrast to medieval legends, Tuchman's article indicates that chivalry involved
- **a.** intellectual requirements.
- **b.** religious convictions.
- **c.** physical endurance.
- **d.** early upbringing.

_____ **2.** According to Tuchman, chivalry was an integration of the Church with the
- **a.** knights' values.
- **b.** stories of heroes.
- **c.** military powers.
- **d.** people's poverty.

_____ **3.** Tuchman's historical research suggests that the twelfth Century Church's construction of chivalry was
- **a.** ruthless.
- **b.** pragmatic.
- **c.** irresponsible.
- **d.** sympathetic.

_____ **4.** According to the article, the concept of chivalry was developed at the time of
- **a.** Sir Gawain and the Green Knight.
- **b.** Columbus's sailing to America.
- **c.** the Enlightenment.
- **d.** the great crusades.

_____ **5.** What was to be the intended result of courtly love on society?
- **a.** Society would be more joyous.
- **b.** Society would be more pious.
- **c.** Society would be less chaotic.
- **d.** Society would be less violent.

_____ **6.** As described by the biographer of Don Pero Niño, the knight's life was
- **a.** a state of deprivation.
- **b.** a series of love affairs.
- **c.** a miserable adventure.
- **d.** a dedication to God.

Name ______________________ Date ______________ Class __________

Selection Test *(continued)*

_____ **7.** According to Tuchman, fighting filled the nobleman's need to
- **a.** do something.
- **b.** serve the Church.
- **c.** create a just society.
- **d.** develop a nation.

_____ **8.** Which knightly quality did King John of Bohemia demonstrate?
- **a.** a deep devotion to battle
- **b.** the bravery of a unique leader
- **c.** the importance of brotherly love in war
- **d.** an ability to overcome a physical handicap

_____ **9.** Which role would a knight probably find most demeaning?
- **a.** biographer
- **b.** sentinel
- **c.** forager
- **d.** scout

_____ **10.** According to Tuchman, which of the following allowed a knight to achieve "gain"?
- **a.** purpose
- **b.** status
- **c.** honor
- **d.** luck

Analyze and Evaluate (30 points total; 10 points each)

Fill in the boxes below with details or examples from the article that illustrate these knightly qualities.

11. Valor	
12. Stamina	
13. Sacrifice	

BIG IDEA Connect (20 points)

Use a separate sheet of paper to answer the following essay question.

14. Using information from Barbara Tuchman's article and from "Sir Gawain and the Green Knight," explain the term "Romantic."

Name ______________________ Date ______________ Class __________

Selection Test

Score

from *Le Morte d'Arthur* (page 198)

Recall and Interpret (35 points total; 5 points each)
Write the letter of the best answer.

_____**1.** The creatures in Arthur's first dream are trying to
a. warn him. **c.** protect him.
b. destroy him. **d.** frighten him.

_____**2.** In Arthur's second dream, Gawain is trying to
a. warn him. **c.** threaten him.
b. comfort him. **d.** bargain with him.

_____**3.** Arthur responds to his second dream by
a. trying to forget it.
b. trying to understand it.
c. acting on the advice received in it.
d. acting counter to the advice received in it.

_____**4.** After the battle, whom does Arthur blame for the deaths of nearly all of his followers?
a. God **c.** Lancelot
b. himself **d.** Mordred

_____**5.** After Arthur kills Mordred, his chief concern is for
a. his survival.
b. the safeguarding of his sword Excalibur.
c. the survival of Sir Lucan and Sir Bedivere.
d. the protection of the wounded from the robbers.

_____**6.** Which of the following leads Sir Bedivere to defy Arthur's order to throw away the sword Excalibur?
a. greed **c.** admiration for the sword
b. ambition **d.** the desire to protect Arthur

_____**7.** After Arthur's death, Sir Bedivere decides to dedicate his life to
a. avenging Arthur's death.
b. praying for Arthur's soul.
c. following Arthur's example.
d. fighting for Arthur's causes.

Vocabulary Practice (20 points total; 5 points each)
Write the letter of the best answer. This exercise is continued on the next page.

_____**8.** It would be normal for a person in **jeopardy** to feel
a. proud. **b.** afraid. **c.** relieved.

Name ______________________ Date ______________ Class ________

Selection Test *(continued)*

_____ **9.** An angry person might **brandish** a
 a. fist. **b.** frown. **c.** temper tantrum.

_____ **10.** One might demonstrate a **doleful** reaction by
 a. weeping. **b.** giggling. **c.** blushing.

_____ **11.** The most common reaction to **peril** is
 a. joy. **b.** fear. **c.** exhaustion.

Analyze and Evaluate (30 points total; 10 points each)
Think about how legends celebrate the heroic qualities of leaders. In the boxes in the left column, identify a quality of Arthur that you think is emphasized in this selection. In the boxes in the right column, give two examples that show how Arthur demonstrates that quality.

12. Quality	How the quality is demonstrated
13. Quality	
14. Quality	

BIG IDEA Connect (15 points)
Use a separate sheet of paper to answer the following essay question.

15. In a paragraph or two, discuss the treatment of Arthur's death in this selection. How important is it? Support your ideas.

Name ______________________ Date ______________ Class __________

Selection Test

Score

Sir Patrick Spens, (page 211) Bonny Barbara Allan, (page 213) and Get Up and Bar the Door (page 215)

Recall and Interpret (40 points total; 5 points each)
Write the letter of the best answer. This exercise is continued on the next page.

_____ **1.** The king chooses Sir Patrick Spens to sail his ship because of Spens's
a. loyalty. **c.** past services to him.
b. ability as a sailor. **d.** status as a nobleman.

_____ **2.** Sir Patrick Spens's attitude toward the voyage is mainly one of
a. dread. **c.** annoyance.
b. terror. **d.** excitement.

_____ **3.** Where are Sir Patrick Spens and his lords at the end of the ballad?
a. adrift at sea
b. sailing toward home
c. at the bottom of the sea
d. at port in a foreign land

_____ **4.** Barbara Allan rejects John Graeme because he
a. lied to her. **c.** flirted with another.
b. stood her up. **d.** insulted her in public.

_____ **5.** John Graeme's dying words reveal that he
a. forgives Barbara Allan.
b. has never loved Barbara Allan.
c. regrets what he did to Barbara Allan.
d. believes that Barbara Allan never loved him.

_____ **6.** In "Get Up and Bar the Door," the wife doesn't fulfill the request that the husband had made because she
a. isn't cold.
b. doesn't hear him.
c. is busy with her housework.
d. doesn't want to be the first to violate their agreement.

_____ **7.** How does the wife respond when the husband finally speaks to the two gentlemen in "Get Up and Bar the Door"?
a. angrily **c.** gratefully
b. sheepishly **d.** triumphantly

Name ______________________ Date ______________ Class ________

Selection Test

(continued)

_____**8.** In order to view "Bonny Barbara Allan" as an example of the standard ballad stanza, the reader must be most flexible in determining

a. how complete the story is.
b. which words are considered rhymes.
c. what syllables are stressed and unstressed.
d. the number of syllables words are considered to have.

Vocabulary Practice (5 points total)
Write the letter of the best answer.

_____**9.** Who **dwells** in a house?

a. tenant **b.** landlord **c.** plumber

Analyze and Evaluate (15 points)
Describe the changes in the refrain in "Bonny Barbara Allan" and what they connote.

10.

BIG IDEA Connect (40 points)
Use a separate sheet of paper to answer the following essay question.

11. What are the chief causes of the troubles experienced by Sir Patrick Spens, Barbara Allan, and the married couple in "Get Up and Bar the Door"? Whose troubles are least deserved, do you think? Are anyone's troubles tragic? Explain.

Name ______________________ Date ______________ Class ________

Open-Book Selection Test

Score

On Monsieur's Departure (page 256) and Speech to the Troops at Tilbury (page 257)

Recall and Interpret (40 points total; 5 points each)
Write the letter of the best answer.

_____ **1.** The first stanza of "On Monsieur's Departure" is mainly about the speaker's
- **a.** internal conflict.
- **b.** desire for peace.
- **c.** love for Monsieur.
- **d.** regrets about the past.

_____ **2.** Line 6 most strongly suggests that Monsieur has left the speaker
- **a.** forever.
- **b.** at her request.
- **c.** for only a short time.
- **d.** without saying good-bye.

_____ **3.** In the second stanza, the speaker communicates the idea that her care is like her shadow in that it
- **a.** frightens her.
- **b.** has no real form.
- **c.** is always with her.
- **d.** seems wholly natural to her.

_____ **4.** In line 14, the speaker reveals that she feels
- **a.** cold.
- **b.** hopeful.
- **c.** worthless.
- **d.** vulnerable.

_____ **5.** The rhyme scheme of the first stanza is
- **a.** *abbacc.*
- **b.** *abcabc.*
- **c.** *aabbcc.*
- **d.** *ababcc.*

_____ **6.** In "Speech to the Troops at Tilbury," the Queen says that she does not fear for her safety among her people because
- **a.** she is the queen.
- **b.** she has ruled justly.
- **c.** she trusts her subjects.
- **d.** she is armed and guarded.

_____ **7.** To keep invaders out of England, the Queen says that she is willing to
- **a.** die with her troops.
- **b.** bargain with the enemy.
- **c.** hire soldiers from abroad.
- **d.** replace the lieutenant general.

_____ **8.** What does the queen promise the soldiers who fight well?
- **a.** her gratitude
- **b.** financial rewards
- **c.** medals for courage
- **d.** positions of command

Name ____________ Date ____________ Class ____________

Open-Book Selection Test *(continued)*

Vocabulary Practice (20 points total; 5 points each)
Write the letter of the best answer.

_____ **9.** A person who is **mute** cannot
a. see. **b.** talk. **c.** hear.

_____ **10.** People involved in **treachery** are
a. disloyal to their leaders.
b. respectful of their leaders.
c. instructive for their leaders.

_____ **11.** To achieve **concord** is to
a. discuss a topic.
b. argue over an issue.
c. reach an agreement.

_____ **12.** Soldiers known for their **valor** in battle are
a. loyal. **b.** intelligent. **c.** courageous.

Analyze and Evaluate (20 points total; 10 points each)

13. How does Elizabeth I use word choice to establish tone in the poem and in the speech?

The tone of the poem suggests . . .	Words that establish this tone are . . .
The tone of the speech suggests . . .	Words and phrases that establish this tone are . . .

BIG IDEA Connect (20 points)
Use a separate sheet of paper to answer the following essay question.

14. In a paragraph, explain how the poem and the speech illustrate the difficult actions and sacrifices Elizabeth undertook to show that England was her priority. Give at least three examples.

Name ______________________ Date ______________ Class __________

Open-Book Selection Test

Score

The Lover Showeth How He Is Forsaken (page 261) and Whoso List to Hunt (page 262)

Recall and Interpret (60 points total; 12 points each)
Write the letter of the best answer.

____ **1.** The tone of "The Lover Showeth How He Is Forsaken" is mainly one of
  a. bitterness.
  b. puzzlement.
  c. acceptance.
  d. sweet yearning.

____ **2.** "The Lover Showeth How He Is Forsaken" is critical of being
  a. fickle.
  b. fun-loving.
  c. materialistic.
  d. old-fashioned.

____ **3.** The quality of the hind most emphasized in "Whoso List to Hunt" is that she is
  a. beautiful.
  b. dangerous.
  c. mysterious.
  d. unattainable.

____ **4.** Which poem has a speaker who once had an intimate relationship with the beloved?
  a. "Whoso List to Hunt"
  b. "The Lover Showeth How He Is Forsaken"
  c. both poems
  d. neither poem

____ **5.** In which poem does the speaker claim to be unworthy of being loved?
  a. "Whoso List to Hunt"
  b. "The Lover Showeth How He Is Forsaken"
  c. both poems
  d. neither poem

Name ______________________ Date ______________ Class __________

Open-Book Selection Test *(continued)*

Analyze and Evaluate (15 points)

Identify an image from one of Wyatt's poems and note two feelings or ideas it conveys.

6.

Image
Feelings and Ideas

BIG IDEA Connect (25 points)

Use a separate sheet of paper to answer the following essay question.

7. Compare the feelings that the speakers of these poems have for the subjects of their poems. Why do you think each speaker feels as he does? Support your ideas with details from the poems.

Name ______________________ Date ______________ Class __________

Open-Book Selection Test

Score

Sonnet 30 (page 267) and Sonnet 75 (page 268)

Recall and Interpret (60 points total; 6 points each)
Write the letter of the best answer.

_____ **1.** In Sonnet 30, how does the lover's rejection affect the speaker?
- **a.** It makes him feel resentful.
- **b.** It makes him love her more deeply.
- **c.** It makes him doubt the power of love.
- **d.** It changes the heat of love to the heat of anger.

_____ **2.** Sonnet 30 suggests that love can overcome the rules of
- **a.** science.
- **b.** religion.
- **c.** morality.
- **d.** psychology.

_____ **3.** How does the speaker in Sonnet 30 expect his love to change?
- **a.** He thinks it will increase.
- **b.** He thinks it will die away.
- **c.** He thinks it will last forever.
- **d.** He thinks it will stay the same.

_____ **4.** Sonnet 30 is constructed around a series of
- **a.** scenes.
- **b.** lessons.
- **c.** realizations.
- **d.** contradictions.

_____ **5.** The rhyme scheme of both sonnets is
- **a.** *abab bcbc cdcd ee.*
- **b.** *abba abba cdec de.*
- **c.** *abab cdcd efef gg.*
- **d.** *aabb ccdd eeff gg.*

_____ **6.** The sonnets are similar in that both present
- **a.** the power of nature.
- **b.** a disdainful woman.
- **c.** the eternality of love.
- **d.** man's ability to persuade.

_____ **7.** In Sonnet 75, the beloved indicates that writing her name in the sand is
- **a.** romantic.
- **b.** pointless.
- **c.** annoying.
- **d.** humiliating.

_____ **8.** In Sonnet 75, the beloved's attitude toward mortality is one of
- **a.** fear.
- **b.** defiance.
- **c.** acceptance.
- **d.** mild curiosity.

Name ______________________________ Date ________________ Class __________

Open-Book Selection Test *(continued)*

_____ **9.** In Sonnet 75, the speaker suggests that all of the following have the power to be immortal except
a. love. **c.** poetry.
b. fame. **d.** goodness.

_____ **10.** How will the beloved become immortal, according to Sonnet 75?
a. She will plunge into the waves.
b. The speaker will remember her.
c. Her name will be scattered like dust.
d. The sonnet will tell readers about her.

Analyze and Evaluate (20 points total; 10 points each)

11. Think about Sonnet 30 as a Spenserian sonnet. Then, in the boxes, summarize the main problem presented or questioned in the three quatrains and the solution, comment, or key point offered in the couplet.

Problem or Question	Solution, Comment, or Key Point

BIG IDEA Connect (20 points)
Use a separate sheet of paper to answer the following essay question.

12. Sir Philip Sidney, in "A Defence of Poesie," claims that the poet is a teacher who "cometh to you with words set in delightful proportion" so that readers can learn about life as they read. What can readers learn from Sonnet 30 and Sonnet 75 about love?

Name ______________________ Date ______________ Class __________

Open-Book Selection Test

Score

Sonnet 31 (page 272) and Sonnet 39 (page 273)

Recall and Interpret (64 points total; 8 points each)
Write the letter of the best answer.

_____ **1.** In Sonnet 31, the speaker assumes that the moon is pale because it
- **a.** merely reflects light.
- **b.** is exhausted from its climb.
- **c.** is suffering from unrequited love.
- **d.** is alone and friendless.

_____ **2.** In Sonnet 31, the speaker suggests that most people see lasting love as being
- **a.** noble.
- **b.** foolish.
- **c.** phony.
- **d.** admirable.

_____ **3.** In Sonnet 31, the speaker believes he is particularly well-qualified to
- **a.** give the moon advice.
- **b.** praise the moon's beauty.
- **c.** predict the moon's future.
- **d.** recognize the moon's problem.

_____ **4.** According to the speaker of Sonnet 39, sleep deals with all people
- **a.** cruelly.
- **b.** equally.
- **c.** selfishly.
- **d.** scornfully.

_____ **5.** What does the speaker of Sonnet 39 expect will happen when he falls asleep?
- **a.** He will dream of Stella.
- **b.** He will sink more deeply into despair.
- **c.** He will temporarily escape his misery.
- **d.** He will come to know what he should do.

_____ **6.** All of the following are personified in Sonnet 39 EXCEPT
- **a.** sleep.
- **b.** despair.
- **c.** a shield.
- **d.** a bedroom.

_____ **7.** In which sonnet does the couplet contain a separate idea, solution, or summation?
- **a.** Sonnet 31
- **b.** Sonnet 39
- **c.** both sonnets
- **d.** neither sonnet

_____ **8.** In which sonnet does the speaker complain about the way he has been treated?
- **a.** Sonnet 31
- **b.** Sonnet 39
- **c.** both sonnets
- **d.** neither sonnet

Name ______________________ Date ______________ Class ________

Open-Book Selection Test *(continued)*

Analyze and Evaluate (16 points total; 8 points each)

In the boxes, answer the questions about the poet's use of apostrophe in these sonnets.

What does the speaker address?	What makes this thing an appropriate choice for the speaker to address?
9. Sonnet 31	
10. Sonnet 39	

BIG IDEA Connect (20 points)

Use a separate sheet of paper to answer the following essay question.

11. Which of these sonnets do you think is more meaningful or relevant to unhappy people? Why? Defend your opinion.

Name ______________________ Date ______________ Class __________

Open-Book Selection Test

Score

The Passionate Shepherd to His Love (page 277)

Recall and Interpret (60 points total; 10 points each)
Write the letter of the best answer.

_____ **1.** With which of the following is the speaker most concerned?
- **a.** security
- **b.** pleasure
- **c.** the constancy of love
- **d.** achieving immortality

_____ **2.** In which stanzas does the speaker make offers to his beloved that it would be unlikely he could provide?
- **a.** stanzas 1 and 2
- **b.** stanzas 2 and 3
- **c.** stanzas 3 and 4
- **d.** stanzas 4 and 5

_____ **3.** From stanza to stanza, the speaker becomes increasingly
- **a.** loving.
- **b.** hopeful.
- **c.** desperate.
- **d.** imaginative.

_____ **4.** What sound effect does the poet use in line 8 to describe the birds' songs?
- **a.** repetition of the *n* sound
- **b.** assonance of the *ir* sound
- **c.** onomatopoeic bird sounds
- **d.** alliteration of the *m* sound

_____ **5.** The speaker describes the world from
- **a.** a wise point of view.
- **b.** a political point of view.
- **c.** a romantic point of view.
- **d.** a scientific point of view.

_____ **6.** In the last line of the poem, the poet
- **a.** mocks the poem's first line.
- **b.** echoes the poem's first line.
- **c.** repeats the poem's first line.
- **d.** contradicts the poem's first line.

Name ______________________ Date ______________ Class __________

Open-Book Selection Test *(continued)*

Analyze and Evaluate (18 points total; 9 points each)

In the boxes, answer the questions about the poem.

7. How do the types of things the shepherd offers his beloved in stanzas 1–3 reflect his point of view of the world?

8. How do the types of things he offers his beloved in stanzas 4 and 5 reflect his point of view of his beloved?

BIG IDEA Connect (22 points)

Use a separate sheet of paper to answer the following essay question.

9. In what ways are the rhyme scheme, simple language, and short lines appropriate to the speaker and the topic?

Name ______________________ Date ______________ Class __________

Open-Book Selection Test

Score

The Nymph's Reply to the Shepherd (page 281)

Recall and Interpret (60 points total; 10 points each)
Write the letter of the best answer.

_____**1.** In the first stanza of "The Nymph's Reply to the Shepherd," the nymph accuses the shepherd of being
- **a.** petty.
- **b.** boring.
- **c.** dishonest.
- **d.** unfaithful.

_____**2.** What does the nymph see as the main obstacle to the life the shepherd has offered her?
- **a.** the passage of time
- **b.** the shepherd's poverty
- **c.** the shepherd's shallowness
- **d.** the harsh realities of rural life

_____**3.** The nymph's assessment of the world is more
- **a.** doubtful than the shepherd's.
- **b.** practical than the shepherd's.
- **c.** romantic than the shepherd's.
- **d.** optimistic than the shepherd's.

_____**4.** In her reply, the nymph counters the "madrigals" in the shepherd's poem with
- **a.** the rivers' raging (line 6).
- **b.** a sudden silence (line 7).
- **c.** the faded blossoms (line 9).
- **d.** a honey tongue (line 11).

_____**5.** In the final stanza, the nymph suggests that she would consider living with the shepherd and being his love if only
- **a.** she were much older.
- **b.** he weren't so foolish.
- **c.** she were much younger.
- **d.** the world were not as it is.

_____**6.** In the final stanza, the nymph's attitude toward the shepherd becomes
- **a.** less patient.
- **b.** less serious.
- **c.** more generous.
- **d.** more accusatory.

Name ______________________ Date ______________ Class ________

Open-Book Selection Test *(continued)*

Analyze and Evaluate (20 points)

7. Describe Raleigh's nymph's attitude towards love, drawing connections between her attitude and the events of Raleigh's own life.

____

____

____

____

____

____

____

____

____

____

____

____

BIG IDEA Connect (20 points)
Use a separate sheet of paper to answer the following essay question.

8. Do you think that "The Nymph's Reply to the Shepherd" is an appropriate response to "The Passionate Shepherd to His Love" (page 277)? Support your opinion.

Name ______________________ Date ______________ Class __________

Selection Test

Score

Of Studies (page 285)

Recall and Interpret (54 points total; 9 points each)
Write the letter of the best answer.

_____ **1.** Which of the following best summarizes the main idea of this essay?
- **a.** People need to engage in activity as well as study.
- **b.** Study has several benefits, each of which is important.
- **c.** To study effectively, one must have a specific purpose in mind.
- **d.** The easier a book is to understand, the less useful it proves to be.

_____ **2.** Bacon says that someone who studies too much is
- **a.** lazy.
- **b.** phony.
- **c.** boring.
- **d.** unhealthy.

_____ **3.** Bacon believes that the main purpose of reading is to
- **a.** win arguments.
- **b.** find support for one's beliefs.
- **c.** be able to weigh and consider ideas.
- **d.** find subjects to talk about in polite society.

_____ **4.** What advice would Bacon give a reader who is presented with a huge array of books and limited time?
- **a.** Skim all of them.
- **b.** Vary the rate and nature of your reading.
- **c.** Read only those that are considered classics.
- **d.** Give up your other activities and read them all.

_____ **5.** According to Bacon, studying the writing of mathematicians is a particularly useful activity for people who have problems with
- **a.** being precise.
- **b.** succeeding in business.
- **c.** making logical argument.
- **d.** keeping their minds focused.

_____ **6.** To what does Bacon compare diseases of the body?
- **a.** books
- **b.** fields of study
- **c.** methods of studying
- **d.** weaknesses in wit

Name ______________________ Date ______________ Class ________

Selection Test

(continued)

Vocabulary Practice (15 points total; 3 points each)
Write the letter of the best answer.

_____ **7.** Which of the following activities requires **discourse**?
a. reading **b.** exercise **c.** conversation

_____ **8.** An example of an **impediment** to a car trip would be
a. a map. **b.** a hitchhiker. **c.** a log across the road.

_____ **9.** Which of the following is most dependent on **rhetoric** for its success?
a. a speech **b.** a marriage **c.** a science experiment

_____ **10.** You could accuse a person of **sloth** by calling him or her a
a. chicken. **b.** lazybones. **c.** tattletale.

_____ **11.** To **execute** an order is to
a. give it. **b.** follow it. **c.** rebel against it.

Analyze and Evaluate (11 points)

12. Consider how Bacon employs parallelism in the boxed quotation. Then underline the words or phrases that create a parallel structure.

> "And therefore, if a man write little, he had need have a great memory; if he confer little, he had need have a present wit; and if he read little, he had need have much cunning to seem to know that he doth not."

BIG IDEA Connect (20 points)
Use a separate sheet of paper to answer the following essay question.

13. What purposes does Bacon believe studies serve? Do you agree? Explain.

Name ________________ Date ____________ Class ________

Open-Book Selection Test

Score

Sonnet 116 (page 295) and Sonnet 130 (page 296)

Recall and Interpret (40 points total; 8 points each)
Write the letter of the best answer.

_____ **1.** What quality of love does the speaker of Sonnet 116 emphasize?
- **a.** passion
- **b.** honesty
- **c.** steadfastness
- **d.** understanding

_____ **2.** Which of the following paraphrases, or restates, the couplet in Sonnet 116?
- **a.** "I have never been wrong about love."
- **b.** "I wouldn't be the least bit surprised if I were proven wrong."
- **c.** "If I am wrong, I will never write another poem or fall in love again."
- **d.** "If I am wrong, then all that I know to be true about the world is also wrong."

_____ **3.** According to Sonnet 116, what cannot change love?
- **a.** the stars
- **b.** the end of life
- **c.** the poet's thoughts
- **d.** the loss of youth and beauty

_____ **4.** In Sonnet 130, what does the speaker suggest about his beloved?
- **a.** She is lovable despite being plain.
- **b.** She is too unattractive to compare to beautiful things.
- **c.** She has made him blind to the beauty and charm of other women.
- **d.** Although many women have been compared to her, none have surpassed her in beauty.

_____ **5.** What comment about love does Sonnet 130 make?
- **a.** Beauty inspires passion.
- **b.** Beauty is in the eye of the beholder.
- **c.** True love makes the world appear beautiful.
- **d.** True love is not concerned with appearances.

Vocabulary Practice (20 points total; 5 points each)
Write the letter of the best answer.

_____ **6.** A tailor makes an **alteration** to a garment when he
- **a.** replaces a button.
- **b.** changes its length.
- **c.** designs the garment.

Name ______________________ Date ______________ Class __________

Open-Book Selection Test *(continued)*

_____ **7.** Which of the following best describes **treading** lightly?
- **a.** stepping softly
- **b.** running silently
- **c.** skipping happily

_____ **8.** A person going to meet his **doom** most likely feels
- **a.** afraid.
- **b.** excited.
- **c.** skeptical.

_____ **9.** Which of the following best characterizes a **tempestuous** relationship?
- **a.** big vacations
- **b.** loud arguments
- **c.** terms of endearment

Analyze and Evaluate (20 points total; 10 points each)
Identify a simile or metaphor that you think is central to each sonnet and tell what is compared in that simile or metaphor. Then indicate the feelings or ideas that it suggests.

10. Sonnet 116

Simile or metaphor	
Compares	. . . to . . .
Feelings and ideas suggested	

11. Sonnet 130

Simile or metaphor	
Compares	. . . to . . .
Feelings and ideas suggested	

BIG IDEA Connect (20 points)
Use a separate sheet of paper to answer the following essay question.

12. Choose one of the sonnets, and explain how it is a good example of the clever thinking that Elizabethan writers and readers admired.

Name ______________________ Date ______________ Class __________

Open-Book Selection Test

Score

Sonnet 73 (page 298) and Sonnet 29 (page 299)

Recall and Interpret (60 points total; 10 points each)
Write the letter of the best answer.

_____ **1.** In Sonnet 73, the speaker says that the friend's love for him is strengthened by
- **a.** passing time.
- **b.** the time of year.
- **c.** the fear of abandonment by the speaker.
- **d.** the understanding that the speaker has little time left.

_____ **2.** To what does the speaker of Sonnet 73 NOT compare the coming of old age?
- **a.** to evening
- **b.** to a dying fire
- **c.** to trees in the winter
- **d.** to friendship forsaken

_____ **3.** "Death's second self" in line 8 of Sonnet 73 is a poetic name for
- **a.** loss.
- **b.** sleep.
- **c.** night.
- **d.** illness.

_____ **4.** Which of the following best represents the shift in mood that takes place in Sonnet 29?
- **a.** despair to ecstasy
- **b.** anger to forgiveness
- **c.** confusion to understanding
- **d.** disappointment to acceptance

_____ **5.** Of which good fortune is the speaker in Sonnet 29 NOT jealous?
- **a.** another man's good looks
- **b.** another man's lovely wife
- **c.** another man's many friends
- **d.** another man's vast knowledge

_____ **6.** What is worth more to the speaker in Sonnet 29 than all that kings have?
- **a.** popularity and wealth
- **b.** the ability to create art
- **c.** the affection of his friend
- **d.** high hopes and good health

Name ______________________ Date ______________ Class __________

Open-Book Selection Test *(continued)*

Analyze and Evaluate (20 points total; 4 points each)

Sonnet 29 is built around a list of similes that use the connecting word "like." Complete the chart to identify three negative comparisons and one positive comparison. Then consider how the fourth simile affects the direction and tone of the poem.

7. First simile, line _____	Compares __________ to __________
8. Second simile, line _____	Compares __________ to __________
9. Third simile, line _____	Compares __________ to __________
10. Fourth simile, line _____	Compares __________ to __________
11. Effect on direction and tone of poem:	

BIG IDEA Connect (20 points)

Use a separate sheet of paper to answer the following essay question.

13. Both sonnets deal with the value of friendship. How does this theme reflect the growing humanism of the Elizabethan period? Use details from the sonnets to support your response.

Name ______________________ Date ______________ Class __________

Open-Book Selection Test

Score

Fear No More the Heat o' the Sun (page 302) and Blow, Blow, Thou Winter Wind (page 303)

Recall and Interpret (40 points total; 8 points each)
Write the letter of the best answer.

_____ **1.** Which of the following paraphrases the speaker of "Fear No More the Heat o' the Sun"?
- **a.** "Rest in peace."
- **b.** "Only the good die young."
- **c.** "The next world is a better place than this world."
- **d.** "Now that you're gone, I have nothing left to lose."

_____ **2.** The person for whom this dirge is sung is compared to
- **a.** a tyrant who has oppressed his people.
- **b.** a lover who has abandoned his beloved.
- **c.** a ghost who has haunted his former home.
- **d.** a worker who has received his pay and gone home.

_____ **3.** Which of the following do the singers of this dirge assert?
- **a.** Young lovers are immortal.
- **b.** Witchcraft can raise the dead.
- **c.** Ill weather affects only the living.
- **d.** Food and clothes are unimportant.

_____ **4.** Which of the following is most probably responsible for the speaker's attitude in "Blow, Blow, Thou Winter Wind"?
- **a.** the speaker's pride
- **b.** the betrayal of loved ones
- **c.** the destructiveness of nature
- **d.** wrongful acts of the speaker

_____ **5.** In "Blow, Blow, Thou Winter Wind" the wind and sky are
- **a.** praised as powerful beings.
- **b.** personified as harsh forces.
- **c.** addressed as sources of comfort.
- **d.** worshipped as benevolent deities.

Vocabulary Practice (20 points total; 5 points each)
Write the letter of the best answer.

_____ **6.** A **keen** kitchen knife
- **a.** cuts quickly.
- **b.** shines brightly.
- **c.** needs sharpening.

Open-Book Selection Test *(continued)*

_____ **7.** Someone who receives **censure** has been
a. praised. **b.** criticized. **c.** welcomed.

_____ **8.** **Tyrants** are usually
a. adored by their subjects.
b. feared by their subjects.
c. admired by their subjects.

_____ **9.** An act of **folly** is likely to
a. fail utterly.
b. receive praise.
c. inspire followers.

Analyze and Evaluate (20 points total; 4 points each)
Complete the chart to decide on the common theme of these two songs.

"Fear No More the Heat o' the Sun"	"Blow, Blow, Thou Winter Wind"
10. What the speakers say people expect of life:	**12.** What the speaker expected of life:
11. What people get in life:	**13.** What the speaker got in life:
14. Common theme of the songs:	

BIG IDEA Connect (20 points)
Use a separate sheet of paper to answer the following essay question.

15. Both songs are sung by characters who have spent their lives at court, either as courtiers or as royalty. What do the songs have to say about the nature of life at court?

Name ______________________ Date ______________ Class __________

Open-Book Selection Test

Score

To be, or not to be, (page 306) All the world's a stage, (page 308) and Our revels now are ended (page 310)

Recall and Interpret (60 points total; 10 points each)
Write the letter of the best answer.

_____ **1.** These passages, spoken by an actor to the audience alone, are called
- **a.** asides.
- **b.** preludes.
- **c.** dialogues.
- **d.** soliloquies.

_____ **2.** A theme of "To be, or not to be," is that the one thing people fear more than life's troubles is
- **a.** death.
- **b.** action.
- **c.** illness.
- **d.** loneliness.

_____ **3.** "To be, or not to be" includes a detailed list of
- **a.** plans for revenge.
- **b.** ways to cheat death.
- **c.** events that are upsetting.
- **d.** countries worth visiting.

_____ **4.** "All the world's a stage" is
- **a.** a personification of a stage.
- **b.** an extended metaphor for life.
- **c.** advice about living a long life.
- **d.** an explanation of people's roles.

_____ **5.** Which is NOT a way, according to Jacques, that old age is like childhood?
- **a.** The memory is diminished.
- **b.** The head has little hair on it.
- **c.** The voice becomes high again.
- **d.** The body shrinks to a small size.

_____ **6.** In "Our revels now are ended," Prospero's description of humankind as "such stuff / As dreams are made on" emphasizes our
- **a.** flimsiness.
- **b.** smallness.
- **c.** fragility.
- **d.** vitality.

Name ______________________ Date ______________ Class ____________

Open-Book Selection Test *(continued)*

Analyze and Evaluate (20 points total; 10 points each)
Describe the voice of two of the three speakers–Hamlet, Jacques, and Prospero–and give examples of the word choices that characterize each voice.

7. First speaker—description of voice:	Examples of word choice from soliloquy:
8. Second speaker—description of voice:	Examples of word choice from soliloquy:

BIG IDEA Connect (20 points)
Use a separate sheet of paper to answer the following essay question.

9. Write a paragraph explaining how the three soliloquies capture the humanist emphasis on the experience of humans living in this world.

Name ______________________ Date ______________ Class __________

Selection Test

Score

The Tragedy of Macbeth, Act 1 (page 317)

Recall and Interpret (30 points total; 5 points each)
Write the letter of the best answer.

_____ **1.** Which of the following best describes the atmosphere of scene 1, in which the witches appear?
- **a.** confused upset
- **b.** horror and shock
- **c.** lighthearted wonder
- **d.** uneasiness and gloom

_____ **2.** Upon hearing the witches' prophecies, Macbeth experiences all of the following except
- **a.** a thrilling fear.
- **b.** scornful disbelief.
- **c.** a desire for more details.
- **d.** the temptation to murder.

_____ **3.** In this act, what causes Macbeth's nervousness and fear?
- **a.** facing enemies in battle
- **b.** being made Thane of Cawdor
- **c.** being tempted to commit murder
- **d.** coming face to face with witches

_____ **4.** In scene 5, Lady Macbeth's immediate reaction upon reading her husband's letter is to express doubt about
- **a.** her own determination.
- **b.** the witches' prophecies.
- **c.** Macbeth's ambition.
- **d.** Macbeth's strength of will.

_____ **5.** Lady Macbeth asks spirits to help her
- **a.** make a decision.
- **b.** trick her husband.
- **c.** overcome temptation.
- **d.** be as cruel as she needs to be.

_____ **6.** Macbeth is reluctant to kill Duncan at Macbeth's castle because of a "double trust," by which he means that Duncan
- **a.** is both his king and his guest.
- **b.** and his two sons are his guests.
- **c.** commands both Macbeth and Lady Macbeth.
- **d.** has named him both Thane of Cawdor and Thane of Glamis.

Vocabulary Practice (20 points total; 5 points each)
Write the letter of the best answer.

_____ **7.** **Direful** information is usually
- **a.** justly deserved.
- **b.** deeply upsetting.
- **c.** wholly unexpected.

Name ______________________ Date ______________ Class ________

Selection Test

(continued)

_____ **8.** Which of the following is most **prophetic**?
- **a.** a good hunch
- **b.** an irrational fear
- **c.** a sneaking suspicion

_____ **9.** A person would probably feel **repentance** for
- **a.** forgetting to do an errand.
- **b.** napping instead of reading.
- **c.** speaking harshly to a friend.

_____ **10.** A **peerless** athlete
- **a.** has no equal or superior.
- **b.** is proud of his achievements.
- **c.** works out several times a week.

Analyze and Evaluate (20 points total; 10 points each)
When a play is performed, lighting, music, costumes, props, and even how the actors' movements are used to establish atmosphere. Summarize each scene below and note what atmosphere you think is appropriate. Then note two things that might be done in staging that scene to help establish the atmosphere.

11. Scene 4 Summary:	What should the atmosphere be?
	What might help to establish this atmosphere?

12. Scene 7 Summary:	What should the atmosphere be?
	What might help to establish this atmosphere?

BIG IDEA Connect (30 points)
Use a separate sheet of paper to answer the following essay question.

13. In scene 7, what approaches, or strategies, does Lady Macbeth use to try to change Macbeth's mind about assassinating Duncan? Why does Macbeth finally agree?

Name ______________________________ Date ____________________ Class __________

Selection Test

Score

The Tragedy of Macbeth, Act 2 (page 338)

Recall and Interpret (30 points total; 5 points each)
Write the letter of the best answer.

_____ **1.** Banquo indicates in scene 1 that his greatest priority is
- **a.** his own advancement.
- **b.** his allegiance to Duncan.
- **c.** his allegiance to Macbeth.
- **d.** seeing the witches' prophecies fulfilled.

_____ **2.** As Lady Macbeth awaits Macbeth at the beginning of scene 2, she is feeling
- **a.** confident.
- **b.** morally uncertain.
- **c.** convinced of failure.
- **d.** jumpy and superstitious.

_____ **3.** The voice that calls out "Sleep no more! Macbeth does murder sleep" is saying that
- **a.** someone has witnessed Duncan's murder.
- **b.** Duncan will never awaken from his "sleep."
- **c.** Macbeth murdered Duncan while Duncan was asleep.
- **d.** Macbeth will never again rest with a clear conscience.

_____ **4.** What does Macbeth suggest was the reason he could not join in the prayer of Malcolm and Donalbain that he overheard?
- **a.** He has lost his faith.
- **b.** He feared being heard.
- **c.** He was overcome with guilt and horror.
- **d.** He was in a hurry to flee the scene of the crime.

_____ **5.** The drunken porter scene serves all of the following functions except to
- **a.** provide comic relief.
- **b.** introduce new information about Duncan's murder.
- **c.** bring Macduff and Lennox into the action of the play.
- **d.** make the murder seem even more awful by the contrast in mood.

_____ **6.** Macbeth murders the king's servants so that they cannot
- **a.** try to get away.
- **b.** investigate the crime.
- **c.** claim they were framed.
- **d.** protect Malcolm and Donalbain.

Name ______________________ Date ______________ Class __________

Selection Test

(continued)

Vocabulary Practice (20 points total; 5 points each)
Write the letter of the best answer.

_____ **7.** Which animal typically demonstrates the greatest **stealth**?
a. cat **b.** bird **c.** horse

_____ **8.** If a person is **surfeited,** he has
a. eaten too little.
b. eaten too much.
c. eaten just enough.

_____ **9.** To **provoke** a fight, one person might
a. insult another.
b. notice another.
c. compliment another.

_____ **10.** A person who has **scruples** would be reluctant to
a. help someone.
b. cook something.
c. steal something.

Analyze and Evaluate (20 points)

11. Identify a motif in this act of *The Tragedy of Macbeth* and explain how it is connected to plot events and theme.

____
____
____
____
____
____
____
____
____
____

BIG IDEA Connect (30 points)
Use a separate sheet of paper to answer the following essay question.

12. What does Macbeth's "dagger soliloquy" reveal about his intentions and his state of mind? Support your answer.

Name ______________________ Date ______________ Class __________

Selection Test

Score

The Tragedy of Macbeth, Act 3 (page 353)

Recall and Interpret (45 points total; 5 points each)
Write the letter of the best answer.

_____ **1.** At the beginning of scene 1, what feeling does Banquo express about the witches' prophecies?
- **a.** a desire to hear more
- **b.** a wish that they not be fulfilled
- **c.** a fear that they have been disastrous for Scotland
- **d.** a hope that they prove true for him as they have for Macbeth

_____ **2.** At the beginning of scene 1, what feeling does Banquo express about Macbeth?
- **a.** envy
- **b.** suspicion
- **c.** loyalty
- **d.** sadness and worry

_____ **3.** Macbeth's statements and behavior suggest that, since Duncan's death, he has felt
- **a.** deceived.
- **b.** smugly satisfied.
- **c.** uneasy and fearful.
- **d.** indecisive and hesitant.

_____ **4.** Macbeth uses all of the following ways to motivate the murderers to act except by
- **a.** threatening them.
- **b.** appealing to their pride.
- **c.** filling them with hatred.
- **d.** hinting at the value of his gratitude.

_____ **5.** Macbeth's desire that his wife be "innocent of the knowledge" of his plan to kill Banquo and Fleance suggests that Macbeth
- **a.** no longer trusts her.
- **b.** has little faith in the plan.
- **c.** is now more decisive on his own.
- **d.** feels guilty about involving her in Duncan's death.

_____ **6.** When Macbeth claims to see a vision at the banquet, Lady Macbeth responds to him with
- **a.** scorn.
- **b.** horror.
- **c.** amusement.
- **d.** bewilderment.

_____ **7.** Lady Macbeth wants the banquet guests to think that Macbeth's odd behavior is the result of
- **a.** a lack of sleep.
- **b.** a recurring illness.
- **c.** worry over Banquo.
- **d.** serious mental problems.

Name ______________________ Date ______________ Class __________

Selection Test

(continued)

_____ **8.** Who has been Macbeth's foil in the first three acts?

a. Banquo
b. Duncan
c. Lady Macbeth
d. Macbeth himself

_____ **9.** By the end of Act 3, who seems to be emerging as Macbeth's new foil?

a. Lennox
b. Macduff
c. Lady Macbeth
d. the murderer of Banquo

Vocabulary Practice (15 points total; 5 points each)
Write the letter of the best answer.

_____ **10.** An **incensed** person usually wears an expression of

a. sorrow.
b. anger.
c. bliss.

_____ **11.** Which, if observed, would be most **appalling** to a compassionate person?

a. suffering
b. celebration
c. athleticism

_____ **12.** To make **amends** after an unkind word to a friend, a person might

a. make a new friend.
b. argue with someone else.
c. apologize for what was said.

Analyze and Evaluate (20 points total)

13. Can a character who serves as a foil have anything in common with the main character? Consider whether the "character" of the ghost at the banquet has anything in common with Macbeth, and explain why or why not.

____

____

____

____

____

____

____

BIG IDEA Connect (20 points)
Use a separate sheet of paper to answer the following essay question.

14. Explain what you think Macbeth means in this statement in scene 4: "I am in blood / Stepped in so far that, should I wade no more, / Returning were as tedious as go o'er."

Name ______________________ Date ______________ Class __________

Selection Test

Score

The Tragedy of Macbeth, Act 4 (page 370)

Recall and Interpret (35 points total; 5 points each)
Write the letter of the best answer.

_____ **1.** The general effect of the first three apparitions in scene 1 is to leave Macbeth feeling
- **a.** angry.
- **b.** confused.
- **c.** despairing.
- **d.** encouraged.

_____ **2.** The apparitions of the eight kings and Banquo in scene 1 are meant to signify to Macbeth that
- **a.** many forces will combine to fight him.
- **b.** Banquo's descendants will become kings.
- **c.** Banquo is the last, or least, of his worries.
- **d.** he has more to fear from the spirit world than from the natural world.

_____ **3.** Macbeth's order to kill Macduff's family is motivated by
- **a.** jealousy.
- **b.** superstition.
- **c.** anger at Macduff.
- **d.** fear of the family's power.

_____ **4.** Lady Macduff calls her husband a "traitor" because she believes that he has betrayed
- **a.** Scotland.
- **b.** Macbeth.
- **c.** Malcolm.
- **d.** his family.

_____ **5.** Lady Macduff responds to her son's questions and statements with
- **a.** confusion.
- **b.** gentle sadness.
- **c.** sharp remarks.
- **d.** frustrated impatience.

_____ **6.** In scene 2, Lady Macduff expresses the belief that
- **a.** evil generates evil.
- **b.** bad things happen to good people.
- **c.** women are completely defenseless.
- **d.** people deserve what happens to them.

_____ **7.** Why does Malcolm describe ways in which he is unworthy to be a king?
- **a.** Honesty forces him to admit his flaws.
- **b.** He wants to test Macduff's loyalty to him.
- **c.** He wants to test Macduff's honesty and loyalty to Scotland.
- **d.** He wants to avoid being urged to fight for the throne, for fear of Macbeth.

Name ______________________ Date ______________ Class __________

Selection Test *(continued)*

Vocabulary Practice (15 points total; 5 points each)
Write the letter of the best answer.

_____ **8.** Which of the following best illustrates **avarice**?
- **a.** refusing to share.
- **b.** enjoying solitude.
- **c.** liking board games.

_____ **9.** A mountaineer famous for his **exploits** has probably
- **a.** exaggerated his successes.
- **b.** suffered climbing injuries.
- **c.** made many difficult climbs.

_____ **10.** Which of the following is an example of someone **redressing** a problem?
- **a.** receiving poor service.
- **b.** asking for a total refund.
- **c.** trying on different outfits.

Analyze and Evaluate (30 points total; 15 points each)

11. Identify which portion of the plot (rising action, falling action, denouement) scene 1 of Act 4 represents.

12. Explain what Macbeth's reactions to the apparitions the witches conjure reveal about his character and mindset.

BIG IDEA Connect (20 points)
Use a separate sheet of paper to answer the following essay question.

13. Using details or ideas from the play, explain how King Edward, as he is described in scene 3, contrasts with Macbeth.

Name ______________________ Date ______________ Class __________

Selection Test

Score

The Tragedy of Macbeth, Act 5 (page 389)

Recall and Interpret (30 points total; 5 points each)
Write the letter of the best answer.

_____ **1.** During her sleepwalking scene, Lady Macbeth seems most consumed by feelings of
- **a.** fear.
- **b.** guilt.
- **c.** anger.
- **d.** longing.

_____ **2.** After observing Lady Macbeth's sleepwalking, her doctor appears to believe that she
- **a.** may harm herself.
- **b.** may harm other people.
- **c.** is under a witch's spell.
- **d.** is in danger from Macbeth.

_____ **3.** Macbeth does not fear death at the hands of the rebels because he has
- **a.** extensive battle experience.
- **b.** faith in the witches' prophecies.
- **c.** little reason to want to go on living.
- **d.** no awareness of the rebels' strength.

_____ **4.** What does the "tomorrow" soliloquy reveal about Macbeth?
- **a.** a desire for redemption
- **b.** a deep love for his dead wife
- **c.** a sense that life is meaningless
- **d.** a regret for "slaughterous" deeds

_____ **5.** In the last scene, Macbeth fights to the death because he
- **a.** is given no other choice.
- **b.** thinks that Macduff can be easily defeated.
- **c.** does not believe Macduff's claim about his birth.
- **d.** prefers an honorable defeat to a humiliating surrender.

_____ **6.** Which of the following best describes Macbeth's tragic flaw?
- **a.** arrogance and conceit
- **b.** an unchecked desire for power
- **c.** a willingness to trust in sorcery
- **d.** a tendency to act without thinking

Vocabulary Practice (25 points total; 5 points each)
Write the letter of the best answer.

_____ **7.** A good gardener tries to **purge** the garden of
- **a.** plants.
- **b.** weeds.
- **c.** flowers.

Name _______________ Date _______________ Class _______________

Selection Test

(continued)

_____ **8.** The **antidote** to exhaustion is
- **a.** a heavy meal.
- **b.** a three-mile run.
- **c.** a good night's sleep.

_____ **9.** A city under **siege** is
- **a.** overrun by the enemy.
- **b.** cut off from supplies and aid.
- **c.** strengthening its defensive walls.

_____ **10.** The athlete with the greatest **prowess**
- **a.** no longer competes.
- **b.** needs to train harder.
- **c.** wins the highest award.

_____ **11.** The **usurper** seeks to obtain a position of power by
a. force. **b.** election. **c.** personality.

Analyze and Evaluate (21 points total; 7 points each)

Readers may have their own ideas about what was most responsible for Macbeth's downfall. For each of the three possible causes common to traditional tragedy, mark the bar graph to show how you would judge its importance. Then explain why you feel as you do.

12. How important is Macbeth's tragic flaw? Why do you think so?	(–) not at all		(+) extremely
13. How important are Macbeth's errors in judgment? Why do you think so?	(–) not at all		(+) extremely
14. How important is fate? Why do you think so?	(–) not at all		(+) extremely

BIG IDEA Connect (24 points)

Use a separate sheet of paper to answer the following essay question.

15. What do you see as the theme of this play? Defend your answer.

Name ______________________ Date ______________ Class __________

Selection Test

Score

Throne of Blood by Daniel Rosenthal (page 406)

Recall and Interpret (60 points total; 10 points each)
Write the letter of the best answer.

_____ **1.** In what way is Kurosawa's adaptation of *The Tragedy of Macbeth* LEAST like the play?
- **a.** Washizu is killed in the final scene.
- **b.** Washizu lacks Macbeth's courage.
- **c.** Asaji's pregnancy alters the plot.
- **d.** Asaji lacks Lady Macbeth's ambition.

_____ **2.** Kurosawa opens the movie with
- **a.** a visitation by an evil spirit.
- **b.** a prediction that Washizu will be king.
- **c.** a battle in which Washizu is victorious.
- **d.** a song about Cobweb Castle being destroyed.

_____ **3.** Both the play and the movie employ
- **a.** heroic actions.
- **b.** a five-act structure.
- **c.** Noh theater traditions.
- **d.** supernatural occurrences.

_____ **4.** Rosenthal claims that Kurosawa improves on the play by
- **a.** producing the play as a movie.
- **b.** having a murder occur offstage.
- **c.** having a ghost appear at a feast.
- **d.** translating the play into Japanese.

_____ **5.** In contrast to Lady Macbeth's madness, Asaji's madness may have been caused in part by
- **a.** the forest spirit.
- **b.** the death of her child.
- **c.** the failure of her plan.
- **d.** the departure of Washizu.

_____ **6.** How does Washizu die?
- **a.** He is killed by Asaji.
- **b.** He is killed by the forest spirit.
- **c.** He is killed by his own soldiers.
- **d.** He is killed by Yoshiteru's soldiers.

Name ______________________ Date ______________ Class __________

Selection Test

(continued)

Analyze and Evaluate (20 points total; 10 points each)

Compare the main characters of the play to those in the movie. What motivates each? Where do they succeed? Why do they fail?

7. Macbeth	What Motivates Him	Where He Succeeds	Why He Fails
8. Washizu	What Motivates Him	Where He Succeeds	Why He Fails

BIG IDEA Connect (20 points)

Use a separate sheet of paper to answer the following essay question.

9. In what ways does the Shakespeare's theme of ambition gone awry differ from the theme of "Throne of Blood"?

Name ______________________ Date ______________ Class __________

Selection Test

Score

Midsummer Night's Spectacle (page 410)

Recall and Interpret (60 points total; 10 points each)
Write the letter of the best answer.

_____ **1.** What is the state of Shakespeare festivals across the nation, according to the article?
- **a.** They are moving indoors.
- **b.** They are attended by few people.
- **c.** They are increasing in popularity.
- **d.** They are concentrated in the inner cities.

_____ **2.** Who assumes most of the roles in outdoor presentations of Shakespeare's plays?
- **a.** local actors
- **b.** amateur actors
- **c.** actors from Hollywood
- **d.** actors trained in England

_____ **3.** How do viewers respond to the plays of other playwrights when they are performed outdoors?
- **a.** Viewers equally enjoy these plays outdoors.
- **b.** Viewers would prefer to see these plays indoors.
- **c.** Viewers think these less known plays should be free.
- **d.** Viewers go to Shakespeare plays instead of these plays.

_____ **4.** The Shakespearean plays that work best outdoors have
- **a.** many soliloquies.
- **b.** history and tradition.
- **c.** action and swordplay.
- **d.** quiet, thoughtful dialogue.

_____ **5.** Shakespeare's early plays perform well outdoors because
- **a.** the bigger casts have more room.
- **b.** they are shorter than the later plays.
- **c.** people know more about the early plays.
- **d.** he wrote them with the open theater in mind.

_____ **6.** Based on the article, it is safe to predict that people will
- **a.** continue to love outdoor performances of Shakespeare's plays.
- **b.** complain about outdoor performances of Shakespeare's plays.
- **c.** demand more performances of Shakespeare's history plays.
- **d.** slowly begin to enjoy viewing Shakespeare's plays indoors.

Name ______________________ Date ______________ Class ________

Selection Test (continued)

Analyze and Evaluate (21 points)

7. List three facts and three opinions that you noted as you read the article.

Fact:	Opinion:
Fact:	Opinion:
Fact:	Opinion:

BIG IDEA Connect (19 points)

Use a separate sheet of paper to answer the following essay question.

8. According to the article, parents want to take their children to see Shakespeare's plays outdoors because "to see these plays under the stars" adds to Shakespeare's universality. How might an outdoor setting add to Shakespeare's universality?

Name ______________________ Date ______________ Class __________

Selection Test

Score

from *the King James Bible* (page 416)

Recall and Interpret (40 points total; 10 points each)
Write the letter of the best answer.

_____ **1.** The most important role of God in the selection from Genesis is that of
a. creator. **c.** protector.
b. teacher. **d.** destroyer.

_____ **2.** The selection from Genesis emphasizes that before people ate from the tree of knowledge, they were
a. perfect. **c.** innocent.
b. godlike. **d.** unfulfilled.

_____ **3.** Psalm 23 communicates the speaker's feelings of
a. guilt. **c.** celebration.
b. sorrow. **d.** reassurance.

_____ **4.** In which of these selections do people express disappointment in God?
a. the selection from Genesis only
b. Psalm 23 only
c. both selections
d. neither selection

Vocabulary Practice (20 points total; 5 points each)
Write the letter of the best answer.

_____ **5.** A person who is **beguiling** is most likely
a. attractive. **b.** uncertain. **c.** dishonest.

_____ **6.** With which of the following pairs is **enmity** most often associated?
a. rivals **b.** friends **c.** teammates

_____ **7.** To **replenish** a supply of something means to
a. share it. **b.** renew it. **c.** exhaust it.

_____ **8.** Someone who gives **abundantly** of his time gives
a. a little bit of time.
b. a great deal of time.
c. a fair amount of time.

Name ______________________ Date ______________ Class ________

Selection Test *(continued)*

Analyze and Evaluate (18 points total; 6 points each)
Describe three aspects of the writing style in this excerpt from Genesis in the King James version of the Bible.

9.
10.
11.

BIG IDEA Connect (22 points)
Use a separate sheet of paper to answer the following question.

12. What are some of the themes or main ideas of the selection from Genesis?

Name ______________________ Date ______________ Class __________

Open-Book Selection Test

Score

Eve's Apology (page 426)

Recall and Interpret (40 points total; 10 points each)
Write the letter of the best answer.

_____ **1.** According to the speaker, to what degree is Eve responsible for the downfall of humanity?
a. completely
b. not at all
c. somewhat, but less than Adam is
d. somewhat, but more than Adam is

_____ **2.** In the second stanza, the speaker stresses that Adam's choice was made
a. lovingly.
b. innocently.
c. deliberately.
d. halfheartedly.

_____ **3.** According to the speaker, which of the following motivated Eve to offer the apple to Adam?
a. curiosity
b. affection
c. ignorance
d. resentment

_____ **4.** In the final stanza, the speaker finds men's boasts of knowledge
a. ironic.
b. frightening.
c. threatening.
d. understandable.

Vocabulary Practice (20 points total; 10 points each)
Write the letter of the best answer.

_____ **5.** Which situation calls for the most **discretion**?
a. thanking someone for a favor
b. declining an invitation to a party
c. congratulating a friend on her success

_____ **6.** Which event would someone most likely have to **endure**?
a. a song played at high volume
b. a boring television show
c. a lecture from a parent

Name ____________________ Date ____________ Class ________

Open-Book Selection Test *(continued)*

Analyze and Evaluate (20 points)

7. What do you think is the main strength of the argument presented in this poem? What is the main weakness? Explain.

____

____

____

____

____

____

____

____

____

BIG IDEA Connect (20 points)
Use a separate sheet of paper to answer the following question.

8. Identify the theme of this poem, and then provide ideas or details from the poem that support that theme.

Name ______________________ Date ______________ Class ________

Open-Book Selection Test

Score

Song, (page 432) A Valediction Forbidding Mourning, (page 433) and Death Be Not Proud (page 435)

Recall and Interpret (63 points total; 7 points each)
Write the letter of the best answer.

_____ **1.** According to "Song," which type of fortune are people able to affect?
- **a.** bad fortune only
- **b.** good fortune only
- **c.** both bad and good fortune
- **d.** neither bad nor good fortune

_____ **2.** According to "Song," fearing that something bad will happen can result in
- **a.** wasted energy.
- **b.** making it happen.
- **c.** taking greater care.
- **d.** losing the joy one has in life.

_____ **3.** The fourth stanza of "Song" suggests that the speaker responds to the beloved's sadness with
- **a.** gratitude.
- **b.** amusement.
- **c.** disapproval.
- **d.** embarrassment.

_____ **4.** Which of the following is the best restatement of the speaker's final thought in "Song"?
- **a.** Our love is what keeps us alive.
- **b.** People who truly need each other should never part.
- **c.** People as close as we are feel great sorrow at being parted.
- **d.** People who are as close as we are can never be truly parted.

_____ **5.** In the second stanza of "A Valediction: Forbidding Mourning," the speaker recommends that the lovers keep their feelings
- **a.** alive.
- **b.** practical.
- **c.** private.
- **d.** obvious to all.

_____ **6.** The simile in lines 21–24 of "A Valediction: Forbidding Mourning" mainly suggests that the relationship between the lovers is
- **a.** strong.
- **b.** delicate.
- **c.** complicated.
- **d.** constantly improving.

Name ______________________ Date ______________ Class ________

Open-Book Selection Test (continued)

_____ **7.** Which of the following is the best restatement of the speaker's final thought in "A Valediction: Forbidding Mourning"?
- **a.** You complete me.
- **b.** Our love is everlasting.
- **c.** I will always return home to you.
- **d.** Without you, I would be nothing.

_____ **8.** Which of the following best describes the overall attitude of the speaker of "Death Be Not Proud" toward death?
- **a.** fearful
- **b.** defiant
- **c.** regretful
- **d.** respectful

_____ **9.** In "Death Be Not Proud," the speaker indicates that death's strength is truly
- **a.** romantic.
- **b.** deceptive.
- **c.** mysterious.
- **d.** considerable.

Analyze and Evaluate (15 points)

10. The rhyme scheme of "Death Be Not Proud" is Petrarchan, but the meter is not consistently iambic. Identify where, specifically, the meter varies from iambic, then explain the effect of this variation.

____

____

____

____

____

____

____

____

____

BIG IDEA Connect (22 points)

Use a separate sheet of paper to answer the following essay question.

11. In a paragraph or two, discuss the qualities that the speakers in "Song" and in "A Valediction: Forbidding Mourning" seem to admire in a beloved. Support your ideas.

Name ______________________ Date ______________ Class ________

Open-Book Selection Test

Score

Meditation 17 (page 439)

Recall and Interpret (45 points total; 9 points each)
Write the letter of the best answer.

_____ **1.** The bell with which Donne is most concerned in "Meditation 17" is one that signals
- **a.** a death.
- **b.** a general alarm.
- **c.** the top of each hour.
- **d.** the time for early morning prayers.

_____ **2.** In one of the most famous sections of "Meditation 17," Donne says that the individual is similar to
- **a.** an island.
- **b.** a country.
- **c.** a continent.
- **d.** a piece of a continent.

_____ **3.** Which of the following best describes Donne's attitude toward death in "Meditation 17"?
- **a.** worried
- **b.** optimistic
- **c.** perplexed
- **d.** unconcerned

_____ **4.** What is Donne's main point about the tolling bell?
- **a.** It rings for the old and sick.
- **b.** It unites the listeners with God.
- **c.** It does not always signal a death.
- **d.** It rings for everyone who hears it.

_____ **5.** What does Donne refer to suffering as?
- **a.** a test
- **b.** a treasure
- **c.** a blessing
- **d.** a bell

Vocabulary Practice (12 points total; 4 points each)
Write the letter of the best answer.

_____ **6.** Someone engaged in **contemplation** is
- **a.** arguing.
- **b.** thinking.
- **c.** breaking the law.

_____ **7.** A **congregation** usually assembles in a
- **a.** church.
- **b.** theater.
- **c.** stadium.

_____ **8.** Someone guilty of **covetousness** is
- **a.** lazy.
- **b.** proud.
- **c.** envious.

Name ______________________ Date ______________ Class ________

Open-Book Selection Test

(continued)

Analyze and Evaluate (24 points total; 4 points each)
Review the metaphysical conceit from "Meditation 17" reproduced below. Then, in each box on the right, identify what the conceit compares to the noted item. In the box at the bottom, answer the question.

"[A]ll mankind is of one author and is one volume; when one man dies, one chapter is not torn out of the book, but translated into a better language; and every chapter must be so translated. God employs several translators; some pieces are translated by age, some by sickness, some by war, some by justice; but God's hand is in every translation, and his hand shall bind up all our scattered leaves [pages] again for that library where every book shall lie open to one another."	**9.** Author
	10. Volume or Book
	11. Chapter
	12. Translation
	13. Library

14. What are two important ideas conveyed through this metaphysical conceit?	

BIG IDEA Connect (19 points)
Use a separate sheet of paper to answer the following essay question.

15. Explain how Donne's meditation leads him to "secure himself," and what that means. Refer to the poem to establish his mood and mindset at the beginning and end of the poem.

Name ______________________ Date ______________ Class __________

Open-Book Selection Test

Score

On My First Son (page 447)

Recall and Interpret (60 points total; 12 points each)
Write the letter of the best answer.

_____ **1.** In lines 5–8 of "On My First Son," the speaker attempts to
a. blame himself.
b. forgive himself.
c. comfort himself.
d. forget what has happened.

_____ **2.** "On My First Son" suggests that parents are mistaken if they think they
a. own their children.
b. deserve their children.
c. appreciate their children enough.
d. sacrifice enough for their children.

_____ **3.** "Seven years wert thou lent to me" means
a. the child was ill for seven years.
b. the child died at seven years of age.
c. Jonson has mourned the child for seven years.
d. Jonson wrote the poem seven years after the child's death.

_____ **4.** Why, according to Jonson, should he envy his child?
a. His child is in heaven.
b. His child is no longer ill.
c. His child is his best piece of poetry.
d. His child has escaped trouble and old age.

_____ **5.** To whom does Jonson speak in the poem?
a. to himself
b. to readers
c. to his wife
d. to his child

Name ______________________ Date ______________ Class __________

Open-Book Selection Test

(continued)

Analyze and Evaluate (20 points)

6. Discuss what Jonson means when he says "O, could I lose all father now!" in line 5. How might the genre (elegy) have affected the realism of this claim?

____

____

____

____

____

____

____

____

____

BIG IDEA Connect (20 points)

Use a separate sheet of paper to answer the following essay question.

7. Many people found Ben Jonson to be "arrogant and argumentative." Are these personality traits evident in the poem? Cite the poem in your answer.

Name ______________________ Date ______________ Class __________

Open-Book Selection Test

Score

Song: To Celia (page 449)

Recall and Interpret (60 points total; 15 points each)

_____ **1.** The speaker of "Song: To Celia" asks for love to be demonstrated by

a. making toasts.
b. exchanging looks.
c. voicing declarations.
d. constant togetherness.

_____ **2.** The speaker of "Song: To Celia" suggests that having Celia's love would be more valuable to him than

a. any other.
b. immortality.
c. nature's beauty.
d. the favor of the gods.

_____ **3.** The rhyme scheme of each four-line section of the poem is

a. *abcb*.
b. *abab*.
c. *aabb*.
d. *abcc*.

_____ **4.** The last four lines of the poem include

a. grim humor.
b. a heartfelt plea.
c. true admiration.
d. an allusion to Jove.

Name ______________________ Date ______________ Class ________

Open-Book Selection Test *(continued)*

Analyze and Evaluate (15 points)

5. Explain which elements of "Song: To Celia" make it a lyric poem.

____

____

____

____

____

____

____

____

____

BIG IDEA Connect (25 points)

Use a separate sheet of paper to answer the following essay question.

6. What effect does Celia have on the wreath sent to her by the speaker? What does this suggest about Celia and her effect on the speaker?

Name ______________________ Date ______________ Class __________

Open-Book Selection Test

Score

To the Virgins, to Make Much of Time (page 457) Carpe Diem (page 459) To Hélène (page 460) and from *the Rubáiyát* (page 461)

Recall and Interpret (60 points total; 6 points each)
Write the letter of the best answer.

_____ **1.** In the first stanza of "To the Virgins, to Make Much of Time," rosebuds are most closely associated with things that are
- **a.** deadly.
- **b.** ageless.
- **c.** spiritual.
- **d.** temporary.

_____ **2.** In the first stanza of "To the Virgins, to Make Much of Time," the gathering of rosebuds is most closely associated with activities that are
- **a.** foolish.
- **b.** enjoyable.
- **c.** productive.
- **d.** respectable.

_____ **3.** Which of the following best states the main idea of the fourth stanza?
- **a.** "Now or never."
- **b.** "Take your time."
- **c.** "Patience is a virtue."
- **d.** "Time is on your side."

_____ **4.** The advice in Herrick's poem is specifically directed toward people who are
- **a.** happy.
- **b.** young.
- **c.** in love.
- **d.** impractical.

_____ **5.** The speaker in "Carpe Diem" advises his friend to
- **a.** drink less wine.
- **b.** enjoy the present.
- **c.** learn about the future.
- **d.** envy those who are old.

_____ **6.** The last line of the poem reminds the friend that tomorrow
- **a.** is a new day.
- **b.** he may be dead.
- **c.** he may grow wiser.
- **d.** will be a better day.

_____ **7.** In "To Hélène" the speaker tells his beloved that she
- **a.** will grieve for him after his death.
- **b.** will someday regret rejecting his love.
- **c.** will learn to card and spin wool into thread.
- **d.** will be glad that she has a good friend in old age.

Name ______________________ Date ______________ Class __________

Open-Book Selection Test *(continued)*

_____ **8.** What is the "it" that Ronsard refers to in line 13?
a. the day that is at hand
b. the entirety of her life
c. the love she has for him
d. the last years of her old age

_____ **9.** Which quatrain of the *Rubáiyát* indicates whom the speaker is addressing?
a. Quatrain 20
b. Quatrain 23
c. Quatrain 26
d. Quatrain 38

_____ **10.** According to quatrain 20, "past regrets and future fears"
a. are like sweet wine filling a cup.
b. keep one from committing new errors.
c. prevent one from enjoying the present.
d. remind one of the preciousness of each day.

Analyze and Evaluate (20 points total; 5 points each)
For each selection (the three poems and the quatrains from the Rubáiyát), choose the line or lines that best state the carpe diem theme for you and explain your choice.

11. From "To the Virgins, to Make Much of Time," line(s) _____ because	**12.** From "Carpe Diem," line(s) _____ because
13. From "To Hélène," lines _____ because	**14.** From the *Rubáiyát*, quatrain _____, because

BIG IDEA Connect (20 points)
Use a separate sheet of paper to answer the following essay question.

15. It has been remarked that cavalier poetry's emphasis on the brevity of life leads to a focus on the secular. How might the carpe diem theme prompt people to think about the sacred instead?

Name ______________________ Date ______________ Class __________

Open-Book Selection Test

Score

The Constant Lover (page 466) and Why So Pale and Wan, Fond Lover? (page 467)

Recall and Interpret (56 points total; 8 points each)
Write the letter of the best answer.

_____ **1.** To the speaker of "The Constant Lover," the three days in which he has been in love seem like
- **a.** no time at all.
- **b.** three very short days.
- **c.** three normal days.
- **d.** three very long days.

_____ **2.** In the first stanza of "The Constant Lover," the speaker indicates that his love will last
- **a.** forever.
- **b.** for no more than three days.
- **c.** for as long as it is convenient.
- **d.** for as long as it takes to win the beloved's heart.

_____ **3.** The speaker uses the phrase "dozen dozen" in "The Constant Lover" to refer to the number of
- **a.** women he has fallen in love with.
- **b.** women he is currently in love with.
- **c.** women spared his attentions in the last three days.
- **d.** suitors competing with him for the woman's love.

_____ **4.** In "Why So Pale and Wan, Fond Lover?" the speaker advises the "fond lover" to
- **a.** admit defeat.
- **b.** play "hard to get."
- **c.** never take no for an answer.
- **d.** give the beloved one last chance.

_____ **5.** The last three lines of "Why So Pale and Wan, Fond Lover?" indicate that the woman's love can only be
- **a.** bought.
- **b.** freely given.
- **c.** taken by force.
- **d.** stolen through trickery.

Name ______________________ Date ______________ Class ________

Open-Book Selection Test *(continued)*

_____ **6.** In which poem does someone undergo a dramatic change of heart?
- **a.** "The Constant Lover" only
- **b.** "Why So Pale and Wan, Fond Lover?" only
- **c.** both poems
- **d.** neither poem

_____ **7.** In which poem is the man's love for the beloved clearly rejected?
- **a.** "The Constant Lover" only
- **b.** "Why So Pale and Wan, Fond Lover?" only
- **c.** both poems
- **d.** neither poem

Analyze and Evaluate (20 points total; 10 points each)
The important shift that occurs in these poems is indicated differently in each. Explain how the form in each poem indicates a major shift in tone or content.

8. "The Constant Lover":
9. "Why So Pale and Wan, Fond Lover?":

BIG IDEA Connect (24 points)
Use a separate sheet of paper to answer the following essay question.

10. Who and/or what does the poet poke fun at in each of these poems? Support your ideas with reference to the poems.

Name ______________________ Date ______________ Class ________

Open-Book Selection Test

Score

To Lucasta, Going to the Wars (page 471) and To Althea, from Prison (page 472)

Recall and Interpret (52 points total; 13 points each)
Write the letter of the best answer.

_____ **1.** In "To Lucasta, Going to the Wars," the main thing that the speaker seeks from Lucasta is her

- **a.** pity.
- **b.** consent.
- **c.** understanding.
- **d.** word of honor.

_____ **2.** What does the speaker of "To Lucasta, Going to the Wars" insist that Lucasta do about his unfaithfulness?

- **a.** copy it
- **b.** ignore it
- **c.** forgive it
- **d.** respect it

_____ **3.** The speaker of "To Althea, from Prison" is least concerned about the state of his

- **a.** soul.
- **b.** body.
- **c.** mind.
- **d.** heart.

_____ **4.** In line 28 of "To Althea, from Prison," the word *That* refers to

- **a.** love.
- **b.** prison.
- **c.** liberty.
- **d.** the soul.

Open-Book Selection Test *(continued)*

Analyze and Evaluate (24 points)

5. What does the poet communicate through his use of paradox in the last stanza of "To Lucasta, Going to the Wars"? Use lines from the poem to support your answer.

____

____

____

____

____

____

____

____

____

BIG IDEA Connect (24 points)
Use a separate sheet of paper to answer the following essay question.

6. Identify the things that the speaker associates with liberty in each stanza of "To Althea, from Prison."

Name ________________________ Date ______________ Class __________

Open-Book Selection Test

Score

To His Coy Mistress (page 476)

Recall and Interpret (50 points total; 10 points each)
Write the letter of the best answer.

_____ **1.** The speaker would like to take all the time in the world to court his mistress because
- **a.** that is what she deserves.
- **b.** courting is what he does best.
- **c.** courting keeps him from growing old.
- **d.** there is nothing he enjoys more than courting.

_____ **2.** The speaker cannot take all the time in the world to court his mistress because
- **a.** he is too impatient.
- **b.** he would eventually tire of her.
- **c.** she would eventually tire of him.
- **d.** old age and death are creeping up on them.

_____ **3.** Hyperbole is used in the first twenty lines of the poem mainly to emphasize the
- **a.** mistress's beauty.
- **b.** speaker's impatience.
- **c.** speaker's love for the mistress.
- **d.** enormity of the mistress's "crime."

_____ **4.** The realization that the speaker comes to in lines 21 and 22 makes him feel
- **a.** angry. **c.** puzzled.
- **b.** anxious. **d.** amused.

_____ **5.** The imagery in lines 33–46 mainly conveys a sense of
- **a.** defiance. **c.** peacefulness.
- **b.** desperation. **d.** energy.

Vocabulary Practice (10 points total; 5 points each)
Write the letter of the best answer.

_____ **6.** What kind of artist is particularly concerned with **hue**?
- **a.** a dancer
- **b.** a painter
- **c.** a musician
- **d.** a dramatist

Name ______________________ Date ______________ Class __________

Open-Book Selection Test

(continued)

_____ **7.** How would the residents of a city experiencing **strife** most likely feel?
- **a.** shy
- **b.** calm
- **c.** fearful
- **d.** confident

Analyze and Evaluate (20 points total)

In the small box, identify a line or set of lines from the poem that contains hyperbole. In the large box, explain the ideas and feelings that the hyperbole conveys.

Line(s)	**8.** Ideas and Feelings Conveyed

BIG IDEA Connect (20 points)

Use a separate sheet of paper to answer the following essay question.

9. In your own words, explain how the lovers will make the sun "run" (lines 45 and 46) and what their doing so means in a literal sense.

Name ______________________ Date ______________ Class __________

Open-Book Selection Test

Score

How Soon Hath Time and When I Consider How My Light Is Spent (page 518)

Recall and Interpret (60 points total; 12 points each)
Write the letter of the best answer.

_____ **1.** In the view of the speaker of "How Soon Hath Time," time has been moving
- **a.** too fast.
- **b.** backwards.
- **c.** in a big circle.
- **d.** in fits and starts.

_____ **2.** In "How Soon Hath Time," the "bud" and "blossom" (line 4) most probably symbolize
- **a.** periods of life.
- **b.** missed opportunities.
- **c.** personal accomplishments.
- **d.** people who are dear to the speaker.

_____ **3.** At which line does the speaker of "How Soon Hath Time" begin to console himself?
- **a.** line 3
- **b.** line 5
- **c.** line 9
- **d.** line 13

_____ **4.** The question asked in line 7 of "When I Consider How My Light Is Spent" is an expression of the speaker's
- **a.** hope.
- **b.** pride.
- **c.** contempt.
- **d.** frustration.

_____ **5.** "When I Consider How My Light Is Spent" emphasizes the idea that God is served whenever one
- **a.** tries hard.
- **b.** accepts God's will.
- **c.** does his or her best.
- **d.** engages in any type of hard labor.

Name ______________________ Date ______________ Class ________

Open-Book Selection Test *(continued)*

Analyze and Evaluate (15 points)

6. Identify the instances of personification that appear in the first stanza of "How Soon Hath Time."

____

____

____

____

____

____

____

BIG IDEA Connect (25 points)

Use a separate sheet of paper to answer one of the following essay questions.

7. In "When I Consider How My Light Is Spent," what does the allusion to the biblical parable of the talents add to your understanding of the poem?

Name ______________________ Date ______________ Class ________

Open-Book Selection Test

Score

from *Paradise Lost* (page 521)

Recall and Interpret (40 points total; 8 points each)
Write the letter of the best answer.

_____ **1.** In which set of lines is the subject of Paradise Lost stated?
- **a.** lines 1–5
- **b.** lines 6–16
- **c.** lines 17–26
- **d.** lines 27–32

_____ **2.** In which set of lines is the purpose of Paradise Lost stated?
- **a.** lines 4–5
- **b.** lines 12–16
- **c.** lines 19–23
- **d.** lines 25–26

_____ **3.** In seeking the aid of the "Heavenly Muse" (line 6 of Paradise Lost), the speaker identifies himself with
- **a.** Satan.
- **b.** Moses.
- **c.** Adam.
- **d.** Christ.

_____ **4.** Paradise Lost indicates that Satan was cast out of Heaven for
- **a.** envying his peers.
- **b.** tempting Adam and Eve.
- **c.** promoting human suffering.
- **d.** challenging God's authority.

_____ **5.** Which of the following does Paradise Lost indicate is most responsible for Satan's fall?
- **a.** lust
- **b.** pride
- **c.** jealousy
- **d.** curiosity

Vocabulary Practice (20 points total; 4 points each)
Write the letter of the best answer.

_____ **6.** Which of the following is an example of **transgression**?
- **a.** stealing
- **b.** traveling
- **c.** conversing

_____ **7.** What amount of rain can be called a **deluge**?
- **a.** a fair amount
- **b.** a huge amount
- **c.** a small amount

_____ **8.** To **discern** an object from afar requires a
- **a.** good eye.
- **b.** sharp ear.
- **c.** keen nose.

Name ______ Date ______ Class ______

Open-Book Selection Test

(continued)

_____ **9.** Which creatures are most likely to be seen in **myriads**?

a. ants
b. whales
c. wolves

_____ **10.** One type of **subterranean** geographic feature is

a. a crag.
b. a cave.
c. a valley.

Analyze and Evaluate (20 points total; 5 points each)

Milton incorporates many allusions into *Paradise Lost.* Four such allusions appear in the opening lines. For each, explain its meaning; use the text notes to help if necessary. Then explain what the use of that allusion adds to the poem.

Allusion	Meaning	What It Adds to the Poem
11. Sinai, 1.7		
12. Sion hill, 1.10		
13. Siloa's brook, 1.11		
14. Aonian mount, 1.15		

BIG IDEA Connect (20 points)

Use a separate sheet of paper to answer one of the following essay questions.

15. In *Paradise Lost*, why does Satan prefer Hell to Heaven? Support your ideas with reference to the poem.

Name ______________________ Date ______________ Class __________

Selection Test

Score

from ***The Pilgrim's Progress*** **(page 534)**

Recall and Interpret (48 points total; 6 points each)
Write the letter of the best answer.

_____ **1.** Christian and Faithful go to Vanity Fair in an effort to
- **a.** complete their journey.
- **b.** buy goods for their journey.
- **c.** take a rest from their journey.
- **d.** find pilgrims to accompany them on their journey.

_____ **2.** The selection indicates that the most popular wares at the fair are those produced by
- **a.** a devil.
- **b.** the British.
- **c.** the French and Italians.
- **d.** the Roman Catholic Church.

_____ **3.** Each of the following immediately draws the townspeople's attention to Christian and Faithful except for the pilgrims'
- **a.** language.
- **b.** appearance.
- **c.** mode of travel.
- **d.** attitude toward the fair's wares.

_____ **4.** Initially, the attitude of Christian and Faithful toward the fair's wares is one of
- **a.** fear.
- **b.** guilt.
- **c.** mockery.
- **d.** lack of interest.

_____ **5.** The selection indicates that the one thing Christian and Faithful would purchase if they could is something that is
- **a.** widely sold at Vanity Fair.
- **b.** never for sale at Vanity Fair.
- **c.** rarely for sale at Vanity Fair.
- **d.** freely given away at Vanity Fair.

_____ **6.** The men who first try Christian and Faithful decide that they are
- **a.** spies.
- **b.** saints.
- **c.** thieves.
- **d.** lunatics.

_____ **7.** What is the last thing that happens to Faithful in this excerpt?
- **a.** He is tortured and dies.
- **b.** He is returned to prison.
- **c.** He is taken up into Heaven.
- **d.** He escapes and continues his journey.

Name ______________________ Date ______________ Class __________

Selection Test

(continued)

______ **8.** Which of the following is typical of Bunyan's style in this excerpt?
- **a.** flowery dialogue
- **b.** unusual capitalization
- **c.** insertion of biblical quotations
- **d.** relatively simple sentence structure

Vocabulary Practice (12 points total; 4 points each)
Write the letter of the best answer.

______ **9.** The most logical answer to an **indictment** would be
a. "Not guilty." **b.** "Fine, thanks." **c.** "You're welcome."

______ **10.** Which of the following best expresses feeling **reconciled** to one's fate?
a. sighing **b.** fighting **c.** complaining

______ **11.** People on a **diverse** diet eat
- **a.** the same things every day.
- **b.** only fruits and vegetables.
- **c.** foods from many cultures.

Analyze and Evaluate (20 points total; 10 points each)

12. Think of this selection as an allegory. What are the origins of the Vanity Fair, and what is the significance of these origins? Where is the town of Vanity located, and what is the significance of its location?

____

____

____

____

____

____

____

BIG IDEA Connect (20 points)
Use a separate sheet of paper to answer the following essay question.

13. Identify two moral lessons that this selection teaches and explain how these lessons are conveyed to the reader.

Name ______________________ Date ______________ Class __________

Open-Book Selection Test

Score

On Her Loving Two Equally (page 544)

Recall and Interpret (45 points total; 9 points each)
Write the letter of the best answer.

_____**1.** In the first stanza, the speaker suggests that if only one man had loved her, she would have
- **a.** come to love the other.
- **b.** been able to return his feelings.
- **c.** cared less for him than she does now.
- **d.** cared twice as much for him as she does now.

_____**2.** Which of the following does the speaker seek from Cupid?
- **a.** advice
- **b.** patience
- **c.** forgiveness
- **d.** deliverance

_____**3.** What will happen if Cupid heeds the speaker's plea?
- **a.** She will discover what true love is.
- **b.** Both men will fall in love with her.
- **c.** Her relationship with one of the men will end.
- **d.** One of the men will fall in love with someone else.

_____**4.** The speaker indicates that when the choice of one man over the other is finally made, she will feel
- **a.** bored.
- **b.** guilty.
- **c.** relieved.
- **d.** heartbroken.

_____**5.** In which stanza does the speaker speak directly to Damon or Alexis?
- **a.** none
- **b.** stanza 1
- **c.** stanza 2
- **d.** stanza 3

Vocabulary Practice (15 points total; 5 points each)
Write the letter of the best answer.

_____**6.** Someone with a **passion** for music
- **a.** prefers silence.
- **b.** will practice daily.
- **c.** listens occasionally.

_____**7.** To **subdue** a bad habit successfully, you must
- **a.** break the habit.
- **b.** pick up the habit.
- **c.** replace the habit with another.

_____**8.** People who are **mourning** are likely to
- **a.** dance.
- **b.** weep.
- **c.** laugh.

Name ______________________ Date ______________ Class ________

Open-Book Selection Test *(continued)*

Analyze and Evaluate (20 points)

In the box on the left, identify an example of inversion in the poem. In the box on the right, write a reason that the poet might have reversed the words in that example.

9. Example of inversion	Possible reason

BIG IDEA Connect (20 points)

Use a separate sheet of paper to answer the following essay question.

10. Consider the possibility that this poem is a satire. If it is, what do you think is being satirized? In other words, who or what is the poet poking fun at? Write a paragraph supporting your ideas.

Name ______________________ Date ______________ Class __________

Selection Test

Score

An Essay of Dramatic Poesy (page 548)

Recall and Interpret (36 points total; 12 points each)
Write the letter of the best answer.

_____ **1.** Which playwright or playwriting team was alive at the time Dryden wrote this essay?
a. Jonson
b. Shakespeare
c. Beaumont and Fletcher
d. none of the above

_____ **2.** Dryden's opinion of Beaumont and Fletcher could best be described as
a. admiring.
b. objective.
c. contemptuous.
d. mixed or undecided.

_____ **3.** Dryden indicates that a Jonson play was least likely to focus on
a. war.
b. love.
c. politics.
d. the common man.

Vocabulary Practice (10 points total; 2 points each)
For each boldface word, write the letter of the word that means the opposite.

_____ **4. insipid** **a.** inadequate
_____ **5. bombast** **b.** disrespect
_____ **6. esteem** **c.** fascinating
_____ **7. superfluous** **d.** subject
_____ **8. monarch** **e.** simplicity

Name ______________________ Date ______________ Class ________

Selection Test

(continued)

Analyze and Evaluate (22 points)

9. What features of this essay make it "informal"? Cite the text to support your answer.

____

____

____

____

____

____

____

BIG IDEA Connect (32 points)

Use a separate sheet of paper to answer the following essay question.

10. Dryden admires Jonson, the "most learned and judicious" dramatist of all time, but he loves Shakespeare. Why might this be so? Support your answer.

Name ______________________ Date ______________ Class __________

Selection Test

Score

from *The Diary of Samuel Pepys* (page 554)

Recall and Interpret (40 points total; 8 points each)
Write the letter of the best answer.

_____ **1.** Which of the following best describes the overall effect of the coronation ceremony on Pepys?
a. It upsets him. **c.** It moves him to tears.
b. It fascinates him. **d.** It secretly amuses him.

_____ **2.** Which of the following is most responsible for Pepys's getting food at the coronation feast?
a. knowing the right people
b. the kindness of strangers
c. refusing to take no for an answer
d. being in the right place at the right time

_____ **3.** On the first day of the London fire, Pepys spends most of his time
a. helping the fire's victims.
b. organizing efforts to stop the fire.
c. observing and talking about the fire.
d. packing up and moving his belongings to safety.

_____ **4.** Government efforts to fight the London fire could best be described as
a. disastrous. **c.** nonexistent.
b. ineffective. **d.** very effective.

_____ **5.** When this excerpt from *The Diary of Samuel Pepys* ends, Pepys's greatest concern is the
a. future of London. **c.** safety of his wife.
b. future of the king. **d.** safety of his valuables.

Vocabulary Practice (20 points total; 5 points each)
Write the letter of the best answer.

_____ **6.** Something commonly used to **quench** a fire is
a. water. **b.** a match. **c.** a furnace.

_____ **7.** A word that means the opposite of **loath** is
a. sorry. **b.** eager. **c.** energetic.

_____ **8.** A **malicious** lie would be one that someone told in order to
a. cause trouble. **b.** seem important. **c.** avoid punishment.

_____ **9.** At which event would you most likely witness a **cavalcade**?
a. at a movie **b.** at a parade **c.** at a concert

Name ______________________ Date ______________ Class __________

Selection Test

(continued)

Analyze and Evaluate (18 points total; 6 points each)

Consider what the diary entries reveal about Pepys's personality and values. In each box on the left, list a trait or value Pepys displays. On the right, note a detail from the diary that exemplifies that trait or value.

Pepys's trait or value:	Detail
10.	
11.	
12.	

BIG IDEA Connect (22 points)

Use a separate sheet of paper to answer the following essay question.

13. In chronicling the fire, Pepys recounts his own effort to see it get under control. Describe the effort Pepys made, and discuss what his rendering of his role suggests about his character and beliefs.

Name ______________________ Date ______________ Class ______________

Selection Test

Score

A Modest Proposal (page 566)

Recall and Interpret (45 points total; 9 points each)
Write the letter of the best answer.

_____ **1.** In "A Modest Proposal," Swift is least concerned with the problem of
a. poverty. **c.** foreign misrule.
b. violent crime. **d.** religious discrimination.

_____ **2.** The tone of "A Modest Proposal" could best be described as
a. playful. **c.** accepting.
b. detached. **d.** mock-earnest.

_____ **3.** The greatest flaw in the "modest proposal" is that it ignores
a. logic. **c.** political reality.
b. human values. **d.** the consequences of the plan.

_____ **4.** In "A Modest Proposal," Swift displays the greatest contempt for
a. politicians. **c.** absentee landlords.
b. the Catholic clergy. **d.** single (unwed) mothers.

_____ **5.** Of the following, who supports British policy in Ireland?
a. only Swift
b. only the speaker of "A Modest Proposal"
c. both Swift and the speaker
d. neither Swift nor the speaker

Vocabulary Practice (15 points total; 5 points each)
Write the letter of the best answer.

_____ **6.** Someone who needs **sustenance** is
a. cold. **b.** tired. **c.** hungry.

_____ **7.** To show **deference** to a king or queen, people often
a. bow. **b.** cheer. **c.** look away.

_____ **8.** Select the sentence in which **digress** is used properly.
a. If you want two, digress that one into halves.
b. When I think of vacation, I digress from my work.
c. Stay in your seat and do not digress to the window.

Name ______________________ Date ______________ Class ________

Selection Test

(continued)

Analyze and Evaluate (20 points)

In the box on the left, identify a human flaw or shortcoming that Swift satirizes in "A Modest Proposal." In the box on the right, explain how Swift satirizes the flaw.

9. "A Modest Proposal"

Flaw	How is it satirized?

BIG IDEA Connect (20 points)

Use a separate sheet of paper to answer the following essay question.

10. Swift created a fictional speaker, or persona, in "A Modest Proposal" whose opinions varied widely from his own. What is the main point the speaker tries to communicate? What is Swift's main point? How does Swift communicate to the reader his opposition to the speaker's views?

Name ______________________ Date ______________ Class ________

Selection Test

Score

from *Gulliver's Travels* (page 575)

Recall and Interpret (50 points total; 10 points each)
Write the letter of the best answer.

_____ **1.** *Gulliver's Travels* is considered a parody because it
  a. offers a humorous criticism of society.
  b. contains exotic and fantastic elements.
  c. is a fictional account of a person's travels.
  d. is a humorous imitation of a particular type of literary work.

_____ **2.** Which of the following motivates the Lilliputians to shoot arrows at Gulliver?
  a. fear   **c.** cruelty
  b. anger   **d.** curiosity

_____ **3.** How does Swift intend the conflicts of the Lilliputians to seem to the reader?
  a. terribly tragic   **c.** surprisingly complex
  b. perfectly ordinary   **d.** remarkably ridiculous

_____ **4.** In offering to share the secret of gunpowder with the King of Brobdingnag, Gulliver gains the king's
  a. trust.   **c.** contempt.
  b. respect.   **d.** loyal devotion.

_____ **5.** How is Gulliver's attitude toward his people affected by the observations of the King of Brobdingnag?
  a. Gulliver's attitude is not affected.
  b. Gulliver adopts a more humble attitude.
  c. Gulliver adopts a more appreciative attitude.
  d. Gulliver adopts an attitude of shame and disgust.

Vocabulary Practice (10 points total; 5 points each)
Write the letter of the best answer.

_____ **6.** To **conjecture** about something is to
  a. make a guess.
  b. offer an observation.
  c. decide one way or the other.

_____ **7.** A measurement of **magnitude** collects data about something's
  a. cost or value.
  b. size or extent.
  c. nature or quality.

Name ______________________ Date ______________ Class __________

Selection Test

(continued)

Analyze and Evaluate (20 points; 10 points each)
Identify two things that Swift parodies in *Gulliver's Travels*, using examples from the text to support your choices.

8.
9.

BIG IDEA Connect (20 points)

10. How do Gulliver's adventures satirize the Enlightenment ideal of rational thought?

Name ______________________ Date ______________ Class ________

Open-Book Selection Test

Score

Epigrams and from An Essay on Man (page 588)

Recall and Interpret (45 points total; 9 points each)
Write the letter of the best answer.

_____ **1.** Why, according to Pope's epigram, is "a little learning . . . a dangerous thing"?
- **a.** Ignorance is the natural state of man.
- **b.** A little learning encourages people to challenge themselves.
- **c.** A little learning makes people feel dissatisfied with their lives.
- **d.** A little learning makes people think they know more than they do.

_____ **2.** In the first two lines of *An Essay on Man*, the speaker indicates that people should focus on learning about
- **a.** the world.
- **b.** God's will.
- **c.** human nature.
- **d.** the relationship between humans and God.

_____ **3.** Which of the following do the contrasts in *An Essay on Man* illustrate?
- **a.** the human condition
- **b.** the differences between man and God
- **c.** the differences between man as he is and man as he might be
- **d.** the differences between man as he is and man as he once was

_____ **4.** In the final line of *An Essay on Man*, the speaker suggests that mankind is all of the following EXCEPT a
- **a.** joke.
- **c.** mistake.
- **b.** triumph.
- **d.** mystery.

_____ **5.** Whether a couplet is a heroic couplet is a matter of
- **a.** its topic.
- **b.** its meter.
- **c.** whether it gives advice.
- **d.** whether it contains a moral.

Vocabulary Practice (15 points total; 5 points each)
Write the letter of the best answer.

_____ **6.** To **commend** someone for his or her work is to
- **a.** criticize its quality.
- **b.** ignore his or her successes.
- **c.** offer him or her compliments.

Name ______________________ Date ______________ Class ________

Open-Book Selection Test *(continued)*

_____ **7.** An example of **discord** is people
- **a.** arguing loudly.
- **b.** agreeing easily.
- **c.** discussing calmly.

_____ **8.** The best way to **disabuse** people of an incorrect idea is to
- **a.** insult their ignorance.
- **b.** teach them the correct idea.
- **c.** threaten them with violence.

Analyze and Evaluate (21 points total; 7 points each)
Paraphrase (express in your own words) the idea or point that each of the following heroic couplets expresses.

	What does this mean?
9. 'Tis education forms the common mind, Just as the twig is bent, the tree's inclined.	
10. Hope springs eternal in the human breast: Man never is, but always to be blest.	
11. A wit's a feather, and a chief's a rod; An honest man's the noblest work of God.	

BIG IDEA Connect (19 points)
Use a separate sheet of paper to answer the following essay question.

12. In this excerpt from "An Essay on Man," what is the attitude of the speaker toward humankind, and why does the speaker feel this way? Support your ideas with reference to the essay.

Name ______________________ Date ______________ Class __________

Open-Book Selection Test

Score

from *The Rape of the Lock* (page 594)

Recall and Interpret (50 points total; 10 points each)
Write the letter of the best answer.

_____**1.** Who are "the heroes and the nymphs" of the poem (1–9)?
- **a.** gods and goddesses
- **b.** the Baron and Belinda
- **c.** the poet and his readers
- **d.** wealthy young men and women

_____**2.** In what activity does Belinda seek victory while at Hampton?
- **a.** a cup of coffee
- **b.** a display of wit
- **c.** a game of cards
- **d.** a dance with a knight

_____**3.** Lines 29-32 foreshadow
- **a.** Belinda's sorrow over the lost lock.
- **b.** the Baron's triumph when he has the lock.
- **c.** the dangers of spilling coffee on expensive fabric.
- **d.** the love that will grow between Belinda and the Baron.

_____**4.** Why does Clarissa give the Baron her scissors?
- **a.** Clarissa loves the Baron.
- **b.** Clarissa dislikes Belinda.
- **c.** The Baron has asked for them.
- **d.** The Baron lies about why he wants them.

_____**5.** The poem concludes that Belinda should not regret the loss of her hair because
- **a.** the event will live forever in the poem.
- **b.** the Baron was just playing a silly prank.
- **c.** her hair will turn to dust one day anyway.
- **d.** her hair is more beautiful than other women's.

Vocabulary Practice (10 points total; 5 points each)
Write the letter of the best answer.

_____**6.** A **stratagem** is characterized by
- **a.** multiple layers.
- **b.** deception or surprise.
- **c.** precious gems.

Name ______________________ Date ______________ Class __________

Open-Book Selection Test *(continued)*

_____ **7.** Which is most likely to **confound** an audience?

a. a pop concert
b. an interesting lecture
c. a complicated magic trick

Analyze and Evaluate (20 points)

8. A mock-epic makes fun of social customs and traditions by exaggerating them. Name two customs that Pope exaggerates in *The Rape of the Lock*, and explain his satirical point.

____

____

____

____

____

____

____

____

____

____

____

BIG IDEA Connect (20 points)

Use a separate sheet of paper to answer the following essay question.

9. Choose two images from the battle scene in Canto V. Describe each image, then comment on its effect in the unfolding story.

Name ______________________ Date ______________ Class __________

Selection Test

Score

Letter to Her Daughter (page 604)

Recall and Interpret (36 points total; 6 points each)
Write the letter of the best answer.

_____ **1.** Montagu writes that her daughter's education was designed chiefly to enable her to be
- **a.** a suitable wife.
- **b.** a brilliant scholar.
- **c.** proud and independent.
- **d.** contented with her fate.

_____ **2.** Which of the following best describes Montagu's attitude toward her daughter's marriage?
- **a.** anxious
- **b.** approving
- **c.** scornful
- **d.** pleasantly surprised

_____ **3.** Montagu argues that her granddaughter should be raised differently than her daughter was because
- **a.** times have changed.
- **b.** their dreams are different.
- **c.** their prospects are different.
- **d.** there is no reason to make the same mistake twice.

_____ **4.** Montagu wants her granddaughter educated for all of the following reasons EXCEPT that it may
- **a.** help her unmask liars.
- **b.** allow her to add to the family's fame.
- **c.** make her more contented with her life.
- **d.** make marriage seem less desirable to her.

_____ **5.** Montagu suggests that her granddaughter "conceal whatever learning she attains" in order to
- **a.** attract a husband.
- **b.** fit in with her friends.
- **c.** avoid offending fools.
- **d.** avoid upsetting her father.

_____ **6.** In the metaphor, "In a lottery where there [are] . . . ten thousand blanks to a prize, it is the most prudent choice not to venture," Montagu compares a lottery to
- **a.** politics.
- **b.** marriage.
- **c.** education.
- **d.** social climbing.

Name ______________________ Date ______________ Class __________

Selection Test

(continued)

Vocabulary Practice (24 points total; 6 points each)
Write the letter of the best answer.

_____ **7.** One would be most likely to find an **edifice** in a publication dealing with
a. fashion. **b.** education. **c.** architecture.

_____ **8.** If someone is an **inveterate** liar, he or she tells lies
a. habitually. **b.** convincingly. **c.** as a last resort.

_____ **9.** If a situation **elates** you, you might say you are
a. satisfied. **b.** uncomfortable. **c.** delighted.

_____ **10.** You are most eager for a **diversion** when you feel
a. tired. **b.** bored. **c.** insecure.

Analyze and Evaluate (21 points; 7 points each)
In the boxes below, answer the questions about the following extended metaphor.

It is the common error of builders and parents to follow some plan they think beautiful (and perhaps is so) without considering that nothing is beautiful that is misplaced. Hence we see so many [buildings] raised that the raisers can never inhabit, being too large for their fortunes. Vistas are laid open over barren heaths, and apartments contrived for a coolness very agreeable in Italy but killing in the north of Britain. Thus every woman endeavors to breed her daughter a fine lady, qualifying her for a station in which she will never appear, and at the same time incapacitating her for that retirement to which she is destined.

11. Identify two pairs of things that the metaphor compares.	
and	*and*
12. Identify two ways in which each of these pairs of things is alike.	
13. What is the main idea that Montague uses the metaphor to convey to her daughter?	

BIG IDEA Connect (19 points)
Use a separate sheet of paper to answer the following essay question.

14. List three character traits of Montagu. Then, in a paragraph or two, explain how her letter reveals these qualities.

Name ______________________ Date ______________ Class __________

Selection Test

Score

from ***The Spectator*** (page 616)

Recall and Interpret (42 points; 6 points each)
Write the letter of the best answer.

_____ **1.** Which of the following best describes the style of these essays?
- **a.** poetic
- **b.** formal
- **c.** hard-hitting.
- **d.** conversational.

_____ **2.** According to the narrator, Sir Roger's peculiar qualities and behaviors make him a particularly good
- **a.** advice giver.
- **b.** judge of character.
- **c.** friend and neighbor.
- **d.** interpreter of the law.

_____ **3.** Which of the following does the narrator indicate had the greatest effect on Sir Roger's life?
- **a.** fighting a duel
- **b.** being disappointed in love
- **c.** kicking a swindler in public
- **d.** explaining a passage in the Game Act

_____ **4.** According to the narrator, manners in the country are different from those in the city mainly in that country manners
- **a.** are less formal.
- **b.** are practically nonexistent.
- **c.** are considerably more formal.
- **d.** vary a great deal from family to family.

_____ **5.** What is the narrator's position on the manners of the countryside and the city?
- **a.** He prefers those of the city.
- **b.** He prefers those of the country.
- **c.** He thinks equally well of both.
- **d.** He doesn't care much for either.

_____ **6.** Where does the narrator suggest that his own natural behavior is likely to be considered ill-mannered?
- **a.** in the city only
- **b.** in the country only
- **c.** in both the city and the country
- **d.** in neither the city nor the country

_____ **7.** According to the narrator, country folk are ahead of the times in
- **a.** fashion only.
- **b.** manners only.
- **c.** both fashion and manners.
- **d.** neither fashion nor manners.

Name ______________________ Date ____________ Class ________

Selection Test

(continued)

Vocabulary Practice (12 points; 4 points each)
Write the letter of the best answer.

_____ **8.** A word that means the opposite of **negligence** is
a. luxury. **b.** care. **c.** generosity.

_____ **9.** Someone who engages in **irrational** behavior is showing a lack of good
a. taste. **b.** sense. **c.** manners.

_____ **10.** Someone who behaves with **complaisance** is
a. agreeable. **b.** interesting. **c.** annoying.

Analyze and Evaluate (24 points; 12 points each)
Joseph Addison is remarked to have been "serious, reserved, and sensible," whereas Sir Richard Steele is remarked to have been "brash, outgoing, and always in debt." Describe how each man's personality manifests itself in his writing style, using examples from the text.

11. Sir Richard Steele, "Sir Roger de Coverley":
12. Richard Addison, "Country Manners":

BIG IDEA Connect (22 points)
Use a separate sheet of paper to answer the following essay question.

13. After reading these two essays, how do you account for the popularity of *The Spectator* in the eighteenth century? Support your ideas with reference to the selections.

Name ______________________ Date ______________ Class ________

Selection Test

Score

from *A Journal of the Plague Year* (page 624); from *The Demon in the Freezer* (page 629); from *History of the Peloponnesian War* (page 635); and from *The Plague* (page 639)

Recall and Interpret (35 points total; 5 points each)

Write the letter of the best answer.

_____**1.** In "A Journal of the Plague Year," the narrator is driven to view the great pit in the churchyard by a sense of
- **a.** guilt.
- **b.** curiosity.
- **c.** religious devotion.
- **d.** duty to his fellow man.

_____**2.** The narrator's reaction to the man who faints in the churchyard could best be described as
- **a.** scornful.
- **b.** embarrassed.
- **c.** concerned.
- **d.** matter-of-fact.

_____**3.** According to "The Demon in the Freezer," which of the following is NOT characteristic of smallpox?
- **a.** The virus is small and airborne.
- **b.** Early symptoms can appear flu-like.
- **c.** The virus hides at first in the lymph cells.
- **d.** Just one inhaled particle can cause the illness.

_____**4.** Why did Ljatif's doctors not recognize that he had smallpox?
- **a.** Ljatif had recently returned from abroad.
- **b.** They had no training in infectious diseases.
- **c.** No cases had been seen in over forty years.
- **d.** Ljatif demonstrated an allergy to penicillin.

_____**5.** Why did the people of Attica stop offering prayers and consulting oracles during the plague, according to Thucydides?
- **a.** They were too full of grief to attend to these activities.
- **b.** These activities reminded them that the gods were angry.
- **c.** These activities brought them neither answers nor relief.
- **d.** They decided to suffer through the plague without complaint.

_____**6.** What grieves the plague survivors most in "*The Plague*"?
- **a.** They are physically weak from illness.
- **b.** They cannot remember those who died clearly.
- **c.** They do not know when the plague will come again.
- **d.** They cannot continue working and living in their city.

Name ______________________ Date ______________ Class __________

Selection Test

(continued)

_____ **7.** What, in the end, does the plague destroy, even among the survivors?
a. love
b. peace
c. patience
d. endurance

Vocabulary Practice (15 points total; 5 points each)
Write the letter of the best answer.

_____ **8.** Which of the following demonstrates feeling **confined**?
a. coloring inside the lines
b. speaking before being spoken to
c. changing lanes on the highway

_____ **9.** People may feel **oppressed** by
a. too much food.
b. too much work.
c. too many friends.

_____ **10.** Which achievement could be described as **prodigious**?
a. fixing dinner for your family
b. preparing to compete in the Olympics
c. turning in an essay in English class on time

Analyze and Evaluate (20 points total; 5 points each)
Defoe's narrator, Thucydides, and Camus's narrator have different perspectives of the plagues they wrote about. Complete the chart to compare their responses in terms of how factual or how fictionalized their accounts are (i.e., the genre in which they were writing).

11. What do the responses of the three narrators have in common?

12. How does Defoe's narrator's response reflect the genre of historical fiction?	**13.** How does Thucydides' response reflect the genre of history?	**14.** How does Camus's narrator's response reflect the genre of fiction?

BIG IDEA Connect (30 points)
Use a separate sheet of paper to answer the following essay question.

15. Having read the excerpt from "The Demon in the Freezer," describe how cultural factors in Yugoslavia in the 1970s affected the smallpox epidemic started by the Pilgrim.

Name ______________________ Date ______________ Class __________

Selection Test

Score

Death by Mosquito (page 644)

Recall and Interpret (60 points total; 12 points each)
Write the letter of the best answer.

_____ **1.** Why were the three million deaths from malaria in 2003 needless?
- **a.** Malaria is easy to get.
- **b.** Malaria need not be fatal.
- **c.** Malaria's comeback was preventable.
- **d.** Malaria kills more children than adults.

_____ **2.** Which is NOT a known method of preventing deaths from malaria?
- **a.** sleeping under treated netting
- **b.** spraying antimosquito pesticides
- **c.** treating sufferers with wormwood
- **d.** eliminating mosquitoes from a region

_____ **3.** Where is malaria always likely to present the most serious problem?
- **a.** tropical regions
- **b.** industrialized areas
- **c.** urban parts of Africa
- **d.** areas with high birth rates

_____ **4.** What effect does the parasite causing malaria have on the mosquito?
- **a.** Positive: the mosquito lives longer.
- **b.** Neutral: the mosquito is only the carrier.
- **c.** Negative: the mosquito will not be able to reproduce.
- **d.** None: the mosquito's short lifespan prevents infection.

_____ **5.** What is most needed to limit the number of malaria cases?
- **a.** research to find a new medicine
- **b.** genetic manipulation of mosquitoes
- **c.** financial assistance from donor nations
- **d.** cooperation of world environmentalists

Name ______________________ Date ______________ Class __________

Selection Test (continued)

Analyze and Evaluate (20 points)

6. Complete the causal chart to explain why malaria cases are on the rise in Africa.

Cause:	Malaria cases are on the rise in Afica.
Cause:	
Cause:	

BIG IDEA Connect (20 points)

Use a separate sheet of paper to answer the following essay question.

7. Explain how an increase in the number of malaria cases can lead to a country's economic decline, and how that decline, in turn, leads to more cases of malaria.

Name ____________________ Date ______________ Class ________

Selection Test

Score

from *A Dictionary of the English Language* (page 650) and Letter to Lord Chesterfield (page 654)

Recall and Interpret (40 points total; 5 points each)
Write the letter of the best answer.

_____ **1.** In the preface to *A Dictionary of the English Language*, Johnson says that critics would be justified in
- **a.** ignoring the publication of *A Dictionary of the English Language*.
- **b.** finding much to fault and to praise in *A Dictionary of the English Language*.
- **c.** finding more to fault in *A Dictionary of the English Language* than to praise.
- **d.** finding nothing deserving of criticism in *A Dictionary of the English Language*.

_____ **2.** In the preface, Johnson characterizes the work of writing the book as mainly
- **a.** dull.
- **b.** easy.
- **c.** thrilling.
- **d.** frustrating.

_____ **3.** Johnson indicates that the circumstances under which the work was done were
- **a.** exciting.
- **b.** refreshing.
- **c.** satisfactory.
- **d.** demoralizing.

_____ **4.** In *A Dictionary of the English Language*, Johnson's definition of lexicographer suggests that he
- **a.** scorns such work.
- **b.** glamorizes such work.
- **c.** has a sense of humor about himself.
- **d.** wishes to distance himself from such work.

_____ **5.** In this excerpt from *A Dictionary of the English Language*, which of the following is used most often to provide examples of words used in context?
- **a.** the Bible
- **b.** Dryden's works
- **c.** Johnson's works
- **d.** Shakespeare's works

_____ **6.** Johnson was motivated to write the "Letter to Lord Chesterfield" by
- **a.** the publication of *A Dictionary of the English Language*.
- **b.** the publication of Chesterfield's praise for *A Dictionary of the English Language*.
- **c.** the publication of Chesterfield's criticism of *A Dictionary of the English Language*.
- **d.** the receipt of Chesterfield's formal offer of patronage.

Name ______________________ Date ____________ Class ________

Selection Test

(continued)

_____ **7.** In the "Letter to Lord Chesterfield," which of the following does Johnson indicate was most responsible for the completion of A *Dictionary of the English Language*?

a. himself
b. his publisher
c. Lord Chesterfield's patronage
d. the hard work of his assistants

_____ **8.** In the "Letter to Lord Chesterfield," Johnson's attitude toward Lord Chesterfield could best be described as

a. bitter.
b. amused.
c. unconcerned.
d. flattering.

Vocabulary Practice (20 points total; 4 points each)

For each boldface word, write the letter of the word that means the OPPOSITE.

_____ **9. intuitive** — **a.** negligence
_____ **10. exultation** — **b.** learned
_____ **11. immutably** — **c.** temporarily
_____ **12. aggregated** — **d.** misery
_____ **13. vigilance** — **e.** individual

Analyze and Evaluate (20 points; 10 points each)

Johnson's "voice," comprised of his writing style and personal qualities, is manifest in the excerpt below. Use Examples from the excerpt to describe these aspects of Johnson's voice.

"Seven years, my Lord, have now passed since I waited in your outward rooms, or was repulsed from your door; during which time I have been pushing on my work through difficulties of which it is useless to complain and have brought it at last to the verge of publication without one act of assistance, one word of encouragement, or one smile of favor. Such treatment I did not expect, for I never had a patron before."

14. Johnson's style
15. Johnson's qualities

BIG IDEA Connect (20 points)

Use a separate sheet of paper to answer the following essay question.

16. In A *Dictionary of the English Language*, Johnson defines a patron as "a wretch who supports with insolence and is paid with flattery." In "Letter to Lord Chesterfield," Johnson asks, "Is not a patron, my Lord, one who looks with unconcern on a man struggling for life in the water and, when he has reached ground, encumbers him with help?" What do these definitions suggest about Johnson's view of the patron and the patron's relationship with the writer?

Name ______________________ Date ______________ Class __________

Selection Test

Score

from *The Life of Samuel Johnson* (page 661)

Recall and Interpret (48 points total; 8 points each)
Write the letter of the best answer.

_____**1.** During their first meeting, Boswell seems to have been most impressed with Johnson's
- **a.** brilliance.
- **b.** friendliness.
- **c.** oddities.
- **d.** modesty.

_____**2.** Johnson's first words to Boswell made him feel
- **a.** proud.
- **b.** angry.
- **c.** relaxed.
- **d.** insecure.

_____**3.** Boswell's account of his first meeting with Johnson focuses on how well-supplied Johnson was with
- **a.** money.
- **b.** opinions.
- **c.** morals.
- **d.** friends.

_____**4.** According to Boswell, Johnson was narrow-minded about
- **a.** religion and politics.
- **b.** literature and philosophy.
- **c.** all four of these topics.
- **d.** nothing at all.

_____**5.** Boswell seems to feel that Johnson's frequent outbursts, especially those directed toward his friends, were justifiable because of Johnson's
- **a.** age.
- **b.** success.
- **c.** health.
- **d.** hard work.

_____**6.** According to Boswell, when could one truly trust Johnson's words?
- **a.** never
- **b.** always
- **c.** when reading what he had written
- **d.** when listening to him speak in public

Vocabulary Practice (15 points total; 3 points each)
Write the letter of the best answer.

_____**7.** Which of the following people is, by definition, **zealous**?
- **a.** a fanatic
- **b.** a clown
- **c.** an actor

_____**8.** Who is likely to receive much public **veneration**?
- **a.** a farmer
- **b.** an award-winning scientist
- **c.** a starlet

Name ______________________ Date ______________ Class __________

Selection Test

(continued)

_____ **9.** Your **precepts** make up your

a. goals. **b.** insecurities. **c.** moral code.

_____ **10.** A career that especially calls for **ingenuity** is

a. lawn care.
b. engineering.
c. coaching soccer.

_____ **11.** An **impetuous** person is

a. impulsive. **b.** generous. **c.** forgetful.

Analyze and Evaluate (20 points total; 5 points each)

Think about what this excerpt from Boswell's biography of Johnson reveals about both men. Then, in each box on the left, identify a strong quality the man indicated possesses. In each box on the right, tell how the quality is revealed in this excerpt.

	Quality:	How it is revealed in the excerpt:
JOHNSON	**12.**	
	13.	

	Quality:	How it is revealed in the excerpt:
BOSWELL	**14.**	
	15.	

BIG IDEA Connect (17 points)

Use a separate sheet of paper to answer the following essay question.

16. From reading the excerpt, which word do you think best describes this biography—biased, balanced, or objective? Support your opinion.

Name ______________________ Date ______________ Class __________

Selection Test

Score

from *Samuel Johnson* (page 670)

Recall and Interpret (60 points total; 12 points each)
Write the letter of the best answer.

_____ **1.** This excerpt focuses mainly on
- **a.** the kind of man Boswell was.
- **b.** the early years of Boswell's life.
- **c.** the work Boswell did for Johnson.
- **d.** the unpublished writings of Boswell.

_____ **2.** What role did Johnson fill in Boswell's life?
- **a.** He taught him to write.
- **b.** He introduced him to London.
- **c.** He became an influential role model.
- **d.** He encouraged him to keep a journal.

_____ **3.** Why did Boswell so greatly want to develop a strict moral code?
- **a.** He wanted to enter the clergy.
- **b.** He wanted his father's approval.
- **c.** Mental instability ran in his family.
- **d.** His natural impulses ran toward excess.

_____ **4.** Which wrong assumption do many readers make about Boswell?
- **a.** that he wrote only "The Life of Samuel Johnson"
- **b.** that he and Johnson were decades apart in age
- **c.** that he longed for but did not achieve fame in his lifetime
- **d.** that he and Johnson were constantly in each other's company

_____ **5.** Why is it important that Boswell referred to Johnson as "Dr. Johnson" in his biography?
- **a.** Johnson was not actually a doctor.
- **b.** Johnson preferred the title "Esquire."
- **c.** Only Boswell was allowed to call him this.
- **d.** Readers have called Johnson "Dr." for two centuries.

Name ______________________ Date ______________ Class __________

Selection Test

(continued)

Analyze and Evaluate (18 points total; 6 points each)

Identify two traits of his family that Boswell tried to change or control in himself. Then explain how he attempted to make these changes.

6. Trait:	**8.** How Boswell tried to make changes:
7. Trait:	

BIG IDEA Connect (22 points)

Use a separate sheet of paper to answer the following essay question.

9. Describe the social and political world of London that Boswell moved in when he visited with Johnson and other eminent men.

Name ______________________ Date ______________ Class __________

Open-Book Selection Test

Score

Elegy Written in a Country Churchyard (page 710)

Recall and Interpret (48 points total; 6 points each)
Write the letter of the best answer.

_____ **1.** In which stanza does it first become clear that this poem's setting is a graveyard?
- **a.** stanza 1
- **b.** stanza 4
- **c.** stanza 6
- **d.** stanza 9

_____ **2.** Which of the following best describes the overall mood of the poem?
- **a.** fearful
- **b.** hopeful
- **c.** yearning
- **d.** melancholy

_____ **3.** The personification of death in line 44 most strongly suggests that death is
- **a.** just.
- **b.** dishonest.
- **c.** uncaring.
- **d.** sentimental.

_____ **4.** Which of the following does the speaker contrast with Hampden, Milton, and Cromwell?
- **a.** those who had no potential
- **b.** those who fulfilled their potential
- **c.** those who had no chance to fulfill their potential
- **d.** those who wasted chances to fulfill their potential

_____ **5.** The speaker maintains that the villagers' situations in life kept them from all of the following except
- **a.** accomplishing great things.
- **b.** committing bold crimes.
- **c.** living useful and happy lives.
- **d.** having their qualities widely recognized.

_____ **6.** In lines 73–76, the speaker suggests that the deceased villagers' lives were
- **a.** joyful.
- **b.** peaceful.
- **c.** miserable.
- **d.** memorable.

_____ **7.** To whom does *thee* refer in line 93?
- **a.** the reader
- **b.** the speaker
- **c.** the honored dead
- **d.** the "unhonored dead"

_____ **8.** In lines 98–116, the shepherd describes a man who is all of the following except
- **a.** lonely.
- **b.** conflicted.
- **c.** energetic.
- **d.** melancholy.

Name ______________________ Date ______________ Class __________

Open-Book Selection Test *(continued)*

Vocabulary Practice (15 points total; 3 points each)
Write the letter of the word that means that OPPOSITE of the given word.

____ **9.** pomp
____ **10.** inevitable
____ **11.** genial
____ **12.** uncouth
____ **13.** kindred

a. preventable
b. alien
c. rude
d. sophisticated
e. squalor

Analyze and Evaluate (17 points)
Use a separate sheet of paper to answer the following essay question.

14. What does the epitaph suggest about what Gray valued in life? Support your ideas with references to the poem.

BIG IDEA Connect (20 points)
Use a separate sheet of paper to answer the following essay question.

15. Select one of the first three stanzas and connect the landscape images therein to the speaker's emotions and the emotions he hopes to conjure in the reader.

Name ______________________ Date ______________ Class __________

Open-Book Selection Test

Score

John Anderson, My Jo (page 719), To a Mouse (page 720), and Auld Lang Syne (page 722)

Recall and Interpret (54 points total; 6 points each)
Write the letter of the best answer.

_____ **1.** The speaker in "John Anderson, My Jo" is most likely
- **a.** John Anderson.
- **b.** the poet himself.
- **c.** John Anderson's wife.
- **d.** John Anderson's mother.

_____ **2.** In "John Anderson, My Jo," the speaker talks directly to
- **a.** Robert Burns.
- **b.** John Anderson.
- **c.** readers of the poem.
- **d.** the British government.

_____ **3.** In the second stanza of "John Anderson, My Jo," the verbs *clamb* and *totter* help define the conditions of
- **a.** good and evil.
- **b.** youth and age.
- **c.** belief and doubt.
- **d.** happiness and anger.

_____ **4.** In "To a Mouse," the line "wee sleekit cow'rin', tim'rous beastie" describes
- **a.** the poet.
- **b.** the mouse.
- **c.** mortal man.
- **d.** hope for the future.

_____ **5.** The speaker in "To a Mouse" is most likely
- **a.** a farmer
- **b.** the mouse.
- **c.** someone from the city.
- **d.** John Anderson as a young man.

_____ **6.** The speaker in "To a Mouse" considers the mouse better off than he is himself because the mouse
- **a.** is just a simple "beastie."
- **b.** has not broken "nature's social union."
- **c.** can, with time and effort, rebuild its burrow.
- **d.** lives only in the present, not the past or future.

_____ **7.** The poem compares the wrecking of the mouse's burrow to the
- **a.** English domination of Scotland.
- **b.** mistreatment of animals by humans.
- **c.** damage done to the earth by humans.
- **d.** ruin of even well-planned human efforts.

_____ **8.** Which of the following phrases is not an example of dialect?
- **a.** "bickering brattle"
- **b.** "wee-bit housie too in ruin"
- **c.** "proving foresight may be vain"
- **d.** "cost thee mony a weary nibble"

Open-Book Selection Test *(continued)*

_____ **9.** How long has the speaker in "Auld Lang Syne" known the person he addresses?
- **a.** his whole life
- **b.** since boyhood
- **c.** for several years
- **d.** just a few weeks

Vocabulary Practice (10 points total; 5 points each)
Write the letter of the best answer.

_____ **10.** **Dominion** is the exercise of
- **a.** faith.
- **b.** control.
- **c.** release.

_____ **11.** Which season would most likely be described as **bleak?**
- **a.** Winter
- **b.** Autumn
- **c.** Spring

Analyze and Evaluate (18 points total; 9 points each)
Paraphrase the lines below in modern Standard English.

DIALECT	STANDARD
"The best laid schemes o' mice an' men / Gang aft a-gley / An' lea'e us nought but grief an' pain / For promised joy."	**12.**
"We twa hae run about the braes, / And pu'd the gowans fine; / But we've wander'd mony a weary foot / Sin' auld lang syne."	**13.**

BIG IDEA Connect (18 points)

14. Discuss what might be lost if "To a Mouse" were written in Standard English rather than dialect. In your answer, consider literary elements such as rhyme, rhythm, and tone, as well as the message of the poem.

Name ______________________ Date ______________ Class __________

Selection Test

Score

from *A Vindication of the Rights of Woman* (page 727)

Recall and Interpret (40 points total; 8 points each)
Write the letter of the best answer.

_____ **1.** According to the writer, women are all too often trained to be
- **a.** good mothers.
- **b.** merely decorative.
- **c.** highly competitive.
- **d.** unnaturally masculine.

_____ **2.** Wollstonecraft states that women should avoid traditionally "masculine" behaviors such as
- **a.** reading and writing.
- **b.** hunting and gambling.
- **c.** dressing well and placing importance on clothing.
- **d.** seeking higher education and getting advanced degrees.

_____ **3.** Throughout the essay, Wollstonecraft argues that women are
- **a.** simple-minded.
- **b.** superior to men.
- **c.** capable of reason.
- **d.** not to be trusted.

_____ **4.** According to the essay, marriages are most successful when based on
- **a.** romantic love.
- **b.** respect and friendship.
- **c.** the man's desire to protect the woman.
- **d.** the woman's ability to care for children.

_____ **5.** Wollstonecraft's argument is primarily directed to
- **a.** both men and women.
- **b.** both parents and educators.
- **c.** women who already feel as she does.
- **d.** men who think things should stay as they are.

Vocabulary Practice (20 points total; 4 points each)
Write the letter of the best answer.

_____ **6.** Which is most likely to excite a person's **indignation**?
- **a.** politics
- **b.** weather
- **c.** music

_____ **7.** A **rational** person is
- **a.** reasonable.
- **b.** hot-headed
- **c.** mild-mannered.

_____ **8.** If in a **congenial** mood, you might
- **a.** give a friend a gift.
- **b.** give a friend grief.
- **c.** ignore your friend.

Name ______________________ Date ______________ Class __________

Selection Test

(continued)

_____ **9.** Someone who has a **faculty** for math
- **a.** likes math.
- **b.** is good at math.
- **c.** does not understand math.

_____ **10.** A person **condescends** when he or she
- **a.** stoops to behavior he or she detests.
- **b.** changes his or her mind about something.
- **c.** stops causing harm to someone else.

Analyze and Evaluate (20 points total; 5 points each)

In the labeled boxes below, note the subject of the essay, the writer's thesis, and two pieces of evidence that support the thesis.

11. Subject	
12. Thesis	
13. Evidence	**14.** Evidence

BIG IDEA Connect (20 points)

Use a separate sheet of paper to answer the following essay question.

15. What concern does Wollstonecraft voice regarding women and physical appearance? In your opinion, is it still a valid concern today? Explain.

Name ______________________ Date ______________ Class __________

Selection Test

Score

Raising Their Voices (page 736)

Recall and Interpret (60 points total; 12 points each)
Write the letter of the best answer.

_____ **1.** What is so unusual about El Degheidi's career as a film director?
- **a.** Muslim film directors are rare.
- **b.** Women film directors are rare.
- **c.** Egyptian film directors are rare.
- **d.** Egyptian women film directors are rare.

_____ **2.** What is women's traditional role in Arab society?
- **a.** leader
- **b.** educator
- **c.** housewife
- **d.** entrepreneur

_____ **3.** What area does the article NOT mention as an area in which Arab women are making progress?
- **a.** athletics
- **b.** education
- **c.** government
- **d.** fiction writing

_____ **4.** Why do many progressive Arab women choose to continue to wear a veil?
- **a.** out of a sense of fashion
- **b.** out of fear of punishment
- **c.** out of devotion to tradition
- **d.** out of a sense of obligation

_____ **5.** What do many progressive Arabs advise about changing women's roles?
- **a.** Change is positive.
- **b.** Change is impossible.
- **c.** Change will be welcomed.
- **d.** Change must occur slowly.

Name ______________________ Date ______________ Class ________

Selection Test

(continued)

Analyze and Evaluate (20 points total; 5 points each)

Complete the cause-and-effect graphic organizer to list the obstacles Arab women face when they try to find work.

6.	Obstacles to Arab women finding work
7.	
8.	
9.	

BIG IDEA Connect (20 points)

Use a separate sheet of paper to answer the following essay question.

10. Which idea important to the Romantics is at work in the current situation of Arab women?

Name ______________________ Date ______________ Class __________

Selection Test

Score

from *The Diary of Fanny Burney* (page 744)

Recall and Interpret (48 points total; 6 points each)
Write the letter of the best answer.

_____ **1.** Burney's discoveries of people's reactions to her book make her feel mainly
- **a.** upset.
- **b.** foolish.
- **c.** delighted.
- **d.** confident.

_____ **2.** When people assume that her book was authored by a man, Burney feels
- **a.** guilty.
- **b.** amused.
- **c.** insulted.
- **d.** embarrassed.

_____ **3.** According to Burney, what was the main reason she gave a poor oral reading of *Evelina* for Mr. Crisp?
- **a.** her illness
- **b.** his behavior
- **c.** delight in fooling him
- **d.** embarrassment in reading something she had written

_____ **4.** What does Burney think will happen as the fame of her book grows?
- **a.** It will receive more negative criticism.
- **b.** It will receive more favorable attention.
- **c.** She will cease to care so much about readers' reactions.
- **d.** Her friends and family will become jealous of her success.

_____ **5.** Mrs. Thrale's first invitation to Streatham has the effect of making Fanny feel all of the following EXCEPT
- **a.** thrilled.
- **b.** insecure.
- **c.** flattered.
- **d.** suspicious.

_____ **6.** Burney is impressed with Mrs. Thrale's efforts to make her feel
- **a.** at ease.
- **b.** ordinary.
- **c.** important.
- **d.** successful.

_____ **7.** When Mr. Crisp confronts Burney about her authorship of *Evelina*, his tone is one of
- **a.** envy.
- **b.** concern.
- **c.** mock anger.
- **d.** deep respect.

_____ **8.** Which of the following does the diary indicate was least important to Burney?
- **a.** her family's reception of *Evelina*
- **b.** the public's reception of *Evelina*
- **c.** the public's interest in the author of *Evelina*
- **d.** the amount of money brought in from sales of Evelina

Name ______________________ Date ______________ Class ________

Selection Test

(continued)

Vocabulary Practice (10 points total; 2 points each)

For each boldface word, write the letter of the word that means the opposite.

____ **9.** droll	**a.** fearful
____ **10.** confound	**b.** shallow
____ **11.** zenith	**c.** boring
____ **12.** sanguine	**d.** bottom
____ **13.** profound	**e.** clarify

Analyze and Evaluate (21 points)

Use a separate sheet of paper to answer the following essay question.

14. In a paragraph, explain why the following passage from Burney's diary is witty. Explain what her use of wit conveys about her attitude toward herself and her novel.

My recovery [from illness] . . . has been slow and sure; but as I could walk hardly three yards in a day at first, I found so much time to spare that I could not resist treating myself with a little private sport with Evelina, a young lady whom I think I have some right to make free with. I had promised Hetty that she should read it to Mr. Crisp . . . but I wrote my excuses and introduced it myself.

BIG IDEA Connect (21 points)

Use a separate sheet of paper to answer the following essay question.

15. In a brief essay, explain how this excerpt shows Burney, like others during the Romantic era, valuing feelings over reason. Provide textual examples to support your position.

Name ______________________ Date ______________ Class __________

Open-Book Selection Test

Score

A Poison Tree (page 756), The Lamb (page 757), and The Tyger (page 758)

Recall and Interpret (60 points total; 6 points each)
Write the letter of the best answer.

_____ **1.** In "A Poison Tree," the speaker contrasts a straightforward approach to anger with
- **a.** quietly planning revenge.
- **b.** secretly poisoning his enemy.
- **c.** resorting to physical violence.
- **d.** trying to forget the whole thing.

_____ **2.** The fate of the speaker's foe suggests that anger can be
- **a.** deadly.
- **b.** useful.
- **c.** controlled.
- **d.** mysterious.

_____ **3.** The argument in "A Poison Tree" is developed by
- **a.** simile.
- **b.** sonnet form.
- **c.** personification.
- **d.** extended metaphor.

_____ **4.** The speaker in "The Lamb" is
- **a.** the Lamb.
- **b.** Jesus Christ.
- **c.** a little child.
- **d.** a Christian minister.

_____ **5.** Descriptive words and imagery in the first stanza of "The Lamb" suggest that the lamb is a symbol of
- **a.** youth.
- **b.** summer.
- **c.** romance.
- **d.** innocence.

_____ **6.** The repeated lines in "The Lamb" are
- **a.** stanzas.
- **b.** refrains.
- **c.** quatrains.
- **d.** enjambment.

_____ **7.** Which of the following phrases does not contribute to the image of the tiger in the poem "The Tyger"?
- **a.** "sinews of thy heart"
- **b.** "fearful symmetry"
- **c.** "fire of thine eyes"
- **d.** "dread grasp"

_____ **8.** In "The Tyger," Blake creates a metaphor that compares the stars to
- **a.** warriors.
- **b.** blacksmiths.
- **c.** fears and terrors.
- **d.** hammers and anvils.

Open-Book Selection Test *(continued)*

_____ **9.** In "The Tyger," the speaker questions
- **a.** whether the Tyger should be chained up.
- **b.** why the Tyger was made in the first place.
- **c.** whether the Tyger and the Lamb had the same creator.
- **d.** what the Tyger will do now that it is free and on the loose.

_____ **10.** The rhyme and meter in both "The Tyger" and "The Lamb" are
- **a.** simple and regular.
- **b.** without clear patterns.
- **c.** repetitious and fast-paced.
- **d.** complicated and sophisticated.

Analyze and Evaluate (20 points total; 10 points each)

In the appropriate box below, list words and images from the three poems that symbolize innocence and experience. List as many examples as you can find for each term.

INNOCENCE	EXPERIENCE
11.	**12.**

BIG IDEA Connect (20 points)

Use a separate sheet of paper to answer the following essay question.

13. After reading these poems, how do you think Blake viewed innocence and experience? Give examples from the poems to support your answer. Do you agree or disagree with Blake's views? Give reasons for your opinion.

Name ______________________ Date ______________ Class __________

Open-Book Selection Test

Score

London (page 760), The Chimney Sweep from *Songs of Innocence* (page 761), and The Chimney Sweep from *Songs of Experience* (page 762)

Recall and Interpret (60 points total; 6 points each)
Write the letter of the best answer.

_____ **1.** The rhyme scheme for each stanza of "London" is
- **a.** *aabb.*
- **b.** *abab.*
- **c.** *abba.*
- **d.** *abcb.*

_____ **2.** Why would Romantic writers be displeased by the idea of "the charter'd Thames"?
- **a.** The Thames gave shape to the city of London.
- **b.** The Thames should be exploited economically.
- **c.** The Thames was the most important river in England.
- **d.** The Thames, as a natural thing, should be accessible to all.

_____ **3.** Which would NOT be an example of "mind-forg'd manacles"?
- **a.** feeling torn by longing
- **b.** feeling fearful of safety
- **c.** feeling wracked by guilt
- **d.** feeling anxious about money

_____ **4.** Why is the setting of the last stanza of "London," which occurs "thro' midnight streets," appropriate to the speaker's observations?
- **a.** He is speaking of illness.
- **b.** He is speaking of marriage.
- **c.** He is speaking of childbirth.
- **d.** He is speaking of prostitution.

_____ **5.** In "The Chimney Sweeper" from *Songs of Innocence*, the comparison of Tom's hair to a lamb's suggests the child's
- **a.** sadness.
- **b.** innocence.
- **c.** blonde coloring.
- **d.** inability to speak.

_____ **6.** Why is it symbolic that the children in the dream come out of coffins?
- **a.** The children's existence is a frightening one.
- **b.** Only death has the power to spare them from work.
- **c.** The beds in which the children sleep are like coffins.
- **d.** Only death will release these children from their misery.

Open-Book Selection Test *(continued)*

_____ **7.** What is the significance of the paleness of the children in the dream?
a. They are in heaven now.
b. They are all very frightened.
c. They are no longer covered in soot.
d. They are lit by a sharp, blinding light.

_____ **8.** What lesson does the speaker draw from Tom's dream?
a. The dreams of children can change their lives.
b. The dreams of children may give them false hope.
c. The children who work hard will be kept safe by God.
d. The children can only experience freedom in their dreams.

_____ **9.** Readers can infer that the person who speaks to the child in the first stanza of "The Chimney Sweep" from *Songs of Experience* is
a. a customer. **c.** the child's mother.
b. a passer-by. **d.** the child's employer.

_____ **10.** Why are the clothes that the child wears referred to as "the clothes of death"?
a. The clothes are filthy and ragged.
b. The clothes belonged to someone who died.
c. The clothes show that his parents have abandoned him.
d. The clothes allow him to do work that will eventually kill him.

Analyze and Evaluate (28 points total; 7 points each)
Describe the idea presented in the stanzas referenced below and the movement that occurs between each and the stanza that follows it.

11. Idea in stanza 2 of "London":	**12.** Idea in stanza 2 of "The Chimney Sweeper" from *Songs of Experience*:
13. Movement from stanza 2 to stanza 3 of "London":	
14. Movement from stanza 2 to stanza 3 of "The Chimney Sweeper" from *Songs of Experience*:	

BIG IDEA Connect (12 points)
Use a separate sheet of paper to answer the following essay question.

15. What Romantic emphasis or idea do the three poems together reinforce?

Name ______________________ Date ______________ Class __________

Selection Test

Score

from *Pride and Prejudice* (page 770)

Recall and Interpret (42 points total; 6 points each)
Write the letter of the best answer.

_____ **1.** Why is it a matter of such importance that Mr. Bingley has moved to the area?
- **a.** He is a wealthy bachelor.
- **b.** He is looking for a bride.
- **c.** He plans to refurbish Netherfield Park.
- **d.** He is expected to participate in local government.

_____ **2.** Which of his daughters does Mr. Bennet prefer?
- **a.** Jane
- **b.** Mary
- **c.** Lydia
- **d.** Elizabeth

_____ **3.** Mr. Bennet shocks Mrs. Bennet by
- **a.** attending a ball.
- **b.** calling on Mr. Bingley.
- **c.** arranging a marriage for Jane.
- **d.** paying attention to her gossip.

_____ **4.** Of what literary element is this sentence from the novel an example: "'If I can but see one of my daughters happily settled at Netherfield,' said Mrs. Bennet to her husband, 'and all the others equally well married, I shall have nothing to wish for.'"
- **a.** theme
- **b.** hyperbole
- **c.** understatement
- **d.** foreshadowing

_____ **5.** Why does Mr. Darcy not dance at the ball?
- **a.** He does not want to be at the ball.
- **b.** He does not dance well and is shy.
- **c.** He does not want to take up the women's time.
- **d.** He does not find the available partners attractive.

_____ **6.** With whom does Mr. Bingley seem quite taken?
- **a.** Jane Bennet
- **b.** Elizabeth Bennet
- **c.** Mr. Darcy's sister
- **d.** Mrs. Long's niece

_____ **7.** What impression does Mr. Darcy make on the Bennet daughters?
- **a.** They find him proud but kind.
- **b.** They find him polite but distant.
- **c.** They find him rude and haughty.
- **d.** They find him attractive and mysterious.

Name ______________________ Date ______________ Class ________

Selection Test

(continued)

Vocabulary Practice (18 points; 6 points each)
Write the letter of the best answer.

_____ **8.** How might someone make an **emphatic** statement?
a. by yelling **b.** by whispering **c.** by speaking gently

_____ **9.** An **acquaintance** cannot also be a
a. friend. **b.** relative. **c.** stranger.

_____ **10.** The opposite of a **hypocritical** person is
a. a lying person.
b. a sincere person.
c. a pessimistic person.

Analyze and Evaluate (20 points)

11. Select one passage of dialogue between Mr. and Mrs. Bennet that reveals an essential aspect of their respective characters and also shows something deeply ingrained about their relationship.

____
____
____
____
____
____
____
____
____
____
____
____
____
____

BIG IDEA Connect (20 points)
Use a separate sheet of paper to answer the following essay question.

12. In what ways is this novel a bridge between the Enlightenment and the Romantic period?

Name ______________________ Date ______________ Class __________

Open-Book Selection Test

Score

The World Is Too Much with Us (page 782), It Is a Beauteous Evening, Calm and Free (page 783), My Heart Leaps Up (page 783), and Composed upon Westminster Bridge, September 3, 1802 (page 784)

Recall and Interpret (60 points total; 10 points each)
Write the letter of the best answer.

_____ **1.** In "The World Is Too Much With Us," the speaker wishes to be
- **a.** able to earn and spend a lot of money.
- **b.** closer to the beauties of the natural world.
- **c.** as strong and powerful as an ancient Greek god.
- **d.** a Pagan, or one who follows an ancient religion.

_____ **2.** Which of the following phrases contains a figure of speech?
- **a.** "It is a beauteous evening. . . ."
- **b.** "Thy nature is not therefore less divine."
- **c.** "So be it when I shall grow old / Or let me die!"
- **d.** "The holy time is quiet as a nun / breathless with adoration."

_____ **3.** In "It Is a Beauteous Evening, Calm and Free," the speaker talks directly to
- **a.** the sun.
- **b.** a child.
- **c.** the ocean.
- **d.** the prophet Abraham.

_____ **4.** In "My Heart Leaps Up," the speaker believes that
- **a.** the old should be allowed to die in peace.
- **b.** nature should be viewed with childlike wonder.
- **c.** nature, symbolized by the rainbow, lasts forever.
- **d.** children should obey "the man," or their parents.

_____ **5.** What is described in "Composed upon Westminster Bridge"?
- **a.** the city of London
- **b.** the beauty of nature
- **c.** the speaker's hopes for success
- **d.** the bridge's elegant construction

_____ **6.** What is conspicuously absent from the scene?
- **a.** human activity
- **b.** natural features
- **c.** the speaker's sister
- **d.** river traffic along the Thames

Name ______________________ Date ______________ Class __________

Open-Book Selection Test *(continued)*

Vocabulary Practice (10 points total; 5 points each)
Write the letter of the best answer.

_____ **7.** Which of the following could be described as **sordid?**
a. a crime **b.** a volunteer project **c.** a donation

_____ **8.** A synonym for **piety** is
a. impiety. **b.** piousness. **c.** patience.

Analyze and Evaluate (10 points total; 5 points each)
Identify two examples of enjambed lines in "It Is a Beauteous Evening, Calm and Free" and explain their effect.

9.
10.

BIG IDEA Connect (20 points)
Use a separate sheet of paper to answer the following essay question.

11. Choose one of the three sonnets from this group of poems, and use its form to explain how it addresses a problem or issue that concerned the Romantics.

Name ______________________ Date ______________ Class __________

Open-Book Selection Test

Score

Lines Composed a Few Miles Above Tintern Abbey (page 786)

Recall and Interpret (48 points total; 8 points each)
Write the letter of the best answer.

_____**1.** Early in the poem "Lines Composed a Few Miles Above Tintern Abbey," Wordsworth admires the country around Tintern Abbey for its
- **a.** natural beauty.
- **b.** prosperous farms.
- **c.** abundance of religious buildings.
- **d.** harmony with man-made structures.

_____**2.** In the five years since the poet's last visit, the land around the abbey has
- **a.** been ruined by other tourists
- **b.** been changed because of a dam on the river.
- **c.** provided the poet with many happy memories.
- **d.** become a home for the poet's sister and "dear, dear Friend."

_____**3.** The poet delights in his sister's reaction to the landscape because she
- **a.** is pure and innocent.
- **b.** has never been there before.
- **c.** feels as he did on his first visit.
- **d.** has spent too much time in the city.

_____**4.** Memories of this area have helped the speaker by
- **a.** giving him subjects for poetry.
- **b.** restoring his calm when under stress.
- **c.** reminding him of children's innocence.
- **d.** enabling him to find his way back to the area.

_____**5.** The diction of this poem is best described as
- **a.** informal and breezy.
- **b.** formal and reverential.
- **c.** optimistic and confident.
- **d.** uncertain and remorseful.

_____**6.** Why is the speaker now able to hear "The still, sad music of humanity"?
- **a.** His age and experience allow him to hear it.
- **b.** The counsel of his sister allows him to hear it.
- **c.** The beauty of the setting allows him to hear it.
- **d.** The memories of childhood allow him to hear it.

Name ______________________ Date ______________ Class ________

Open-Book Selection Test *(continued)*

Vocabulary Practice (12 points total; 6 points each)
Write the letter of the best answer.

_____ **7.** A **secluded** room is
- **a.** noisy.
- **b.** private.
- **c.** luxurious.

_____ **8.** Which person is **reposing**?
- **a.** someone lying down for a nap
- **b.** someone photographing a scene
- **c.** someone nailing shingles to a roof

Analyze and Evaluate (20 points total; 10 points each)
Explain how Wordsworth's diction (specifically in the underlined phrases below) suggests mood and/or deeper meaning in the overall context of the poem.

9. "These plots of cottage ground, these orchard tufts . . . Are clad in one green hue, and lose themselves / 'Mid groves and copses . . . . " (lines 11-14):
10. "[W]hen the fretful stir / Unprofitable, and the fever of the world, / Have hung upon the beatings of my heart—":

BIG IDEA Connect (20 points)
Use a separate sheet of paper to answer the following essay question.

11. In "Lines Composed a Few Miles Above Tintern Abbey," Wordsworth speculates that perhaps the "best portion of a good man's life" may be the "little, nameless, unremembered, acts / Of kindness and of love." Do you agree or disagree with this sentiment? Give examples to support your opinion.

Name ______________________ Date ______________ Class ________

Selection Test

Score

from *The Journals of Dorothy Wordsworth* (page 797)

Recall and Interpret (40 points total; 10 points each)
Write the letter of the best answer.

_____ **1.** Based on this journal entry, Dorothy Wordsworth's main interest appears to be
- **a.** the rights of women.
- **b.** the English countryside.
- **c.** weather patterns in England.
- **d.** her famous brother, William.

_____ **2.** For Dorothy Wordsworth, the high point of the walk is
- **a.** the daffodils.
- **b.** the lake itself.
- **c.** the strong wind.
- **d.** the people of the countryside.

_____ **3.** In this entry, Wordsworth includes
- **a.** only information that can be proved or disproved.
- **b.** an idealized, fictionalized tale of a day in the country.
- **c.** physical descriptions and her reactions to the countryside.
- **d.** an account of events that took place when she was absent.

_____ **4.** Which of the following passages from the journal entry contains personification?
- **a.** "We fancied that the lake had floated the seeds ashore. . . ."
- **b.** "The bays were stormy, and we heard the waves at different distances. . . ."
- **c.** ". . . daffodils rested their heads upon these stones as on a pillow for weariness. . . ."
- **d.** ". . . wood-sorrel flowers, the anemone, scentless violets, and that starry yellow flower. . . ."

Name ______________________ Date ______________ Class __________

Selection Test

(continued)

Analyze and Evaluate (36 points total; 6 points each)
Fill in the chart below with information from the journal.

5. Topic of journal entry:	
Wordsworth's descriptions of the countryside: **6.** **7.**	What her descriptions imply about how she feels: **8.** **9.**
10. What freedoms and restrictions are unique to journal writing? How is writing in a journal different from writing a poem? What tools can both a journal writer and a poet make use of? Explain.	

BIG IDEA Connect (24 points)
Use a separate sheet of paper to answer the following essay question.

11. Explain how Dorothy Wordsworth's journal reflects the Romantics' respect for nature. Use examples from the text for support.

Name ______________________ Date ______________ Class __________

Open-Book Selection Test

Score

Kubla Khan (page 801)

Recall and Interpret (60 points total; 12 points each)
Write the letter of the best answer.

_____ **1.** The poem "Kubla Khan" conveys
- **a.** a series of memorable images.
- **b.** the tales of a traveler in the Far East.
- **c.** historical facts about the king of China.
- **d.** an account of the brave deeds of a ruling family.

_____ **2.** Which of the following phrases contains an example of simile?
- **a.** ". . .Where blossomed many an incense-bearing tree."
- **b.** ". . . Through caverns measureless to man / Down to a sunless sea."
- **c.** ". . . As e'er beneath a waning moon was haunted / By woman wailing for her demon lover!"
- **d.** "Huge fragments vaulted like rebounding hail, / Or chaffy grain beneath the thresher's flail:"

_____ **3.** Which literary device is used in line 25: "Five miles meandering with a mazy motion"?
- **a.** metaphor
- **b.** repetition
- **c.** hyperbole
- **d.** alliteration

_____ **4.** At what point in the poem do the speakers who cry "Beware!" end their speech?
- **a.** They speak through the end of line 49.
- **b.** They speak through the end of line 50.
- **c.** They speak through the end of line 51.
- **d.** They speak through the end of line 54.

_____ **5.** The last lines of the poem insist that true poetic inspiration is
- **a.** part of the Romantic tradition.
- **b.** alarming to those who witness it.
- **c.** necessary to the writing of good poetry.
- **d.** harmful to the person who experiences it.

Open-Book Selection Test

(continued)

Analyze and Evaluate (20 points)

Coleridge uses alliteration throughout the poem. Two consonants are used alliteratively in lines 37-44 (below). Identify these consonants and explain the general pattern of their appearance, noting any lines in which alliteration is NOT prevalent.

A damsel with a dulcimer
In a vision I once saw:
It was an Abyssinian maid,
And on her dulcimer she played,
Singing of Mount Abora.
Could I revive within me
Her symphony and song,
To such a deep delight 'twould win me....

6.

BIG IDEA Connect (20 points)

Use a separate sheet of paper to answer the following essay question.

7. How does Kubla's pleasure dome incorporate elements important to Romantic poets?

Name ______________________ Date ______________ Class ________

Open-Book Selection Test

Score

The Rime of the Ancient Mariner (page 805)

Recall and Interpret (45 points total; 9 points each)
Write the letter of the best answer.

_____ **1.** In The "Rime of the Ancient Mariner," the tale of the ill-fated ship is told by the
- **a.** Pilot's son.
- **b.** Wedding guest.
- **c.** Ancient Mariner.
- **d.** Hermit of the Wood.

_____ **2.** Which phrase does not contain imagery?
- **a.** "'Oh let me be awake, my God! / Or let me sleep alway.'"
- **b.** "'Brown skeletons of leaves that lag / My forest brook along;'"
- **c.** ". . . 'and through the drifts, the snowy clifts / Did send a dismal sheen'"
- **d.** "'With throats unslaked, with black lips baked, / Agape they heard me call.'"

_____ **3.** As part of his punishment, the Mariner must
- **a.** never kill another feathered creature.
- **b.** watch as other sailors starve or drown.
- **c.** periodically repeat the tale he told the Hermit.
- **d.** constantly work to save all creatures great and small.

_____ **4.** Who rescues the Mariner after his ship sinks?
- **a.** the Pilot
- **b.** Life-in-Death
- **c.** the Polar Spirit
- **d.** the Wedding Guest

_____ **5.** What is the setting for the mariner's recital of his tale?
- **a.** on the shore with a clear view of the sea
- **b.** on a rock in a secluded area of the country
- **c.** on the docks among sailors preparing to sail
- **d.** outside a home where a wedding is taking place

Name ______________________ Date ______________ Class ________

Open-Book Selection Test *(continued)*

Vocabulary Practice (15 points total; 5 points each)
Write the letter of the best answer.

_____ **6.** What kind of weather produces a **dismal** day?
- **a.** drizzle, chilly wind, and rain clouds
- **b.** heat, humidity, and a cloudless sky
- **c.** sunshine, breezes, and puffy clouds

_____ **7.** Someone might choose to do **penance** after
- **a.** submitting an idea.
- **b.** committing a crime.
- **c.** making a new friend.

_____ **8.** The opposite of **impart** is
- **a.** enjoy.
- **b.** receive.
- **c.** benefit.

Analyze and Evaluate (21 points; 7 points each)
Identify three places where, in the course of this narrative poem, the "present" narrative breaks through the "past" narrative of the mariner's tale. (Note: do not refer to any of the first five stanzas.)

9.
10.
11.

BIG IDEA Connect (19 points)
Use a separate sheet of paper to answer the following essay question.

12. Why does nature come to the aid of the mariner, even after he has pointlessly killed the albatross?

Name ______________________ Date ______________ Class __________

Selection Test

Score

from *In Patagonia* (page 829)

Recall and Interpret (60 points total; 12 points each)
Write the letter of the best answer.

_____ **1.** In what century did the disastrous voyage of the *Desire* occur?
a. 1500s
b. 1600s
c. 1700s
d. 1800s

_____ **2.** The author describes Captain John Davis and says, "Before him were two books of seamanship and six fatal cuts of a Japanese pirate's sword." This sentence
a. lists Davis's credentials.
b. foreshadows Davis's death.
c. celebrates Davis's accomplishments.
d. comments on Davis's industriousness.

_____ **3.** Of what did Davis's dying commanding officer, Cavendish, accuse Davis?
a. stealing
b. abandonment
c. ignoring orders
d. endangering sailors

_____ **4.** Why did the crew kill thousands of penguins?
a. to defend themselves
b. to lay in food supplies
c. to rid an island of the birds
d. to take revenge on the native people

_____ **5.** When the *Desire* finally made port in Ireland,
a. the worms had finally died off.
b. Captain Davis lay ill in his cabin.
c. the crew had recovered from scurvy.
d. only five men could still stand and sail.

Name ______________________ Date ______________ Class __________

Selection Test

(continued)

Analyze and Evaluate (20 points total; 10 points each)

Use the chart below to characterize Captain John Davis.

6. What Davis did:	What the action says about him:
7. What Davis did:	What the action says about him:

BIG IDEA Connect (20 points)

Use a separate sheet of paper to answer the following essay question.

8. What would Coleridge have made of the captain's decision to attack native peoples and kill twenty-thousand birds that had no fear of humans?

Name ______________________ Date ______________ Class __________

Selection Test

Score

from **The Introduction to *Frankenstein*** (page 835)

Recall and Interpret (40 points total; 10 points each)
Write the letter of the best answer.

_____**1.** During their marriage, the poet Percy Bysshe Shelley
- **a.** wrote several popular gothic novels.
- **b.** cared for the couple's seven children.
- **c.** often encouraged the literary efforts of his wife, Mary.
- **d.** refused to allow Mary Shelley to pursue a literary calling.

_____**2.** The original Frankenstein was
- **a.** an evil German count.
- **b.** a writer of several gothic novels.
- **c.** a monster made of spare human parts.
- **d.** a doctor who created a living-dead monster.

_____**3.** Shelley attributes her desire to write to being
- **a.** the wife of a poet.
- **b.** the child of two writers.
- **c.** the reader of many Gothic novels.
- **d.** the mother of a child who loves stories.

_____**4.** Who suggested that Shelley and others write ghost stories?
- **a.** Byron
- **b.** Mary Shelley
- **c.** Percy Shelley
- **d.** Byron's doctor, Polidori

Vocabulary Practice (20 points total; 5 points each)
Write the letter of the best answer.

_____**5.** An **acute** but **transient** pain is one that
- **a.** causes mild but constant pain.
- **b.** is very strong but does not last.
- **c.** often causes the death of the patient.

_____**6.** To **incite** someone to act is to
- **a.** enable him or her to act.
- **b.** encourage him or her to act.
- **c.** prevent him or her from acting.

_____**7.** Which person is best described as **illustrious**?
- **a.** a famous pop singer
- **b.** a Nobel prize-winning scientist
- **c.** a middle school band director

Name ______________________ Date ______________ Class __________

Selection Test *(continued)*

_____ **8.** A child might be asked to **relinquish** his toy if he is
- **a.** breaking it.
- **b.** playing with it.
- **c.** sharing it with a friend.

Analyze and Evaluate (20 points)

A gothic novel is said to have a "gloomy, ominous setting" and "elements of mystery, horror, or the supernatural." What information in Mary Shelley's Introduction indicates that her novel *Frankenstein* had both?

9.

BIG IDEA Connect (20 points)

Use a separate sheet of paper to answer the following essay question.

10. Shelley writes that "Invention . . . does not consist in creating out of void, but out of chaos; the materials must, in the first place, be afforded: it can give form to dark, shapeless substances but cannot bring into being the substance itself."
Explain how this is a Romantic approach to writing.

Name ______________________ Date ______________ Class __________

Open-Book Selection Test

Score

She Walks in Beauty (page 844) and from *Childe Harold's Pilgrimage* (page 845)

Recall and Interpret (45 points total; 5 points each)
Write the letter of the best answer.

_____ **1.** The color of the woman's hair in the poem "She Walks in Beauty" is
- **a.** red.
- **b.** brown.
- **c.** black.
- **d.** blonde.

_____ **2.** Byron compares the woman to the night sky in "cloudless climes" because
- **a.** he sees her by moonlight.
- **b.** he has seen her only in good weather.
- **c.** she reminds him of a night lit by stars.
- **d.** she is most beautiful by candlelight.

_____ **3.** To the speaker, the woman's beauty represents
- **a.** power.
- **b.** innocence.
- **c.** spirituality.
- **d.** intelligence.

_____ **4.** In the line "One shade the more, one ray the less," the poet uses
- **a.** refrain.
- **b.** comparison.
- **c.** parallel form.
- **d.** internal rhyme.

_____ **5.** The main subject of the excerpt from "Childe Harold's Pilgrimage" is
- **a.** the speaker's youth.
- **b.** the speaker's love of the ocean.
- **c.** the extraordinary beauty of nature.
- **d.** the mighty empires that have dominated the seas.

_____ **6.** What did the speaker in "Childe Harold's Pilgrimage" do at the ocean as a boy?
- **a.** swim
- **b.** sail
- **c.** fish
- **d.** sunbathe

_____ **7.** Which of the following is not a reason that the speaker loves the ocean?
- **a.** It is unchanging.
- **b.** It is beautiful.
- **c.** It is untouched by man.
- **d.** It is the site of great battles.

Name ______________________ Date ______________ Class ________

Open-Book Selection Test

(continued)

_____ **8.** The ocean's attitude toward man is
- **a.** love.
- **b.** disdain.
- **c.** comfort.
- **d.** indifference.

_____ **9.** The poet refers to sailing ships as the ocean's "toys" (line 34). This is an example of
- **a.** repetition.
- **b.** hyperbole.
- **c.** juxtaposition.
- **d.** personification.

Vocabulary Practice (10 points total; 5 points each)
Write the letter of the best answer.

_____ **10.** If you **spurn** someone, you
- **a.** reject him or her.
- **b.** embrace him or her.
- **c.** tease him or her.

_____ **11.** Spilling coffee on your pants would do what to them?
- **a.** enhance them
- **b.** mar them
- **c.** adorn them

Analyze and Evaluate (20 points)
Describe two ways in which the poet juxtaposes two contrasting images, using references to the poem.

12.
13.

BIG IDEA Connect (25 points)
Use a separate sheet of paper to answer the following essay question.

14. In the excerpt from "Childe Harold's Pilgrimage" and in the poem "She Walks in Beauty," Byron describes things he finds beautiful. List these things. What do you find beautiful? Does your list echo Byron's in any way? Explain.

Name ______________________ Date ______________ Class __________

Open-Book Selection Test

Score

Ozymandias (page 852)

Recall and Interpret (60 points total; 12 points each)
Write the letter of the best answer.

_____ **1.** The tone of "Ozymandias" is
- **a.** ironic.
- **b.** comic.
- **c.** tragic.
- **d.** bitter.

_____ **2.** According to Shelley, the sculptor has read well Ozymandias's
- **a.** figure.
- **b.** egotism.
- **c.** power.
- **d.** strength.

_____ **3.** The traveler speaks to
- **a.** the poet.
- **b.** ye Mighty.
- **c.** the sculptor.
- **d.** Ozymandias.

_____ **4.** Which part(s) of Ozymandias do NOT remain in the desert?
- **a.** legs
- **b.** face
- **c.** hands
- **d.** pedestal

_____ **5.** Which of the following best describes the sands of the desert where Ozymandias can be seen?
- **a.** clean
- **b.** empty
- **c.** decayed
- **d.** flattened

Name ______________________ Date ______________ Class __________

Open-Book Selection Test

(continued)

Vocabulary Practice (20 points total; 5 points each)
Write the letter of the best answer.

_____**6.** What might you hear at a funeral?
a. a dirge **b.** a ditty **c.** an aria

_____**7.** A synonym for **cleave** is
a. join. **b.** inspect. **c.** split.

_____**8.** You could expect **tumult** during a(n)
a. fire. **b.** concert. **c.** worship service.

_____**9.** After eating the Thanksgiving dinner, Anna felt
a. peckish. **b.** satiety. **c.** morose.

Analyze and Evaluate (10 points)
How is the message "Look on my works, ye Mighty, and despair!" ironic by the time the traveler sees Ozymandias?

10.

BIG IDEA Connect (10 points)
Use a separate sheet of paper to answer the following essay question.

11. "Ozymandias" is, among other things, a commentary on the nature of power. What is Shelley's attitude toward power? Write a paragraph explaining Shelley's message.

Name ______________________ Date ______________ Class __________

Open-Book Selection Test

Score

Ode to the West Wind (page 854) and To a Skylark (page 858)

Recall and Interpret (56 points total; 7 points each)
Write the letter of the best answer.

_____**1.** "Ode to the West Wind" is set in
a. spring. **c.** fall.
b. summer. **d.** winter.

_____**2.** The rhyme scheme of the terza rima used in "Ode to the West Wind"
a. *aba cdc* . . . **c.** *abc cba* . . .
b. *abc def* . . . **d.** *aba bcb* . . .

_____**3.** Each of the separate sections of "Ode to the West Wind" is
a. a couplet. **c.** an ode.
b. a sonnet. **d.** a ballad.

_____**4.** In "Ode to the West Wind," the speaker does not compare himself to a
a. wave. **c.** cloud.
b. leaf. **d.** stream.

_____**5.** The tone of the last line of "Ode to the West Wind" is one of
a. hope. **c.** resignation.
b. despair. **d.** awe of nature.

_____**6.** What figure of speech dominates the first twelve stanzas of "To a Skylark"?
a. simile
b. alliteration
c. hyperbole
d. assonance

_____**7.** The line length and rhythm of the lines in "To a Skylark" is meant to remind the reader of
a. a bird's song.
b. the hills of Italy.
c. a summer evening.
d. the flight of a skylark.

_____**8.** The diction of "To a Skylark" is
a. wispy and light.
b. haughty and ornate.
c. formal and energetic.
d. melancholic and remorseful.

Name ______________________ Date ______________ Class __________

Open-Book Selection Test

(continued)

Analyze and Evaluate (24 points total; 8 points each)

Explain the effect of the diction Shelley uses in these lines from "Ode to the West Wind." Pay careful attention to the underlined portions.

9. "O wild West Wind, thou breath of Autumn's being" (line 1):

10. "(Driving sweet buds like flocks to feed in air)" (line 11):

11. "The sea-blooms and the oozy woods which wear The sapless foliage of the ocean, know" (lines 39-40):

BIG IDEA Connect (20 points)

Use a separate sheet of paper to answer the following essay question.

12. What does Shelley ask of the West Wind in Part 4, and how does this represent a shift in the shape and/or meaning of the poem? You may refer to other parts (1-5) of the poem to support your answer.

Name ______________________ Date ______________ Class __________

Open-Book Selection Test

Score

La Belle Dame Sans Merci (page 867) and When I Have Fears That I May Cease to Be (page 869)

Recall and Interpret (60 points total; 10 points each)
Write the letter of the best answer.

_____**1.** "La Belle Dame Sans Merci" is set in
- **a.** spring.
- **b.** summer.
- **c.** fall.
- **d.** winter.

_____**2.** The tone of "La Belle Dame Sans Merci" is
- **a.** ironic.
- **b.** comic.
- **c.** fearful.
- **d.** mournful.

_____**3.** "La Belle Dame Sans Merci" is
- **a.** an ode.
- **b.** a sonnet.
- **c.** a ballad.
- **d.** a mock epic.

_____**4.** Which of the following is not something Keats fears in "When I Have Fears That I May Cease to Be"?
- **a.** never growing rich
- **b.** never chasing romance
- **c.** never seeing his beloved again
- **d.** never writing the books he wants

_____**5.** "When I Have Fears That I May Cease To Be" is
- **a.** a sonnet.
- **b.** a ballad.
- **c.** an ode.
- **d.** a terza rima.

_____**6.** To what does Keats compare the verse he is writing and will write?
- **a.** to stars in the sky
- **b.** to a beautiful woman
- **c.** to characters in a book
- **d.** to a rich harvest of grain

Name ______________________ Date ______________ Class __________

Open-Book Selection Test

(continued)

Vocabulary Practice (15 points total; 5 points each)
Write the letter of the best answer.

_____ **7.** A common sign in a storefront reads, "No
a. purchasing." **b.** loitering." **c.** shopping."

_____ **8.** If you **glean** something, you
a. collect it. **b.** abhor it. **c.** discard it.

_____ **9.** An antonym for **teeming** is
a. sparse. **b.** overflowing. **c.** lovely.

Analyze and Evaluate (10 points)
Explain the aspects of the form of "La Belle Dame Sans Merci" that make it a ballad.

10.

BIG IDEA Connect (15 points)
Use a separate sheet of paper to answer the following essay question.

11. From reading these two poems, how does Keats seem to have felt about the world and about love? Do you think his view was positive or negative? Write one or two paragraphs describing Keats's attitudes as they are revealed in the poems.

Name ______________________ Date ______________ Class __________

Open-Book Selection Test

Score

Ode on a Grecian Urn (page 872)

Recall and Interpret (40 points total; 8 points each)
Write the letter of the best answer.

_____**1.** Which of the following is NOT something that Keats associates with the urn in "Ode on a Grecian Urn"?
a. a bride
b. a child
c. a historian
d. a legend

_____**2.** Which scene is depicted on the front side of the urn (stanzas 1–3)?
a. figures dancing to music
b. farmers in a field
c. a concert
d. a play being performed

_____**3.** Which scene is depicted on the back of the urn (stanza 4)?
a. a town festival
b. a mountain road
c. a religious procession
d. a city by a river

_____**4.** In the final stanza of "Ode on a Grecian Urn," Keats addresses
a. the urn itself.
b. nature personified.
c. the maker of the urn.
d. a character on the urn.

_____**5.** To what does the "mad pursuit" in line 9 refer?
a. The poet's search for the urn's meaning.
b. The lesson the urn teaches about how to live.
c. The chase scene engraved on the side off the urn.
d. The speaker's desire to find the owner of the urn.

Name ______________________ Date ______________ Class __________

Open-Book Selection Test

(continued)

Vocabulary Practice (20 points total; 10 points each)
Write the letter of the best answer.

_____ **6.** Which are examples of **deities**?
- **a.** our best friends
- **b.** Olympic athletes
- **c.** Apollo and Aphrodite

_____ **7.** Which landscape is most likely to be **desolate**?
- **a.** a barren desert
- **b.** a lush coastline
- **c.** a cultivated field

Analyze and Evaluate (20 points total; 10 points each)

8. Explain how Keats uses apostrophe, a common element of odes.

9. An ode is typically elevated in terms of tone and style. Select one example of elevated diction in "Ode on a Grecian Urn" and explain how it is elevated.

BIG IDEA Connect (20 points)
Use a separate sheet of paper to answer the following essay question.

10. Keats writes that "Heard melodies are sweet, but those unheard / Are sweeter. . . ." How does this line from "Ode on a Grecian Urn" reflect Romantic ideas about the imagination?

Name ______________________ Date ______________ Class __________

Open-Book Selection Test

Score

To Autumn (page 877), Haiku for Four Seasons (page 880), To John Keats, Poet, at Springtime (page 882), and Untying the Knot from *Pilgrim at Tinker Creek* (page 884)

Recall and Interpret (48 points total; 6 points each)
Write the letter of the best answer.

_____ **1.** In the second stanza of "To Autumn," Keats addresses
- **a.** nature.
- **b.** the sun.
- **c.** a farmer.
- **d.** autumn itself.

_____ **2.** Which of the following is not part of what Keats calls the "music" of autumn?
- **a.** skylarks singing
- **b.** lambs bleating
- **c.** crickets singing
- **d.** swallows twittering

_____ **3.** An ode is a poem that
- **a.** is written in an irregular stanza.
- **b.** addresses the subject of love.
- **c.** celebrates a person or object.
- **d.** was written by the Roman poet Horace.

_____ **4.** In "Haiku for Four Seasons," in which of the haiku does the speaker appear?
- **a.** "Spring"
- **b.** "Summer"
- **c.** "Autumn"
- **d.** "Winter"

_____ **5.** Why must the poet write in "To John Keats, Poet, at Springtime"?
- **a.** He is moved by the poetry of Keats.
- **b.** He is moved by the beauty of spring.
- **c.** He is saddened by the early death of Keats.
- **d.** He is maddened by the sweet smells of spring.

_____ **6.** What makes the poet feel that Keats is still somehow alive?
- **a.** Keats's grave is like "death's dark door."
- **b.** The poet hears "a harp that grieves" for Keats.
- **c.** Keats's poetry is part of the beauty of this spring.
- **d.** The poet has written a poem to honor John Keats.

_____ **7.** What task does Dillard undertake and fail at in the essay "Untying the Knot"?
- **a.** She tries to untangle a knot in a snakeskin.
- **b.** She tries to free a snake from a broken aquarium.
- **c.** She tries to explain why the earth heats and cools slowly.
- **d.** She tries to understand why people like the change of seasons.

Name ______________________ Date ______________ Class __________

Open-Book Selection Test

(continued)

_____ **8.** To what does Dillard compare time, as she explains why it is hard to "catch the seasons"?

a. to a bible verse
b. to a planting calendar
c. to a looped snakeskin
d. to time at Tinker Creek

Vocabulary Practice (10 points total; 5 points each)
Write the letter of the best answer.

_____ **9.** A synonym for **conspiring** is
a. ignoring. **b.** conjoining. **c.** plotting.

_____ **10.** What might a wheel leave in the ground?
a. mound **b.** a furrow **c.** a seedling

Analyze and Evaluate (24 points total; 6 points each)
Think about the power of haiku to create a strong image and mood with very few words. For each of the haiku by Bashō, identify the central image and the mood it creates.

Haiku	Central Image	Mood
11. "Spring"		
12. "Summer"		
13. "Autumn"		
14. "Winter"		

BIG IDEA Connect (18 points)
Use a separate sheet of paper to answer the following essay question.

15. What is Romantic about naturalist Annie Dillard's approach to nature? What in her approach reflects an understanding of nature that is more characteristic of the Enlightenment?

Name ______________________ Date ______________ Class __________

Open-Book Selection Test

Score

from **In Memoriam A. H. H.** (page 924), **Crossing the Bar** (page 928), **Tears, Idle Tears** (page 929)

Recall and Interpret (42 points total; 6 points each)
Write the letter of the best answer.

_____ **1.** Section 7 of *In Memoriam* takes place in front of
- **a.** the home of a dead friend of the speaker.
- **b.** an old haunted house owned by the speaker.
- **c.** the deserted childhood home of the speaker.
- **d.** a family home in which the speaker's father died.

_____ **2.** The rhyme scheme of each of the stanzas from *In Memoriam* is
- **a.** *abab.*
- **b.** *aabb.*
- **c.** *abca.*
- **d.** *abba.*

_____ **3.** At the end of section 54, the speaker is feeling
- **a.** angry and bitter.
- **b.** helpless and fearful.
- **c.** trusting and peaceful.
- **d.** joyous and confident.

_____ **4.** The bells in section 106 are ringing to
- **a.** commemorate Hallam's burial.
- **b.** mark the wedding of a young bride.
- **c.** celebrate the coming of a new year.
- **d.** announce the birth of the speaker's son.

_____ **5.** The theme of "Crossing the Bar" is that
- **a.** there is no place like home.
- **b.** true sailors must return to the sea.
- **c.** friends should not part with sadness.
- **d.** death reunites the faithful with God.

_____ **6.** The tears in "Tears, Idle Tears" are idle because they
- **a.** are shed for no reason.
- **b.** cannot bring back the past.
- **c.** come during a happy occasion.
- **d.** mourn a love that is not returned.

_____ **7.** The first two lines of "Tears, Idle Tears" include examples of which poetic device?
- **a.** alliteration
- **b.** onomotopoeia
- **c.** consonance
- **d.** oxymoron

Name ______________________ Date ______________ Class ________

Open-Book Selection Test *(continued)*

Vocabulary Practice (20 points total; 5 points each)
Write the letter of the best answer.

_____ **8.** The **diffusive** light rays
- **a.** focused on one spot.
- **b.** shone brightly.
- **c.** spread widely.

_____ **9.** If John wants to get into medical school, he'll have to break his **slothful** habits.
- **a.** quiet **b.** lazy **c.** sneaky

_____ **10.** A sign of his **license** is his
- **a.** spendthrift ways.
- **b.** excessive exercise.
- **c.** continual lecturing.

_____ **11.** It was only a **feigned** illness.
- **a.** minor **b.** short-lived **c.** imagined

Analyze and Evaluate (18 points)
What phrases are used rhythmically as a sort of refrain in section 106 of "In Memoriam A.H.H.", and how are the content and effect of these repeated phrases apt for this poem?

12.

BIG IDEA Connect (20 points)
Use a separate sheet of paper to answer the following essay question.

13. How does the speaker in "In Memoriam A.H.H." appear to embody the typical Victorian ideals of "self-improvement, moral earnestness, and the value of work"?

Name ________________________ Date ________________ Class __________

Open-Book Selection Test

Score

Ulysses (page 932)

Recall and Interpret (50 points total; 10 points each)
Write the letter of the best answer.

_____ **1.** As the poem opens, Ulysses's mood might best be described as
- **a.** tired.
- **b.** bitter.
- **c.** complacent.
- **d.** restless.

_____ **2.** When Ulysses says, "I am become a name," he means that
- **a.** all he has left is his kingly title.
- **b.** his exploits have made him a legend.
- **c.** he has brought honor to the family name.
- **d.** he has become an object of people's ridicule.

_____ **3.** Ulysses believes that his son Telemachus is more
- **a.** prudent and gentle than he is.
- **b.** famous and respected than he is.
- **c.** brave and adventurous than he is.
- **d.** ruthless and self-centered than he is.

_____ **4.** Line 46 includes an example of which sound device?
- **a.** consonance.
- **b.** assonance.
- **c.** alliteration.
- **d.** internal rhyme.

_____ **5.** In Ulysses's opinion, old age is a time for
- **a.** rest and relaxation.
- **b.** settling old scores.
- **c.** seeking new experiences.
- **d.** spending more time with family.

Vocabulary Practice (10 points total; 5 points each)
Write the letter of the best answer.

_____ **6.** The tricky situation called for her to act with **prudence** and
a. regret. **b.** caution. **c.** tiredness.

_____ **7.** He wondered which friends would **abide**
- **a.** during the performance of the play.
- **b.** before his mother sold the house.
- **c.** after he graduated from school.

Name ______________________ Date ______________ Class ________

Open-Book Selection Test *(continued)*

Analyze and Evaluate (20 points total)

Select one example of consonance and one example of assonance from the poem and explain their effects.

8. Assonance:
9. Consonance:

BIG IDEA Connect (20 points)

Use a separate sheet of paper to answer the following essay question.

10. Identify the ideas that Ulysses expresses in lines 18-23 and explain how they reflect popular notions of the Victorian era.

Name ______________________ Date ______________ Class __________

Open-Book Selection Test

Score

Sonnet 43 (page 941), Love Is Not All: It Is Not Meat nor Drink (page 943), and Simone de Beauvoir to Nelson Algren (page 944)

Recall and Interpret (60 points total; 10 points each)
Write the letter of the best answer.

_____**1.** In lines 9–10 of "Sonnet 43," the speaker implies that her love is
- **a.** enduring.
- **b.** childish.
- **c.** grievous.
- **d.** passionate.

_____**2.** The rhyme scheme of the first eight lines of "Sonnet 43" is
- **a.** *aabbccdd.*
- **b.** *abababab.*
- **c.** *abbaabba.*
- **d.** *abcdabcd.*

_____**3.** Which of the following lines of "Love Is Not All . . ." includes an example of alliteration?
- **a.** line 1
- **b.** line 9
- **c.** line 12
- **d.** line 14

_____**4.** The first six lines of "Love Is Not All . . ." express which of the following views of love?
- **a.** rational
- **b.** sarcastic
- **c.** sentimental
- **d.** passionate

_____**5.** In lines 9–13 of "Love Is Not All . . .," the speaker implies that she might
- **a.** die for her love.
- **b.** go mad over her love.
- **c.** trade her love for some necessity.
- **d.** beg her love to release her from their marriage.

_____**6.** In her letter to Nelson Algren, de Beauvoir describes Paris as
- **a.** dangerous and full of armed soldiers.
- **b.** the most beautiful city in the world.
- **c.** mostly deserted, dull, and cloudy.
- **d.** the place where she left her heart.

Name ______________________ Date ______________ Class ________

Open-Book Selection Test *(continued)*

Analyze and Evaluate (18 points total; 6 points each)

Select one example of repetition from each text and explain how it contributes to tone.

7. Barrett Browning's Sonnet 43:

8. St. Vincent Millay's "Love is not All: It Is Not Meat nor Drink":

9. de Beauvior's Letter to Nelson Algren:

BIG IDEA Connect (22 points)

Use a separate sheet of paper to answer the following essay question.

10. Although de Beauvoir and the speakers of both poems make strong statements about their love, the works reveal some important differences about their attitudes toward love. Compare and contrast what the three writings say about love and how they say it.

Name ______________________ Date ______________ Class __________

Open-Book Selection Test

Score

In My Life (page 946)

Recall and Interpret (60 points total; 10 points each)
Write the letter of the best answer.

_____**1.** What is the first thing the speaker mentions remembering?
- **a.** places he used to know
- **b.** his first real sweetheart
- **c.** his many childhood friends
- **d.** songs he often sang in school

_____**2.** The second stanza of the song contains an example of
- **a.** onomatopoeia.
- **b.** slant rhyme.
- **c.** end rhyme.
- **d.** oxymoron.

_____**3.** Whom does the speaker address?
- **a.** an old friend
- **b.** the idea of love
- **c.** a current lover
- **d.** his own memory

_____**4.** What is the speaker's attitude toward people and things from the past?
- **a.** He wishes they would not change.
- **b.** He tries to visit them often.
- **c.** He thinks them insignificant.
- **d.** He remembers them fondly.

_____**5.** Which literary device does Lennon use in the last stanza of the song?
- **a.** internal rhyme
- **b.** assonance
- **c.** repetition
- **d.** simile

_____**6.** The tone of "In My Life" is best described as
- **a.** bitter.
- **b.** melancholy.
- **c.** excited.
- **d.** affectionate.

Name ______________________ Date ______________ Class ________

Open-Book Selection Test

(continued)

Analyze and Evaluate (20 points total; 10 points each)

Although "In My Life" is a song, Lennon uses standard literary devices found in poems. In the chart below, list two poetic devices Lennon uses, examples of each, and the effects of these devices.

Literary Device	Example	Effect
7.		
8.		

BIG IDEA Connect (20 points)

Use a separate sheet of paper to answer the following essay question.

9. Discuss how Lennon depicts the relationship between love and memory in this song. Explain whether his viewpoint on the subject is optimistic or not.

Name ______________________ Date ______________ Class ________

Selection Test

Score

What Is Love? (page 948)

Recall and Interpret (60 points total; 6 points each)
Write the letter of the best answer.

_____**1.** Until recently, most scientists thought love was
- **a.** best assessed by chemists and physicists.
- **b.** a primal emotion like anger and fear.
- **c.** ecstasy and torment, freedom and slavery.
- **d.** too difficult to measure and study accurately.

_____**2.** According to the article, one factor that may account for the rise in interest in the subject of love is
- **a.** an increase in the amount of leisure time people have.
- **b.** a greater number of female biologists and anthropologists.
- **c.** the ascendance of poetry as a form of entertainment.
- **d.** the return to eighteenth century courting rituals.

_____**3.** Who is generally credited with inventing the notion of love?
- **a.** playwrights, poets, and other writers
- **b.** psychologists and anthropologists
- **c.** William Shakespeare
- **d.** Cole Porter

_____**4.** What is the connotation of the word "idle" in the following sentence: "Among the prime suspects are the 12th century French troubadours who more or less invented the Art of Courtly Love, an elaborate and artificial ritual for idle aristocrats?"
- **a.** lazy
- **b.** bored
- **c.** relaced
- **d.** thoughtful

_____**5.** According to the article, today love helps
- **a.** people focus on their work.
- **b.** researchers communicate with each other.
- **c.** build communities all over the world.
- **d.** sell a wide range of products.

_____**6.** The writer cites the 17th century tulip craze in Holland as an example of
- **a.** dramatic irony.
- **b.** non-romantic love.
- **c.** phony emotion.
- **d.** mass hallucination.

_____**7.** Those who argue that love is just a cultural fantasy claim that love is the domain of
- **a.** British peasants.
- **b.** rich nobles.
- **c.** French artists.
- **d.** skilled hunters.

Name ______________________ Date ______________ Class __________

Selection Test (continued)

_____ **8.** What was the conclusion of the study conducted by Jankowiak and Fischer?
- **a.** Love is a universal phenomenon.
- **b.** Roses are a common symbol of love.
- **c.** Courtship rituals indicate of the presence of love.
- **d.** People are genetically programmed to love certain types.

_____ **9.** According to the article, what happens in cultures where marriage is not necessarily based on love?
- **a.** Couples turn their attention to education.
- **b.** People fall in love and love each other in secret.
- **c.** Women make most of the decisions about money.
- **d.** The divorce rate is much higher than in other cultures.

_____ **10.** At the end of the article, the writer states that more and more scientists believe
- **a.** love determines most of the decisions adults make in life.
- **b.** love is generally expressed in the same way across cultures.
- **c.** human beings have a biological predisposition to love.
- **d.** human beings use love as a resource to combat illness.

Analyze and Evaluate (20 points total; 10 points each)

In the boxes below, describe the connotations of each of the underlined words listed from the article.

Word	Connotation
11. "But romantic love, and all the attendant sighing and swooning and sonnet writing, . . ."	
12. "Then a shadow falls over his certainty."	

BIG IDEA Connect (20 points)

Use a separate sheet of paper to answer the following essay question.

13. Discuss the writer's tone in this article and describe how he creates that tone. Include some mention of how the writer himself seems to think about love.

Name ______________________ Date ______________ Class __________

Open-Book Selection Test

Score

Pied Beauty (page 953) and Spring and Fall: To a Young Child (page 954)

Recall and Interpret (60 points total; 10 points each)
Write the letter of the best answer.

_____ **1.** What the speaker of "Pied Beauty" admires most in the world is its
- **a.** symmetry.
- **b.** variety.
- **c.** color.
- **d.** mystery.

_____ **2.** Line 6 of "Pied Beauty" contains an example of
- **a.** onomatopoeia.
- **b.** assonance.
- **c.** oxymoron.
- **d.** alliteration.

_____ **3.** The tone of "Pied Beauty" could best be described as
- **a.** solemn.
- **b.** exuberant.
- **c.** humorous.
- **d.** fearful.

_____ **4.** The first four lines of "Spring and Fall . . ." suggest that Margaret has been
- **a.** crying.
- **b.** singing.
- **c.** praying.
- **d.** misbehaving

_____ **5.** Lines 5–8 of "Spring and Fall. . ." assure Margaret that as she grows older she will
- **a.** mourn less over changing seasons.
- **b.** accept her limitations.
- **c.** appreciate her early discipline.
- **d.** become less rebellious.

_____ **6.** The "blight" man was born for (line 14 in "Spring and Fall. . .") is
- **a.** the yearly onset of winter.
- **b.** our sense of shame.
- **c.** human mortality.
- **d.** the loss of memory.

Name ______________________ Date ______________ Class __________

Open-Book Selection Test *(continued)*

Analyze and Evaluate (18 points)

How is the title of "Spring and Fall" related to Hopkin's practice of "sprung rhythm"?

7.

BIG IDEA Connect (22 points)

Use a separate sheet of paper to answer the following essay question.

8. Hopkins's two poems both refer to the idea of change, a staple of the Victorian era, though Hopkin's notions of change have a somewhat bleaker connotation. Compare and contrast the views on change expressed in the two poems, identifying the tone of each poem.

Name ______________________ Date ______________ Class __________

Open-Book Selection Test

Score

Jabberwocky (page 958)

Recall and Interpret (60 points total; 10 points each)
Write the letter of the best answer.

_____ **1.** Overall, "Jabberwocky" is an account of
- **a.** father-son tensions.
- **b.** a young man's brave act.
- **c.** the joys of young love.
- **d.** a young man's first job.

_____ **2.** The main event of the poem takes place in a
- **a.** city.
- **b.** village.
- **c.** swamp.
- **d.** forest.

_____ **3.** Which of the following effects is created by the rhythm and rhyme scheme of the poem?
- **a.** a sense of doom
- **b.** a sense of celebration
- **c.** a sense of playfulness
- **d.** a sense of mysteriousness

_____ **4.** According to the poem, the Jubjub bird is a
- **a.** good omen.
- **b.** menace.
- **c.** trickster.
- **d.** fool.

_____ **5.** The second and fifth lines are spoken by the
- **a.** hero of the poem.
- **b.** hero's father.
- **c.** wise counselor.
- **d.** Jabberwock.

_____ **6.** Given the context, it is clear that "brillig," "vorpal," and "manxome" function as which part of speech?
- **a.** verb
- **b.** adjective
- **c.** adverb
- **d.** interjection

Name ______________________ Date ______________ Class __________

Open-Book Selection Test

(continued)

Analyze and Evaluate (20 points total; 5 points each)

Although "Jabberwocky" is classified as nonsense verse, it makes its own kind of sense because of the way language works. Pick two nonsense verbs and two nonsense adjectives from the poem and write them in the left column of the chart. In the right column, define each term based on the context in which it is used.

Nonsense verbs:	What each means:
7.	
8.	
Nonsense adjectives:	What each means:
9.	
10.	

BIG IDEA Connect (20 points)

Use a separate sheet of paper to answer the following essay question.

11. Carroll's "nonsense verse" might be considered a kind of Victorian inventiveness—a new way to do an old thing; a new way to tell an old story. How does the "new" language of this Victorian poem tell an "old" story like those of "Beowulf" or "Sir Gawain and the Green Knight"?

Name ______________________ Date ____________ Class ________

Selection Test

Score

Jabberwocky (page 960)

Recall and Interpret (60 points total; 10 points each)
Write the letter of the best answer.

_____**1.** Coleman uses the phrase "mirror image" to refer to
- **a.** the intellectual loneliness of her childhood.
- **b.** physical likeness beyond physical beauty.
- **c.** the Jabberwock's resemblance to zoo creatures.
- **d.** a style of writing in which two authors write alike.

_____**2.** Where did Coleman see images of Black children in the literature she read as a child?
- **a.** in magazines such as *Esquire*
- **b.** in Lewis Carroll's books
- **c.** at the library
- **d.** almost nowhere

_____**3.** Why did Coleman read so much as a child?
- **a.** She sought the solace and escape of literature.
- **b.** Her teachers encouraged her to read poetry.
- **c.** She was confined inside by a bout of pneumonia.
- **d.** Her family lived in a remote rural community.

_____**4.** Who gave Coleman a copy of "Alice's Adventures in Wonderland and Through the Looking-Glass"?
- **a.** her cousin
- **b.** her father
- **c.** her mother
- **d.** her teacher

_____**5.** What genre of writing does Coleman seem to especially love?
- **a.** plays
- **b.** non-fiction
- **c.** poetry
- **d.** fables

_____**6.** Coleman states that reading Carroll's works made
- **a.** her feel more lonely and isolated.
- **b.** no sense to her until she was a adult.
- **c.** a lasting impression on her own writing.
- **d.** her seek out the writings of Tennyson.

Name ______________________ Date ______________ Class __________

Selection Test

(continued)

Analyze and Evaluate (20 points total; 10 points each)

In the boxes below, describe the differences between the childhood world Coleman grew up in and the world she found in books. Cite details from the essay.

7. Childhood World	**8.** World of Books

BIG IDEA Connect (20 points)

Use a separate sheet of paper to answer the following essay question.

9. Discuss how Coleman "rewrote" Alice during her frequent readings of Lewis Carroll's books. Explain what the central appeal of his books was to Coleman.

Name ______________________ Date ______________ Class __________

Selection Test

Score

from *Jane Eyre* (page 968)

Recall and Interpret (50 points total; 10 points each)
Write the letter of the best answer.

____ **1.** What does Bessie do?
- **a.** She is a servant in the Reed household.
- **b.** She acts as Jane's tutor in mathematics.
- **c.** She drives the carriage for Mr. Brocklehurst.
- **d.** She is an archdeacon in the Church of England.

____ **2.** How does Jane feel when she is called to the breakfast room?
- **a.** indifferent
- **b.** delighted
- **c.** frightened
- **d.** exhausted

____ **3.** Upon meeting her, Mr. Brocklehurst asks Jane whether she is
- **a.** happy at the Reeds.
- **b.** capable of gardening.
- **c.** a curious student.
- **d.** a good child.

____ **4.** Mrs. Reed is best described as
- **a.** intelligent and shy.
- **b.** cruel and efficient.
- **c.** sickly and frail.
- **d.** friendly and cheerful.

____ **5.** Lowood is devoted to raising children
- **a.** in a simple and harsh manner.
- **b.** as if they were already adults.
- **c.** only from the wealthiest families.
- **d.** to become artistic geniuses.

Vocabulary Practice (10 points total; 5 points each)
Write the letter of the best answer.

____ **6.** A person would **advocate** on behalf of
a. an enemy. **b.** a lawyer. **c.** a child.

____ **7.** The doctor found that she wanted to act in **retaliation** for the
- **a.** crime that had been committed.
- **b.** gift a patient had given her.
- **c.** award she was about to receive.

Name ______________________ Date ______________ Class ________

Selection Test

(continued)

Analyze and Evaluate (20 points total; 10 points each)

In the boxes below, note the physical description of each character and what those descriptions indicate about each character's personality.

Physical Description	Personality
8. Mr. Brocklehurst:	
9. Mrs. Reed:	

BIG IDEA Connect (20 points)

Use a separate sheet of paper to answer the following essay question.

10. What does the selection indicate about the differing states of children in Victorian England? Make specific references to the selection to support your ideas.

Name ______________________ Date ______________ Class ________

Open-Book Selection Test

Score

My Last Duchess (page 981)

Recall and Interpret (50 points total; 10 points each)
Write the letter of the best answer.

____ **1.** The person listening to the speaker in "My Last Duchess" is
- **a.** a tourist.
- **b.** the speaker's friend.
- **c.** the speaker's bride-to-be.
- **d.** an emissary from a nobleman.

____ **2.** In lines 13–15, the speaker in "My Last Duchess" begins to reveal his
- **a.** jealous nature.
- **b.** fond memories of the past.
- **c.** reasons for wanting to remarry.
- **d.** anguish over his ex-wife's untimely death.

____ **3.** Lines 21–31 suggest that the last Duchess was
- **a.** shallow.
- **b.** generous.
- **c.** arrogant.
- **d.** talkative.

____ **4.** Lines 49–54 imply that the speaker wants to remarry
- **a.** for companionship.
- **b.** because he has fallen in love.
- **c.** in order to increase his wealth.
- **d.** because he will gain another title.

____ **5.** The speaker implies that his last duchess
- **a.** remarried and died in childbirth.
- **b.** was put to death or banished by the Duke.
- **c.** ran away with a servant and is presumed dead.
- **d.** was killed in a riding or boating accident.

Name ____________________ Date ____________ Class ________

Open-Book Selection Test

(continued)

Vocabulary Practice (10 points total; 5 points each)
Write the letter of the best answer.

____ **6.** The king tried to read the queen's **countenance** by
- **a.** winding his watch.
- **b.** reading a book on botany.
- **c.** looking at her face.

____ **7.** The princess showed her **munificence** by
- **a.** leaving the room abruptly.
- **b.** funding the building of a library.
- **c.** tripping over her ball-gown.

Analyze and Evaluate (20 points total)
The speakers in dramatic monologues often reveal more about themselves than they intend to. In the boxes below, indicate how the speaker in "My Last Duchess" sees himself, what his monologue reveals about his true character, and which lines communicate his true character.

8. "My Last Duchess"		
How the speaker sees himself:	What the speaker is truly like:	What lines reveal the speaker's true nature:

BIG IDEA Connect (20 points)
Use a separate sheet of paper to answer the following essay question.

9. Discuss the feelings and mood of the speaker at the end of "My Last Duchess" and how they exemplify realism in Browning's writing.

Name ______________________ Date ______________ Class ________

Selection Test

Score

from *Oliver Twist* (page 986)

Recall and Interpret (50 points total; 10 points each)
Write the letter of the best answer.

_____ **1.** Who is the narrator of this selection?
- **a.** Oliver Twist
- **b.** Mr. Bumble
- **c.** a board member
- **d.** an unnamed observer

_____ **2.** During the meeting, the board members treat Oliver with
- **a.** patience.
- **b.** contempt.
- **c.** sadness.
- **d.** curiosity.

_____ **3.** Why does the board decide to change the workhouse?
- **a.** because the building needed repairs
- **b.** in order to make greater profits
- **c.** because paupers were leaving to work abroad
- **d.** in order to employ more children

_____ **4.** Oliver and the other boys in the workhouse suffer most acutely from
- **a.** loneliness.
- **b.** tuberculosis.
- **c.** influenza.
- **d.** starvation.

_____ **5.** How does the master react to Oliver's request?
- **a.** with shock
- **b.** with admiration
- **c.** by crying
- **d.** by leaving

Vocabulary Practice (10 points total; 5 points each)
Write the letter of the best answer.

_____ **6.** Upon seeing the **extraordinary** animal, the boy
- **a.** clapped his hands in excitement.
- **b.** decided to do his homework.
- **c.** picked it up to take to the veterinarian.

_____ **7.** The **inseparable** puppies were found
- **a.** huddled close together.
- **b.** sleeping for three days straight.
- **c.** barking at a squirrel.

Name ______________________ Date ______________ Class __________

Selection Test

(continued)

Analyze and Evaluate (20 points total; 5 points each)

In the boxes to the right, briefly describe the characters, setting, and situation in this excerpt from *Oliver Twist*.

	Exposition:
8. Oliver	
9. Mr. Bumble	
10. Setting	
11. Situation	

BIG IDEA Connect (20 points)

Use a separate sheet of paper to answer the following essay question.

12. Explain Dickens' use of characterization to create sympathy for the poor in this excerpt. How do his characterizations of Oliver and the board members exemplify realism?

Name ______________________ Date ______________ Class __________

Selection Test

Score

Dover Beach (page 996)

Recall and Interpret (50 points total; 10 points each)
Write the letter of the best answer.

_____ **1.** At the beginning of "Dover Beach," the speaker is
- **a.** standing on a beach in a French vacation resort.
- **b.** looking out a window on the English coast.
- **c.** peering at the ocean through a telescope.
- **d.** getting ready to go for a swim.

_____ **2.** The speaker's dramatic monologue is directed to
- **a.** a poet.
- **b.** the reader.
- **c.** a loved one.
- **d.** an imaginary friend.

_____ **3.** The tone of "Dover Beach" is best described as
- **a.** bitter.
- **b.** melancholy.
- **c.** indifferent.
- **d.** dispassionate.

_____ **4.** In the third stanza, faith is compared to the
- **a.** ebbing and flowing tides.
- **b.** works of ancient writers.
- **c.** fading lights of France.
- **d.** white cliffs of Dover.

_____ **5.** In the last stanza, the speaker concludes that the modern world is
- **a.** calm and peaceful.
- **b.** bloodied by wars.
- **c.** full of confusion and doubt.
- **d.** very like the ancient world.

Name ______________________ Date ______________ Class __________

Selection Test

(continued)

Analyze and Evaluate (30 points total; 15 points each)

Describe the meter's effect on the first and last stanzas of "Dover Beach."

	Effect of meter
6. First stanza	
7. Last stanza	

BIG IDEA Connect (20 points)

Use a separate sheet of paper to answer the following essay question.

8. Arnold once said that Victorians lived between two worlds, "one dead, the other powerless to be born." Explain how "Dover Beach" illustrates that judgment.

Name ______________________ Date ______________ Class __________

Open-Book Selection Test

Score

To an Athlete Dying Young (page 1000) and When I Was One-and-Twenty (page 1001)

Recall and Interpret (56 points total; 8 points each)
Write the letter of the best answer.

_____**1.** The first time the athlete in "To an Athlete Dying Young" was brought home "shoulder-high" was when
- **a.** he was injured.
- **b.** he won a race.
- **c.** he retired from competition.
- **d.** he broke a world record.

_____**2.** The "stiller town" of line 8 refers to
- **a.** the realm of death.
- **b.** the quiet of retirement.
- **c.** a place far from the stadium.
- **d.** the village where the athlete retired.

_____**3.** The speaker says the athlete is "smart" because he
- **a.** used good racing strategy.
- **b.** died while his fame was fresh.
- **c.** didn't become too greedy.
- **d.** knew how to handle success.

_____**4.** Line 20 of "To An Athlete . . ." refers to situations in which
- **a.** athletes burn out early.
- **b.** athletes lose their perspective.
- **c.** athletes' reputations are ruined.
- **d.** athletes' fame dies out.

_____**5.** The main advice of the "wise man" in "When I Was One-and-Twenty" is to
- **a.** be thrifty.
- **b.** give away all wealth.
- **c.** be careful in love.
- **d.** be generous to loved ones.

_____**6.** What did the speaker do, apparently, in his twenty-first year?
- **a.** fell in love
- **b.** rejected his parents
- **c.** gave away all his money
- **d.** invested in precious stones

_____**7.** The tone of "When I Was One-and-Twenty" might best be described as
- **a.** angry.
- **b.** happy.
- **c.** satisfied.
- **d.** remorseful.

Name ______________________ Date ______________ Class ________

Open-Book Selection Test

(continued)

Analyze and Evaluate (20 points total; 10 points each)

Lyric poems are characterized as being short and highly musical. Describe the "musical" qualities in each of Housman's lyric poems, and tell how they reinforce the tone of each poem.

8. "To an Athlete Dying Young"	**9.** "When I Was One-and-Twenty"
Musical Elements:	Musical Elements:
How musical elements reinforce tone of poem:	How musical elements reinforce tone of poem:

BIG IDEA Connect (24 points)

Use a separate sheet of paper to answer the following essay question.

10. Based on your reading of these poems, how do you think Housman might have responded to the old saying, "Youth is wasted on the young"? Point to specific passages from each poem to establish Housman's views as precisely as possible. Then explain how your own views on the matter compare to Housman's.

Name ______________________ Date ______________ Class __________

Open-Book Selection Test

Score

The Darkling Thrush, The Man He Killed, and "Ah, Are You Digging on My Grave?"

Recall and Interpret (54 points total; 6 points each)
Write the letter of the best answer.

_____ **1.** The physical setting for the first stanza of "The Darkling Thrush" is
a. a rural landscape. **c.** a battlefield.
b. a cemetery. **d.** a mountain.

_____ **2.** The second stanza suggests that the events in "The Darkling Thrush" take place
a. just after a war. **c.** at the end of a century.
b. after a fierce battle. **d.** after the death of a friend.

_____ **3.** The thrush's song makes the speaker in "The Darkling Thrush"
a. want to despair. **c.** answer a fundamental question.
b. wish for hope. **d.** be romantically inspired.

_____ **4.** The speaker of "The Man He Killed" is
a. a traitor. **c.** a wounded officer.
b. a fierce patriot. **d.** an ordinary soldier.

_____ **5.** The speaker of "The Man He Killed" realizes that the man he killed was
a. a deadly enemy. **c.** a fierce patriot.
b. a distant relative. **d.** an ordinary man.

_____ **6.** The theme of "The Man He Killed" is best expressed by which of the following phrases?
a. the camaraderie of war
b. the excitement of war
c. the financial cost of war
d. the absurdity of war

_____ **7.** The first speaker's loved one in "Ah, Are You Digging on My Grave?" has not visited her grave because
a. he'd been killed in an accident.
b. he didn't know she had died.
c. he'd married someone else.
d. he was too despondent.

_____ **8.** In the second stanza, the first speaker assumes that which of the following is digging on her grave?
a. her loved one **c.** a secret admirer
b. an old school mate **d.** her relatives

Name ________________ Date ________________ Class ________

Open-Book Selection Test

(continued)

_____ **9.** The speaker's dog has come to her grave to

- **a.** bury a bone.
- **b.** pay his respects.
- **c.** laugh at her fate.
- **d.** bring her a tribute.

Analyze and Evaluate (21 points total; 7 points each)

Each of Hardy's poems includes an example of either verbal or situational irony. In the boxes below, identify and describe the ironic words or situations in each poem.

10. "The Darkling Thrush"
11. "The Man He Killed"
12. "Ah, Are You Digging on My Grave?"

BIG IDEA Connect (25 points)

Use a separate sheet of paper to answer the following essay question.

13. Hardy is often labeled a pessimist because his view of life seems bleak. Hardy rejected that label, saying that he was a "meliorist" who believed that the world's problems were caused by "man's inhumanity to man." The world's problems could therefore be cured. Using these poems as evidence, would you describe Hardy as a pessimist or a meliorist? Explain, using specific passages to support your view.

Name ______________________ Date ______________ Class ________

Selection Test

Score

A Cup of Tea (page 1047), Village People (page 1054), The Parable of Lazarus and the Rich Man (page 1057), and from the Qur'an (page 1059)

Recall and Interpret (54 points total; 6 points each)
Write the letter of the best answer.

_____ **1.** In "A Cup of Tea," Rosemary could be described as
- **a.** vain.
- **b.** cruel.
- **c.** violent.
- **d.** distracted.

_____ **2.** Why does Rosemary like the shop on Curzon Street?
- **a.** Her husband owns it.
- **b.** The shopkeeper flatters her.
- **c.** It is the best place to go for tea.
- **d.** It is always full of people she knows.

_____ **3.** The winter weather Rosemary experiences reflects her
- **a.** illness.
- **b.** selfishness.
- **c.** depression.
- **d.** vulnerability.

_____ **4.** Rosemary brings home
- **a.** a friend.
- **b.** a beggar.
- **c.** a new servant.
- **d.** the shopkeeper.

_____ **5.** The author of "Village People" believes people in poverty survive because they have
- **a.** health.
- **b.** foreign help.
- **c.** dignity.
- **d.** medical supplies.

_____ **6.** What might the author say is one of the most valuable aspects of the lives of the poverty stricken?
- **a.** education
- **b.** independence
- **c.** technology
- **d.** community

_____ **7.** The crowd reacts to the old woman's needs by
- **a.** sobbing.
- **b.** staring at her.
- **c.** laughing.
- **d.** ignoring her.

_____ **8.** In "The Parable of Lazarus and the Rich Man," the rich man asks Abraham to
- **a.** tell Lazarus to stop begging.
- **b.** save his wife from going to hell.
- **c.** keep his wife from stealing.
- **d.** send Lazarus to comfort him.

Name ______________________ Date ______________ Class ________

Selection Test

(continued)

_____ **9.** According to the excerpt from the Qur'an, alms should be given to
a. the traveler in need.
b. state employees.
c. boastful men.
d. the family elders.

Vocabulary Practice (6 points total; 2 points each)
Write the letter of the best answer.

_____ **10.** If you met a **quaint** person, you might describe him as
a. unique. **b.** royal. **c.** mature.

_____ **11.** Something that is **odious** is
a. beautiful. **b.** incomprehensible. **c.** hateful.

_____ **12.** To **retort** is to
a. move back. **b.** respond. **c.** fight.

Analyze and Evaluate (20 points total; 10 points each)
In both stories, you read of someone helping another; however, the actions, motives, and results of the acts of helping are quite different. Complete the boxes below to show the similarities and differences between the kinds of help provided in the stories.

	Rosemary, "A Cup of Tea"	Narrator, "Village People"
Action taken:	**13.**	**14.**
Motives:		
Result:		

BIG IDEA Connect (20 points)
Use a separate sheet of paper to answer the following essay question.

15. Compare and contrast the attitudes toward the poor in "The Parable of Lazarus and the Rich Man" and the excerpt from the Qur'an. Cite examples from each selection to support your ideas.

Name ______________________ Date ______________ Class __________

Selection Test

Score

Down and Out in Europe (page 1062)

Recall and Interpret (60 points total; 10 points each)
Write the letter of the best answer.

_____ **1.** Where does Big Sid mainly live?
- **a.** in a Paris shelter
- **b.** in the Caribbean
- **c.** on the streets of London
- **d.** on the dock in Brighton

_____ **2.** What are Big Sid's two favorite phrases?
- **a.** inside and outside
- **b.** short-term and long-term
- **c.** big-hearted and big-up
- **d.** bitter and better

_____ **3.** Only a small number of the homeless people in Europe
- **a.** have health problems.
- **b.** live on the street.
- **c.** are single men.
- **d.** speak English.

_____ **4.** Why does the author say it is surprising that Europe's homeless problem is so widespread?
- **a.** because European countries have extensive social safety nets
- **b.** because Europe's housing market has been growing rapidly
- **c.** because education is seen as a priority in most of Europe
- **d.** because alcohol and drug abuse rates are very low in Europe

_____ **5.** According to the article, one reason for the rise in the number of homeless women with families is
- **a.** higher rates of divorce.
- **b.** increased fertility rates.
- **c.** restrictive immigration laws.
- **d.** lack of medical resources for women.

_____ **6.** Why does the West London hostel run by Broadway charge its residents a fee?
- **a.** to pay for fees charged by the British government
- **b.** to encourage residents to leave the hostel quickly
- **c.** to discourage homeless people with abuse problems from staying
- **d.** to help residents learn how to deal with real-world chores

Name ______________________ Date ______________ Class __________

Selection Test

(continued)

Analyze and Evaluate (20 points total; 10 points each)

The author profiles two homeless people, Big Sid and Christelle, in the article. In the boxes below, describe why each person is probably homeless, where he or she is living when interviewed by the author, and what his or her situation indicates about the problem of homelessness in Europe.

	Why Homeless?	Living Situation	What It Indicates
7. Big Sid			
8. Christelle			

BIG IDEA Connect (20 points)

Use a separate sheet of paper to answer the following essay question.

9. Discuss what Europe's traditional response to homelessness has been and what the author says needs to happen now in order to address the growing problem.

Name ______________________ Date ______________ Class __________

Selection Test

Score

Miss Youghal's *Sais* (page 1070)

Recall and Interpret (56 points total; 8 points each)
Write the letter of the best answer.

_____ **1.** The narrator of "Miss Youghal's *Sais*" is
- **a.** Strickland.
- **b.** an Indian spy.
- **c.** Dulloo.
- **d.** a British friend.

_____ **2.** Strickland's "extraordinary theory" about police work was that the police
- **a.** are criminals themselves.
- **b.** should never use force.
- **c.** should get to know local customs.
- **d.** should never talk to civilians.

_____ **3.** Strickland's methods of police work rely heavily on
- **a.** a fast car.
- **b.** many disguises.
- **c.** multiple weapons.
- **d.** his physical strength.

_____ **4.** Strickland's successes at solving crimes
- **a.** earn him promotions.
- **b.** make the natives fear him.
- **c.** get him lots of publicity.
- **d.** make his peers jealous.

_____ **5.** The Youghals object to Strickland's proposal to marry their daughter because
- **a.** he is British.
- **b.** they distrust him.
- **c.** their daughter is too young.
- **d.** he has insulted them.

_____ **6.** The incident that causes Strickland to reveal his true identity is
- **a.** a General's flirtation.
- **b.** a General's command.
- **c.** his anger at Mr. Youghal.
- **d.** the indignities of his job as a *sais*.

_____ **7.** When the General learns of Strickland's engagement, he
- **a.** threatens to tell Mr. Youghal.
- **b.** threatens to arrest Strickland.
- **c.** laughs and offers help.
- **d.** gives Strickland a pony.

Name ______________________ Date ______________ Class ________

Selection Test

(continued)

Vocabulary Practice (8 points total; 2 points each)
Write the letter of the best answer.

_____**8.** If you meet an **unsavory** person, you might find that he
- **a.** spends money foolishly.
- **b.** talks too loud.
- **c.** is dishonest.

_____**9.** As **compensation** for his work on the robbery, the officer was
a. fired. **b.** fined. **c.** given a bonus.

_____**10.** A publishing house intent on **suppressing** a book would most likely
- **a.** print a second edition.
- **b.** print an illustrated version.
- **c.** not print it.

_____**11.** At the performance of a **farce**, an audience would most likely
a. laugh. **b.** cry. **c.** sing along.

Analyze and Evaluate (18 points total; 6 points each)
In the boxes below, describe how the story might have been different if told from the point of view of each character listed.

12. Strickland:
13. Mr. Youghal:
14. The General:

BIG IDEA Connect (18 points)
Use a separate sheet to answer the following essay question.

15. Write a character sketch of the narrator, discussing the specific perspective, personality, and set of values he brings to the story. Make specific references to the story to support your statements.

Name ______________________ Date ______________ Class __________

Selection Test

Score

Shooting an Elephant (page 1079)

Recall and Interpret (50 points total; 10 points each)
Write the letter of the best answer.

_____ **1.** Which of the following best describes the natives' feeling toward the narrator of "Shooting an Elephant," a British police officer in Burma?

- **a.** they hate him
- **b.** they respect him
- **c.** they fear him
- **d.** they pity him

_____ **2.** Which of the following best describes the narrator's feelings about his own position in Burma?

- **a.** proud of his role as an officer of the British Empire
- **b.** ashamed of the power he holds over the Burmese people
- **c.** torn between hatred of Empire and rage against the Burmese
- **d.** fearful of being assassinated by the people he is meant to protect

_____ **3.** The narrator realizes he'll have to shoot the elephant when he

- **a.** sees the dead coolie.
- **b.** realizes the crowd expects him to shoot.
- **c.** realizes the elephant's owner is hours away.
- **d.** hears about the damage the elephant has done.

_____ **4.** The mood of the crowd that follows the narrator could best be described as

- **a.** festive.
- **b.** fearful.
- **c.** angry.
- **d.** passive.

_____ **5.** According to the narrator, the primary goal of British officials in the East was to

- **a.** bring civilization to the area.
- **b.** exploit the local resources.
- **c.** avoid being laughed at.
- **d.** learn about local culture.

Vocabulary Practice (10 points total; 2 points each)
Write the letter of the best answer.

_____ **6.** If Tom is going to **supplant** Phil as the starting quarterback, Tom will

- **a.** replace Phil.
- **b.** celebrate Phil's record.
- **c.** coach Phil.

_____ **7.** A **despotic** athletic coach would

- **a.** insist on strict obedience.
- **b.** seek ways to make practices enjoyable.
- **c.** encourage players to make strategic decisions.

Name ______________________ Date ______________ Class __________

Selection Test

(continued)

_____ **8.** A person who wished to escape from a **labyrinth** would be helped most by a

a. shovel. **b.** car. **c.** guide.

_____ **9.** When Ethan's mother said his room was **squalid**, she was commenting on its

a. size. **b.** condition. **c.** colors.

_____ **10.** To remark that a person's clothes are **garish** is to say that they are

a. subdued and stylish.
b. expensive but ugly.
c. bright and tasteless.

Analyze and Evaluate (20 points)

In the boxes below, describe what the elephant may symbolize in the essay. Then identify a phrase describing the elephant and explain what this description conveys about the elephant and what it symbolizes.

What Elephant Symbolizes	Phrase	What It Conveys
11.		

BIG IDEA Connect (20 points)

Use a separate sheet of paper to answer the following essay question.

12. At one point in the essay, Orwell says, "I perceived in this moment that when the white man turns tyrant it is his own freedom that he destroys." Explain what he means by this statement. Why did this thought occur to him at this moment?

Name ______________________ Date ______________ Class __________

Open-Book Selection Test

Score

The Soldier (page 1091)

Recall and Interpret (60 points total; 15 points each)
Write the letter of the best answer.

_____ **1.** The speaker of the poem will consider himself an Englishman
- **a.** eternally.
- **b.** for a long time.
- **c.** until there is a new king.
- **d.** as long as he lives in England.

_____ **2.** Which of the following best describes the speaker's feelings about the possibility of death?
- **a.** fear
- **b.** denial
- **c.** worry
- **d.** resignation

_____ **3.** In line 5, the speaker metaphorically asserts that England
- **a.** fed him.
- **b.** gave birth to him.
- **c.** bathed him.
- **d.** educated him.

_____ **4.** The mood at the end of the poem is best described as
- **a.** peaceful.
- **b.** complex.
- **c.** fierce.
- **d.** bored.

Name ______________________ Date ______________ Class __________

Open-Book Selection Test *(continued)*

Analyze and Evaluate (20 points total; 10 points each)

In the boxes below, cite two images from the poem. Then say what mood each image expresses.

Image	Mood It Expresses
5.	
6.	

BIG IDEA Connect (20 points)

Use a separate sheet of paper to answer the following essay question.

7. Discuss Brooke's attitude toward the war, citing examples from the poem to support your ideas. Then explain what you think about the poet's attitude toward war.

Name ______________________ Date ______________ Class __________

Open-Book Selection Test

Score

Dreamers (page 1095)

Recall and Interpret (48 points total; 12 points each)
Write the letter of the best answer.

_____ **1.** In the first stanza, the speaker claims a soldier has little control over his
- **a.** fate.
- **b.** family.
- **c.** battle.
- **d.** emotions.

_____ **2.** The speaker asserts that during war a soldier is preoccupied with
- **a.** dying.
- **b.** home.
- **c.** the battle.
- **d.** his career.

_____ **3.** What mocks the soldiers at the end of the poem?
- **a.** death
- **b.** the sun
- **c.** longing
- **d.** the enemy

_____ **4.** The speaker's tone is best described as
- **a.** ferocious.
- **b.** indifferent.
- **c.** melancholic.
- **d.** humorous.

Vocabulary Practice (12 points total; 4 points each)
Write the letter of the best answer.

_____ **5.** To avoid one's **destiny** is
a. praiseworthy. **b.** impossible. **c.** deadly.

_____ **6.** The **feud** between the two sisters
- **a.** happened last Tuesday.
- **b.** lasted for years and years.
- **c.** was removed by surgery.

_____ **7.** In the opera's **fatal** climax, the hero
- **a.** dies.
- **b.** sings.
- **c.** cries.

Name ______________________ Date ______________ Class ________

Open-Book Selection Test

(continued)

Analyze and Evaluate (20 points)

In the boxes below, describe who the dreamers in Sassoon's poem are, what they dream of, and why you think Sassoon used "Dreamers" as the title of the poem.

Dreamers	What They Dream Of	Why This Title?
8.		

BIG IDEA Connect (20 points)

Use a separate sheet of paper to answer the following essay question.

9. Discuss how Sassoon contrasts images of the battlefield with images of home in the poem. Cite specific examples from the poem to support your ideas.

Name ______________________ Date ______________ Class ________

Open-Book Selection Test

Score

Dulce et Decorum Est (page 1099)

Recall and Interpret (48 points total; 12 points each)
Write the letter of the best answer.

_____ **1.** The first verse paragraph of "Dulce et Decorum Est" portrays the soldiers as
- **a.** lost.
- **b.** lazy.
- **c.** hungry.
- **d.** exhausted.

_____ **2.** In lines 9–16, the speaker describes a soldier who cannot
- **a.** fire his gun.
- **b.** march in place.
- **c.** put on his gas mask.
- **d.** follow his commander.

_____ **3.** What happens to the soldier in the final verse paragraph?
- **a.** He dies a painful death.
- **b.** He is carried by the speaker.
- **c.** He fights and kills the enemy.
- **d.** He is reprimanded for moving slowly.

_____ **4.** If the speaker in the poem met a young man who aspired to go to battle, the speaker would tell him that war is
- **a.** a way to prove his manhood.
- **b.** probably not what he expects.
- **c.** only for the strong and quick.
- **d.** an experience that will better him.

Vocabulary Practice (12 points total; 4 points each)
Write the letter of the best answer.

_____ **5.** The hiker found she had to **trudge**
- **a.** on the paved road.
- **b.** under a blue sky.
- **c.** through deep snow.

_____ **6.** The child displayed a sense of **ecstasy** upon
- **a.** getting on the school bus.
- **b.** opening a desired present.
- **c.** watching an old TV show.

_____ **7.** I found that the **vile** odor came from
- **a.** the rotting carcass of an animal.
- **b.** the flowering trees over the hill.
- **c.** a tiny drop of spilled kerosene.

Name ______________________ Date ______________ Class ________

Open-Book Selection Test

(continued)

Analyze and Evaluate (20 points)

Choose a verse paragraph from the poem. In the boxes below, indicate which lines the verse paragraph consists of and what the paragraph's main idea is. Then write two details that support the main idea.

Lines	Main Idea	Supporting Details
8.		

BIG IDEA Connect (20 points)

Use a separate sheet of paper to answer the following essay question.

9. Discuss what Owen says "the old Lie" is and which images he uses in the poem to provide evidence that the statement is, in fact, a lie.

Name ______________________ Date ______________ Class __________

Selection Test

Score

from *The Great War and Modern Memory* (page 1101)

Recall and Interpret (60 points total; 10 points each)
Write the letter of the best answer.

_____ **1.** Fussell estimates that the total length of the trenches used in World War I was equal to
- **a.** the circumference of the earth.
- **b.** the perimeter of France.
- **c.** 3000 miles.
- **d.** 300 meters.

_____ **2.** At the beginning of the excerpt, Fussell notes that some survivors of trench warfare have imagined
- **a.** covering the trenches with gold.
- **b.** digging trenches to Australia.
- **c.** seeing the whole line of trenches at once.
- **d.** living in the trenches for the rest of their lives.

_____ **3.** The Staff used the term "wastage" to refer to
- **a.** the left-over lumber from building floors.
- **b.** the sumps used under the boards of the trenches.
- **c.** the deeper holes dug for officers meetings.
- **d.** soldiers killed or wounded in the trenches.

_____ **4.** Reserve lines were typically
- **a.** kept at home in England.
- **b.** behind support trench lines.
- **c.** used to send letters to relatives.
- **d.** fifty yards from enemy counterparts.

_____ **5.** Communication trenches often began
- **a.** underground.
- **b.** in towns.
- **c.** as "funk-holes."
- **d.** with sticks and rushes.

_____ **6.** The Allies used barbed wire to
- **a.** keep the enemy from throwing grenades.
- **b.** restrain wild animals from entering the trenches.
- **c.** protect crops of vegetables in French towns.
- **d.** provide autumnal scenery similar to England.

Name ______________________ Date ______________ Class ________

Selection Test

(continued)

Analyze and Evaluate (20 points)

In the boxes below, describe the three kinds of trenches and the purpose of each.

Kind of Trench	Purpose
7.	

BIG IDEA Connect (20 points)

Use a separate sheet of paper to answer the following essay question.

8. Describe Fussell's tone in this excerpt. Discuss the ways in which he describes his subject and what he chooses to focus on, and cite examples to support your viewpoint.

Name ______________________ Date ______________ Class __________

Open-Book Selection Test

Score

The Lake Isle of Innisfree and When You Are Old (page 1108)

Recall and Interpret (60 points total; 10 points each)
Write the letter of the best answer.

_____ **1.** The speaker wants to go to Innisfree to
- **a.** write a poem.
- **b.** escape from school.
- **c.** live alone.
- **d.** learn music.

_____ **2.** According to lines 11–12 of the poem, Innisfree will be in the heart of the speaker
- **a.** whenever he is in the city.
- **b.** wherever he goes.
- **c.** whenever he is near water.
- **d.** wherever there are birds.

_____ **3.** Which of these best describes what the speaker feels at Innisfree?
- **a.** love
- **b.** pride
- **c.** serenity
- **d.** amusement

_____ **4.** In the first stanza of "When You Are Old," the speaker asks the woman he addresses to
- **a.** read his book.
- **b.** kiss his hand.
- **c.** forget they met.
- **d.** go on a pilgrimage.

_____ **5.** The speaker of "When You Are Old" wants the woman to feel
- **a.** pity.
- **b.** regret.
- **c.** hostility.
- **d.** numbness.

_____ **6.** In which line does the speaker claim to have loved the woman more deeply than any other man has loved her?
- **a.** 4
- **b.** 6
- **c.** 5
- **d.** 7

Open-Book Selection Test *(continued)*

Analyze and Evaluate (20 points total; 10 points each)

In the boxes below, describe the structures and rhyme schemes Yeats uses in both poems. Say what the effect of each rhyme scheme is.

Structure	Rhyme Scheme	Effect of Rhyme Scheme
7. "The Lake Isle of Innisfree"		
8. "When You Are Old"		

BIG IDEA Connect (20 points)

Use a separate sheet of paper to answer the following essay question.

9. Describe how Yeats uses contrasts and the tension between opposites in "The Lake Isle of Innisfree" and "When You Are Old." What effects does using these contrasts have?

Name ______________________ Date ______________ Class __________

Open-Book Selection Test

Score

Sailing to Byzantium (page 1111) and The Second Coming (page 1112)

Recall and Interpret (48 points total; 8 points each)
Write the letter of the best answer.

_____ **1.** In "Sailing to Byzantium," which line presents a metaphor for an aged body?
- **a.** 5
- **b.** 10
- **c.** 14
- **d.** 17

_____ **2.** The speaker prefers Byzantium over his own world, because his world
- **a.** is crowded.
- **b.** rejects the elderly.
- **c.** is dangerous.
- **d.** is full of aging men.

_____ **3.** Line 22 of "Sailing to Byzantium" refers to the speaker's
- **a.** body.
- **b.** memory.
- **c.** clothes.
- **d.** poetry.

_____ **4.** Which line of "The Second Coming" best portrays chaos?
- **a.** 1
- **b.** 2
- **c.** 4
- **d.** 7

_____ **5.** In "The Second Coming," who lacks all conviction?
- **a.** the best
- **b.** the Sphinx
- **c.** the sun
- **d.** desert birds

_____ **6.** Which of the following causes the greatest feeling of dread for the speaker?
- **a.** falcon
- **b.** falconer
- **c.** cradle
- **d.** Sphinx

Name ______________________ Date ______________ Class __________

Open-Book Selection Test

(continued)

Vocabulary Practice (12 points total; 3 points each)
Write the letter of the best answer.

_____ **7.** Every **artifice** is
a. lifelike. **b.** motorized. **c.** human-made.

_____ **8.** A state of **anarchy** is usually
a. disorderly. **b.** agreeable. **c.** nervous.

_____ **9.** To give up a **conviction** is
a. costly. **b.** honorable. **c.** difficult.

_____ **10.** Comments that **vex** you make you feel
a. irritated. **b.** downcast. **c.** proud.

Analyze and Evaluate (20 points total; 10 points each)
In the boxes below, describe the structure of each poem. Then describe what the effect of each structure is.

	Structure	Effect of Structure
11. "Sailing to Byzantium"		
12. "The Second Coming"		

BIG IDEA Connect (20 points)
Use a separate sheet of paper to answer the following essay question.

13. Compare and contrast the moods of the two poems and discuss how Yeats uses imagery to convey mood in the poems.

Name ______________________ Date ______________ Class ________

Open-Book Selection Test

Score

Preludes (page 1119)

Recall and Interpret (50 points total; 10 points each)
Write the letter of the best answer.

_____ **1.** At what time of year does prelude I take place?
- **a.** spring
- **b.** summer
- **c.** fall
- **d.** winter

_____ **2.** To the speaker, physical decay is analogous to the decline of
- **a.** the mind.
- **b.** education.
- **c.** society.
- **d.** the body.

_____ **3.** The tone of the first prelude can best be described as
- **a.** depressing.
- **b.** gruesome.
- **c.** shocking.
- **d.** horrifying.

_____ **4.** The "worlds" in the final prelude are
- **a.** people who are ill.
- **b.** people who are alone.
- **c.** people who are evil.
- **d.** people who are aging.

_____ **5.** The images suggest that the most urgent problem in society is
- **a.** disease.
- **b.** isolation.
- **c.** murder.
- **d.** lack of privacy.

Vocabulary Practice (10 points total; 5 points each)
Write the letter of the best answer.

_____ **6.** The cake batter was **constituted**
- **a.** under the covered bridge.
- **b.** of sugar, flour, and eggs.
- **c.** so we had to throw it out.

_____ **7.** The **infinitely** long tunnel
- **a.** pierced the mountain.
- **b.** connected the islands.
- **c.** took forever to dig.

Name ______________________ Date ______________ Class __________

Open-Book Selection Test

(continued)

Analyze and Evaluate (20 points total; 10 points each)

In the boxes below, cite two images from "Preludes." Explain which sense each image appeals to and the feeling conveyed by each image.

Image	Sense	Feeling
8.		
9.		

BIG IDEA Connect (20 points)

Use a separate sheet of paper to answer the following essay question.

10. Discuss how Eliot creates a sense of alienation and despair in "Preludes." Cite examples from the poem.

Name ______________________ Date ______________ Class __________

Selection Test

Score

The Rocking-Horse Winner (page 1124)

Recall and Interpret (48 points total; 6 points each)
Write the letter of the best answer.

_____ **1.** What is the biggest problem for the people in this family?
- **a.** The parents are divorced.
- **b.** The parents are unemployed.
- **c.** Objects in the house can talk.
- **d.** Their wants exceed their means.

_____ **2.** According to the mother, the best way to obtain money is through
- **a.** luck.
- **b.** stealing.
- **c.** hard work.
- **d.** inheritance.

_____ **3.** The mother is raising her children out of a sense of
- **a.** deep concern.
- **b.** maternal love.
- **c.** obligation.
- **d.** affection for kids.

_____ **4.** The only person who knows that the rocking horse helps Paul determine the winning racehorse is
- **a.** Uncle Oscar.
- **b.** Mother.
- **c.** Bassett.
- **d.** Paul.

_____ **5.** After Paul's mother receives the money, what happens to the voices in the house?
- **a.** They stop entirely.
- **b.** They become quiet.
- **c.** They only occur on her birthday.
- **d.** They grow louder and more urgent.

_____ **6.** Paul panics when his mother speaks of sending him to the seaside because he
- **a.** is afraid of being alone.
- **b.** wants to stay with his friends.
- **c.** hopes to continue making bets.
- **d.** thinks his luck will change.

_____ **7.** Which of the following events foreshadows the tragic ending?
- **a.** Paul's horse loses a race.
- **b.** Bassett discovers Paul's secret.
- **c.** Uncle Oscar loses all his money.
- **d.** Mother experiences anxiety attacks.

_____ **8.** Which of these is an example of personification?
- **a.** ". . . she felt she must cover up some fault in herself."
- **b.** ". . . the voices in the house . . . simply trilled and screamed . . ."
- **c.** ". . . there was always the grinding sense of shortage of money."
- **d.** "When he had ridden to the end of his mad little journey, he climbed down."

Name ______________________ Date ______________ Class ________

Selection Test

(continued)

Vocabulary Practice (12 points total; 3 points each)
Write the letter of the best answer.

_____ **9.** If you **emancipate** something, you
a. free it. **b.** mock it. **c.** believe in it.

_____ **10.** To **reiterate** a command is to
a. defy it. **b.** follow it. **c.** repeat it.

_____ **11.** You might **parry** a question you desire to
a. avoid. **b.** answer. **c.** ask.

_____ **12.** Another word for **obstinately** is
a. reasonably. **b.** dangerously. **c.** stubbornly.

Analyze and Evaluate (20 points total; 10 points each)
In the boxes below, cite two examples of foreshadowing from the story and tell what each example foreshadows.

Example	What It Foreshadows
13.	
14.	

BIG IDEA Connect (20 points)
Use a separate sheet of paper to answer the following essay question.

15. What does this selection suggest about D. H. Lawrence's view toward greed and material possessions? Do you agree or disagree with his viewpoint?

Name ______________________ Date ______________ Class __________

Selection Test

Score

Araby (page 1140)

Recall and Interpret (45 points total; 5 points each)
Write the letter of the best answer.

_____**1.** The street on which the narrator lives is
- **a.** quiet.
- **b.** dirty.
- **c.** somber.
- **d.** dangerous.

_____**2.** The narrator's love for Mangan's sister is best described as
- **a.** unrequited.
- **b.** lasting.
- **c.** mature.
- **d.** noncommittal.

_____**3.** As the story progresses, the narrator's feelings for Mangan's sister become feelings of
- **a.** respect.
- **b.** superiority.
- **c.** obsession.
- **d.** amusement.

_____**4.** What plans do the narrator and Mangan's sister make regarding Araby?
- **a.** He will take her there.
- **b.** He will photograph it for her.
- **c.** He will not go if she cannot go.
- **d.** He will buy her something there.

_____**5.** Which of the following statements best describes the narrator during the days before the bazaar?
- **a.** He counts down the days on a calendar.
- **b.** He is distracted and time passes slowly.
- **c.** He desires more time because he is nervous.
- **d.** He is happy that school makes the time pass quickly.

_____**6.** What causes a delay on the day he is supposed to go to Araby?
- **a.** His uncle is late.
- **b.** Mrs. Mercer talks too much.
- **c.** He plays with friends.
- **d.** His mother makes him drink tea.

_____**7.** Why does the narrator compare the bazaar to a church?
- **a.** It is crowded.
- **b.** It smells like incense.
- **c.** He sees many priests.
- **d.** It is silent and still.

Name ______________________ Date ______________ Class __________

Selection Test

(continued)

_____ **8.** At the end of the story, what does the narrator discover about his relationship with Mangan's sister?
- **a.** He is one of many suitors.
- **b.** He will never have her.
- **c.** He is lost without her.
- **d.** He does not want her.

_____ **9.** At what point does the narrator experience this revelation?
- **a.** during tea with his aunt
- **b.** as he stands alone at the bazaar
- **c.** on the train ride home from the bazaar
- **d.** when he discovers the dead priest's books

Vocabulary Practice (15 points total; 5 points each)
Write the letter of the best answer.

_____ **10.** A **converging** intersection is one in which the streets
a. come together. **b.** move apart. **c.** are at an angle.

_____ **11.** An **imperturbable** person is not easily
a. amused. **b.** taught. **c.** disturbed.

_____ **12.** To **impinge** is to
a. operate. **b.** collide. **c.** manufacture.

Analyze and Evaluate (20 points)
The narrator of the story experiences a major epiphany. In the boxes below, identify when the narrator has the epiphany and what insight(s) the narrator gains as a result of this experience.

When Epiphany Occurs	What Insight(s) He Gains
13.	

BIG IDEA Connect (20 points)
Use a separate sheet of paper to answer the following essay question.

14. Describe how "Araby" is both traditional and innovative in its techniques and subject matter.

Name ______________________ Date ______________ Class ________

Selection Test

Score

from **A Room of One's Own** (page 1151)

Recall and Interpret (35 points total; 5 points each)
Write the letter of the best answer.

_____ **1.** Which of these is not presented as a reason why sixteenth-century women did not write?
- **a.** Women had no place to write.
- **b.** Women had to tend to household duties.
- **c.** Women had to tend to their children.
- **d.** Women were denied formal education.

_____ **2.** Woolf's description of Shakespeare as a youth encourages the reader to view him as
- **a.** odd.
- **b.** ordinary.
- **c.** superior.
- **d.** a prodigy.

_____ **3.** The bishop who contrasted sixteenth-century women to Shakespeare also asserted
- **a.** pets have no souls.
- **b.** Shakespeare was godly.
- **c.** women are wicked.
- **d.** Shakespeare had a sister.

_____ **4.** Which of the following is not mentioned by Woolf as a possible fate of a sixteenth-century female writer?
- **a.** loss of life.
- **b.** loss of health.
- **c.** loss of sanity.
- **d.** loss of dowry.

_____ **5.** According to Woolf, who may have been Anon?
- **a.** a man.
- **b.** Shakespeare.
- **c.** a woman.
- **d.** Shakespeare's sister.

_____ **6.** The purpose of the passage that mentions Anon is to
- **a.** inform.
- **b.** amuse.
- **c.** instruct.
- **d.** persuade.

_____ **7.** Although sarcastic at times, Woolf concludes with an air of
- **a.** shame.
- **b.** vengeance.
- **c.** anger.
- **d.** resignation.

Vocabulary Practice (25 points total; 5 points each)
Write the letter of the best answer.

_____ **8.** To **guffaw** is to
- **a.** choke.
- **b.** beg.
- **c.** laugh.

Name ______________________ Date ______________ Class __________

Selection Test

(continued)

_____ **9.** If you **thwart** an action, you
- **a.** facilitate it.
- **b.** prevent it.
- **c.** encourage it.

_____ **10.** One who is **hindered** is
- **a.** delayed.
- **b.** ridiculed.
- **c.** rejected.

_____ **11.** If a person is **morbid**, the person is
- **a.** alone.
- **b.** sleeping.
- **c.** gloomy.

_____ **12.** A common reaction to a **dilemma** is
- **a.** joy.
- **b.** anxiety.
- **c.** fatigue.

Analyze and Evaluate (20 points)

In the boxes below, state the main argument that Woolf makes in this essay. Then name two ways in which she supports her argument.

Argument	Support for Argument
13.	

BIG IDEA Connect (20 points)

Use a separate sheet of paper to answer the following essay question.

14. What group of people might be identified as repressed in our society today? What might Woolf say is the cause of their repression?

Name ______________________ Date ______________ Class ________

Selection Test

Score

from *Mrs. Dalloway* (page 1157)

Recall and Interpret (50 points total; 10 points each)
Write the letter of the best answer.

_____ **1.** Whom does Mrs. Dalloway recall fondly throughout the excerpt?
- **a.** Peter Walsh
- **b.** Hugh Whitbread
- **c.** Richard Dalloway
- **d.** Evelyn Whitbread

_____ **2.** Clarissa Dalloway lives
- **a.** with Lady Bexborough.
- **b.** in Westminster.
- **c.** in Buckingham Palace.
- **d.** in India.

_____ **3.** What has just ended?
- **a.** Clarissa's party
- **b.** Clarissa's marriage
- **c.** World War I
- **d.** World War II

_____ **4.** Hugh Whitbread is Clarissa's
- **a.** second cousin.
- **b.** former lover.
- **c.** childhood friend.
- **d.** younger brother.

_____ **5.** What time of year is it?
- **a.** midwinter
- **b.** early spring
- **c.** late autumn
- **d.** early summer

Vocabulary Practice (10 points total; 2 points each)
Write the letter of the best answer.

_____ **6.** A person with an **ailment** might visit
a. a doctor. **b.** her sister. **c.** a banker.

_____ **7.** A **solemn** person would be most likely to
a. scream. **b.** frown. **c.** jump.

Name ______________________ Date ______________ Class ________

Selection Test

(continued)

_____ **8.** If you give someone a **cordial** greeting, you are being
a. friendly. **b.** noisy. **c.** standoffish.

_____ **9.** A person who is **presumably** intelligent is most likely
a. confused. **b.** dull-witted. **c.** smart.

_____ **10.** A **perpetual** noise seems
a. bearable. **b.** delightful. **c.** unending.

Analyze and Evaluate (20 points)

In the boxes below, write a passage from the selection that displays stream of consciousness and then explain what the passage tells the reader about Mrs. Dalloway.

Passage	Insights into Mrs. Dalloway
11.	

BIG IDEA Connect (20 points)

Use a separate sheet of paper to answer the following essay question.

12. The selection concludes with Clarissa thinking, "Oh if she could have had her life over again!" Explain why she thinks this and describe the character's personality and how Woolf conveys her personality.

Name ______________________ Date ______________ Class __________

Selection Test

Score

Be Ye Men of Valor (page 1168)

Recall and Interpret (48 points total; 8 points each)
Write the letter of the best answer.

_____ **1.** Which of the following statements best summarizes Churchill's speech?
- **a.** We must win at any cost.
- **b.** We must conserve our resources.
- **c.** We must put a quick end to this terrible war.
- **d.** We must not sacrifice any more lives to win the war.

_____ **2.** Churchill opens his speech with a description of
- **a.** a heroic soldier.
- **b.** a particular battle.
- **c.** those who have died,
- **d.** the state of the prisoners of war.

_____ **3.** Churchill's goal is to elicit which of the following from his citizens?
- **a.** shame
- **b.** peace
- **c.** horror
- **d.** unity

_____ **4.** Which of the following does Churchill use to persuade?
- **a.** figures and statistics
- **b.** emotional patriotism
- **c.** harsh, scolding words
- **d.** gruesome descriptions

_____ **5.** The expression "unless we conquer, as conquer we must; as conquer we shall," is an example of
- **a.** hyperbole.
- **b.** repetition.
- **c.** alliteration.
- **d.** personification.

_____ **6.** Churchill describes the condition of suffering in Holland to increase his country's
- **a.** sympathy for Dutch.
- **b.** pride in British soldiers.
- **c.** realization of the urgent situation.
- **d.** understanding of Holland's errors.

Vocabulary Practice (12 points total; 3 points each)
Write the letter of the best answer.

_____ **7.** Which of these might **ravage** a countryside?
- **a.** an enemy
- **b.** an environmentalist
- **c.** a farmer

Name ______________________ Date ______________ Class ________

Selection Test *(continued)*

_____ **8.** The student **grappled** with an assignment that was
a. remedial. **b.** average. **c.** difficult.

_____ **9.** Which of these is cause for **imperious** action by school children?
a. recess **b.** physical education **c.** a fire alarm

_____ **10.** The **indomitable** character was
a. peaceful. **b.** restrained easily. **c.** impossible to overcome.

Analyze and Evaluate (20 points total; 10 points each)
In the boxes below, give two examples of appeals to logic and two examples of appeals to emotion that Churchill uses to persuade his audience.

Appeal to Logic	Appeal to Emotion
11.	
12.	

BIG IDEA Connect (20 points)
Use a separate sheet of paper to answer the following essay question.

13. Do you think Churchill appealed more to people's feelings or to their reason? What is the effect of this type of rhetoric? Support your answer with references to the selection.

Name ______________________ Date ______________ Class ________

Selection Test

Score

The Demon Lover (page 1176)

Recall and Interpret (40 points total; 5 points each)
Write the letter of the best answer.

_____ **1.** At the beginning of the story, the homes in London have been abandoned because of

a. war. **c.** disease.
b. famine. **d.** construction.

_____ **2.** Upon entering the house, Mrs. Drover appears to be

a. happy. **c.** distressed.
b. excited. **d.** broken-hearted.

_____ **3.** What is Mrs. Drover's reaction to seeing a letter on the hall table?

a. pleasure **c.** disappointment
b. curiosity **d.** astonishment

_____ **4.** After reading the letter, Mrs. Drover begins to feel

a. dread. **c.** concern.
b. sadness. **d.** hostility.

_____ **5.** Mrs. Drover's thoughts of the soldier could best be described as

a. a dream. **c.** a metaphor.
b. an allusion. **d.** a flashback.

_____ **6.** Which of the following describes Mrs. Drover's fiancée?

a. He looks like everyone.
b. His face is utterly sinister.
c. She cannot remember his face.
d. He could be seen only by Mrs. Drover.

_____ **7.** What would Mrs. Drover do again if she got the chance?

a. take the taxi
b. get engaged to the soldier
c. marry William Drover
d. visit her house in London

_____ **8.** Which of these statements most likely reflects the author's attitude toward the war?

a. The war produced many heroes.
b. The war decreased national patriotism.
c. The war had little effect on the people of London.
d. The war caused psychological problems in some people.

Name ______________________ Date ______________ Class __________

Selection Test

(continued)

Vocabulary Practice (20 points total; 4 points each)
Write the letter of the best answer.

_____ **9.** Someone working **impassively** might
a. stare. **b.** smile. **c.** frown.

_____ **10.** From a teacher, there might **emanate** a
a. student. **b.** command. **c.** desk.

_____ **11.** If rain is **intermittent**, it
a. stops immediately. **b.** lasts all day. **c.** starts and stops.

_____ **12.** The **prosaic** woman looked
a. unruly. **b.** ordinary. **c.** exotic.

_____ **13.** Something spoken **precipitately** is spoken
a. quickly. **b.** with delay. **c.** quietly.

Analyze and Evaluate (20 points)
In the boxes below, describe the flashback that occurs in the story. Describe what effect the flashback has.

Flashback	Effect
14.	

BIG IDEA Connect (20 points)
Use a separate sheet of paper to answer the following essay question.

15. Define *suspense* and discuss how the author uses suspense at the end of this story. Does it create an effective ending? Why or why not?

Name ______________________ Date ______________ Class __________

Open-Book Selection Test

Score

Musée des Beaux Arts (page 1186) and The Unknown Citizen (page 1187)

Recall and Interpret (48 points total; 8 points each)
Write the letter of the best answer.

_____ **1.** According to Auden, the Old Masters were "never wrong" about suffering because they knew that most people viewed it with
- **a.** understanding.
- **b.** indifference.
- **c.** sympathy.
- **d.** contempt.

_____ **2.** In Auden's view, Brueghel's painting captures what quality of the human condition?
- **a.** its communal spirit
- **b.** its inherent evil
- **c.** its isolation
- **d.** its absurdity

_____ **3.** The speaker's tone in "Musée des Beaux Arts" is best described as
- **a.** resigned.
- **b.** loving.
- **c.** passionate.
- **d.** angry.

_____ **4.** Which word best describes the Unknown Citizen?
- **a.** intense
- **b.** brilliant
- **c.** mean
- **d.** average

_____ **5.** The Unknown Citizen has
- **a.** two point three children.
- **b.** everything a Modern Man needs.
- **c.** a job at the Bureau of Statistics.
- **d.** no health insurance.

_____ **6.** The speaker of "The Unknown Citizen" wants to know if the Unknown Citizen was
- **a.** fired from the factory.
- **b.** happy and free.
- **c.** rich and famous.
- **d.** portrayed in a novel.

Name ______________________ Date ______________ Class ________

Open-Book Selection Test

(continued)

Vocabulary Practice (12 points total; 4 points each)
Write the letter of the best answer.

_____ **7.** The man behaved **reverently** while he was in the
a. night club. **b.** church. **c.** stadium.

_____ **8.** The **forsaken** child
a. danced around. **b.** hugged everyone. **c.** wept.

_____ **9.** Although the plan was **sensible**, the committee
a. rejected it. **b.** discussed it. **c.** accepted it.

Analyze and Evaluate (20 points total; 10 points each)
Auden uses both verbal and dramatic irony in these two poems. In the boxes below, write an example of irony from each of the two poems and indicate what type of irony it represents.

Example of Irony	Verbal or Dramatic?
10. "Musée des Beaux Arts"	
11. "The Unknown Citizen"	

BIG IDEA Connect (20 points)
Use a separate sheet of paper to answer the following essay question.

12. Describe Auden's opinion about modern life as he expresses it in "The Unknown Citizen." Cite examples from the poem to support your answer.

Name ______________________ Date ______________ Class __________

Selection Test

Score

A Shocking Accident (page 1194)

Recall and Interpret (42 points total; 7 points each)
Write the letter of the best answer.

_____ **1.** Jerome's father had worked as a
- **a.** diplomat.
- **b.** gangster.
- **c.** travel writer.
- **d.** member of the Secret Service.

_____ **2.** After telling Jerome of his father's death, Mr. Wordsworth apparently "shook with emotion" because he was
- **a.** grieving.
- **b.** laughing.
- **c.** angry.
- **d.** sympathizing.

_____ **3.** When Jerome starts public school, he realizes that listeners find the story of his father's death
- **a.** tragic.
- **b.** gruesome.
- **c.** funny.
- **d.** boring.

_____ **4.** When Jerome tells the story of his father's death in a detailed, leisurely way, he is trying to make the story
- **a.** boring.
- **b.** accurate.
- **c.** exciting.
- **d.** suspenseful.

_____ **5.** Before he marries, Jerome worries that Sally may
- **a.** think he's dull.
- **b.** not take him seriously.
- **c.** not appreciate his sensitivities.
- **d.** laugh at the story of his father's death.

_____ **6.** The speaker implies that Jerome's work as an accountant means he is
- **a.** sensible.
- **b.** wealthy.
- **c.** brilliant.
- **d.** greedy.

Vocabulary Practice (15 points total; 3 points each)
Write the letter of the best answer.

_____ **7.** Someone who wants to avoid being charged with **callousness** might try to be
- **a.** cautious.
- **b.** fast.
- **c.** sympathetic.

_____ **8.** At which occasion would you most likely offer people your **commiseration**?
- **a.** a funeral
- **b.** a graduation
- **c.** a wedding

_____ **9.** A plan that is **intrinsically** flawed is
- **a.** immoral.
- **b.** poorly expressed.
- **c.** based on faulty ideas.

Name ________________________ Date ______________ Class __________

Selection Test

(continued)

_____ **10.** Which of the following would be notable for its **brevity**?

a. a novel **b.** a haiku **c.** an epic

_____ **11.** To **appease** students' fears about grades, a teacher might

a. draw lots for grades.
b. give an F to all first assignments.
c. announce that everyone will receive an A.

Analyze and Evaluate (20 points total; 10 points each)

In the boxes below, name two characters from in story. Then identify each character as round or flat and as static or dynamic, and describe the character's function in the story.

Character	Round or Flat	Static or Dynamic	Function in Story
12.			
13.			

BIG IDEA Connect (23 points)

Use a separate sheet of paper to answer the following essay question.

14. Describe which aspects of British society Greene satirizes in this story. Cite examples from the story to support your answer.

Name ______________________ Date ______________ Class __________

Open-Book Selection Test

Score

Fern Hill (page 1202) and Do Not Go Gentle into That Good Night (page 1204)

Recall and Interpret (48 points total; 8 points each)
Write the letter of the best answer.

_____ **1.** Which of the following best describes the tone of the first stanza of "Fern Hill"?
- **a.** comic
- **b.** remorseful
- **c.** joyful
- **d.** melancholy

_____ **2.** In the second stanza, phrases such as "mercy of his means," "green and golden," and "clear and cold" are examples of which poetic device?
- **a.** onomatopoeia
- **b.** alliteration
- **c.** assonance
- **d.** metaphor

_____ **3.** What quality of childhood does the speaker of "Fern Hill" prize most highly?
- **a.** physical energy
- **b.** absence of fear
- **c.** creativity and freedom
- **d.** freedom from sin

_____ **4.** In line 28, "the farm, like a wanderer white," is an example of which poetic device?
- **a.** simile
- **b.** metaphor
- **c.** synecdoche
- **d.** hyperbole

_____ **5.** How does Thomas organize stanzas 2 through 5 in "Do Not Go Gentle into That Good Night"?
- **a.** by varieties of death
- **b.** by intensities of pain
- **c.** by types of men
- **d.** by stages of decline

_____ **6.** How many different pairs of end rhymes are in "Do Not Go Gentle into That Good Night"?
- **a.** one in each stanza
- **b.** four
- **c.** three
- **d.** two

Name ______________________ Date ______________ Class ________

Open-Book Selection Test *(continued)*

Vocabulary Practice (12 points total; 3 points each)
Write the letter of the best answer.

_____ **7.** To **hail** the result of an election is to
a. protest it. **b.** disregard it. **c.** applaud it.

_____ **8.** The **spellbound** woman was utterly
a. engrossed. **b.** filthy. **c.** ignored.

_____ **9.** The accident was caused by a **heedless**
a. driver. **b.** axle. **c.** roadway.

_____ **10.** Because he is **frail,** the teacher walks
a. boldly. **b.** carefully. **c.** rapidly.

Analyze and Evaluate (20 points total; 10 points each)
In the boxes below, write examples of assonance and consonance from each poem.

Assonance	Consonance
11. "Do Not Go Gentle into That Good Night"	
12. "Fern Hill"	

BIG IDEA Connect (20 points)
Use a separate sheet of paper to answer the following essay question.

13. Think about the strong beliefs and convictions conveyed in Thomas's two poems. Write a paragraph explaining how the poems together might suggest the poet's view of life.

Name ______________________ Date ______________ Class __________

Open-Book Selection Test

Score

Not Waving but Drowning (page 1244)

Recall and Interpret (60 points total; 12 points each)
Write the letter of the best answer.

_____ **1.** In "Not Waving but Drowning," the bystanders
- **a.** doubt the man.
- **b.** question the man.
- **c.** assist the man.
- **d.** misunderstand the man.

_____ **2.** When did the man experience times of "not waving but drowning"?
- **a.** often
- **b.** always
- **c.** rarely
- **d.** sometimes

_____ **3.** How did the man feel while alive?
- **a.** abused
- **b.** isolated
- **c.** violated
- **d.** insulted

_____ **4.** The bystanders believe the man enjoyed
- **a.** waving.
- **b.** swimming.
- **c.** joking.
- **d.** exercising.

_____ **5.** What killed the man?
- **a.** cold
- **b.** larking
- **c.** illness
- **d.** drowning

Name ______________________ Date ______________ Class __________

Open-Book Selection Test *(continued)*

Analyze and Evaluate (20 points total; 10 points each)

In the boxes below, list two speakers in the poem; then select lines that show how the main speaker is misunderstood by the others.

Speaker	Lines That Show Misunderstanding
6.	
7.	

BIG IDEA Connect (20 points)

Use a separate sheet of paper to answer the following essay question.

8. How does this poem contrast with earlier British poetry and reflect post–World War II Britain?

Name ______________________ Date ______________ Class ________

Selection Test

Score

At the Pitt-Rivers (page 1248)

Recall and Interpret (45 points total; 9 points each)
Write the letter of the best answer.

_____ **1.** The narrator observes that the Pitt-Rivers is usually
- **a.** dark.
- **b.** quiet.
- **c.** closed.
- **d.** cold.

_____ **2.** Upon seeing her the first time, the narrator thinks the woman is
- **a.** attractive.
- **b.** too skinny.
- **c.** about fifty.
- **d.** ordinary looking.

_____ **3.** Which of the following sentences contains dialect?
- **a.** "As a matter of fact I've been in love myself twice."
- **b.** "I write quite a lot of poetry."
- **c.** "They stopped in front of a case and I could see their faces quite clearly."
- **d.** "I thought he seemed like a nice bloke, whatever you thought about him and her and all that."

_____ **4.** What is the narrator's first reaction to seeing the couple?
- **a.** disgust
- **b.** curiosity
- **c.** fear
- **d.** indifference

_____ **5.** What does the speaker do with the poem he is writing at the end of the story?
- **a.** He gives it to the woman.
- **b.** He decides to rewrite the ending.
- **c.** He tears it up.
- **d.** He sends it to his girlfriend.

Name ______________________ Date ______________ Class ________

Selection Test

(continued)

Vocabulary Practice (15 points total; 5 points each)
Write the letter of the best answer.

_____ **6.** The **benign** dog
- **a.** licked its owner's face.
- **b.** growled at the boy.
- **c.** ate an entire pizza.

_____ **7.** She tried to be **explicit** so that she
- **a.** would be admired.
- **b.** would not be misunderstood.
- **c.** might recognize others' mistakes.

_____ **8.** Garth was **envious** of his friend's
- **a.** long illness.
- **b.** smart girlfriend.
- **c.** blue sweater.

Analyze and Evaluate (20 points total; 10 points each)
In the boxes below, write two examples of vernacular from the story. Then "translate" the vernacular into standard American English.

Example of Vernacular	Translation
9.	
10.	

BIG IDEA Connect (20 points)
Use a separate sheet of paper to answer the following essay question.

11. Discuss how the love story the narrator observes is traditional and how it is nontraditional. Cite examples from the story to support your ideas.

Name ______________________ Date ______________ Class __________

Open-Book Selection Test

Score

Follower (page 1260), Mnemonic (page 1262), and Photograph from *Running in the Family* (page 1264)

Recall and Interpret (60 points total; 10 points each)
Write the letter of the best answer.

_____ **1.** Which pair of lines in "Follower" makes use of slant rhyme?
- **a.** 2 and 3
- **b.** 13 and 15
- **c.** 17 and 18
- **d.** 22 and 24

_____ **2.** When the speaker in "Follower" was young, he admired his father's
- **a.** intelligence.
- **b.** expertise.
- **c.** physical strength.
- **d.** shrewdness.

_____ **3.** As a boy, the speaker hoped to become a
- **a.** poet.
- **b.** horse trainer.
- **c.** plowman.
- **d.** professor.

_____ **4.** In "Mnemonic," the speaker says his father had a good
- **a.** job.
- **b.** memory.
- **c.** singing voice.
- **d.** pitching arm.

_____ **5.** In Ondaatje's piece, the photograph is of two people
- **a.** dancing the jitterbug.
- **b.** at a basketball game.
- **c.** making a meal.
- **d.** on their honeymoon.

_____ **6.** The people in the photograph express a sense of
- **a.** humor.
- **b.** regret.
- **c.** anger.
- **d.** freedom.

Open-Book Selection Test *(continued)*

Analyze and Evaluate (21 points total; 7 points each)

In the boxes below, describe what each of the speakers in the three selections realizes by thinking about his past.

Speaker	What Speaker Realizes
7. "Follower"	
8. "Mnemonic"	
9. "Photograph"	

BIG IDEA Connect (19 points)

Use a separate sheet of paper to answer the following essay question.

10. Compare and contrast the tones of the three selections and the attitude of each of the speakers toward his parent or parents.

Name ______________________ Date ______________ Class __________

Open-Book Selection Test

Score

Wind (page 1269)

Recall and Interpret (45 points total; 9 points each)
Write the letter of the best answer.

_____ **1.** At the beginning of the poem, Hughes compares the house to
- **a.** a ship at sea.
- **b.** a rocking horse.
- **c.** a covered wagon.
- **d.** a roller coaster.

_____ **2.** What does the speaker do in the middle of the day?
- **a.** He walks along the side of the house.
- **b.** He climbs the roof to fix a shingle.
- **c.** He calls the fire marshal for help.
- **d.** He helps his mother chop wood.

_____ **3.** Which line displays personification?
- **a.** 5
- **b.** 7
- **c.** 13
- **d.** 17

_____ **4.** The speaker's tone can best be described as
- **a.** dramatic.
- **b.** happy.
- **c.** angry.
- **d.** exhausted.

_____ **5.** In the midst of the storm, the people in the house are
- **a.** busy and active.
- **b.** calm and confident.
- **c.** fearful and tense.
- **d.** preoccupied with other problems.

Vocabulary Practice (15 points total; 5 points each)
Write the letter of the best answer.

_____ **6.** The boy was **floundering** after he
- **a.** ate too much ice cream.
- **b.** slipped on the icy sidewalk.
- **c.** received his highest test score ever.

_____ **7.** The **luminous** moon
- **a.** disappeared from sight.
- **b.** was a sliver in the sky.
- **c.** shed light on the landscape.

Open-Book Selection Test *(continued)*

_____ **8.** Lydia **grimaced** upon seeing
- **a.** the leftover taco on her pillow.
- **b.** her best friend at the train station.
- **c.** the fireworks on the Fourth of July.

Analyze and Evaluate (20 points total; 10 points each)
In the boxes below, note two things that Hughes personifies in the poem. Then state the lines in which those things are personified.

Personification	Lines
9.	
10.	

BIG IDEA Connect (20 points)
Use a separate sheet of paper to answer the following essay question.

11. Describe the portrayal of nature in "Wind." What effect does nature have on the people in the house?

Name ______________________ Date ______________ Class __________

Selection Test

Score

That's All (page 1273)

Recall and Interpret (40 points total; 10 points each)
Write the letter of the best answer.

_____ **1.** Who is the "she" that Mrs. A refers to in the dialogue?
a. a former housekeeper
b. a relative
c. a former neighbor
d. her best friend

_____ **2.** How does Mrs. A learn about the unnamed woman's shopping habits?
a. The woman called her.
b. She called the woman.
c. She called the butcher.
d. She met the woman by chance.

_____ **3.** Which of the following characteristics marks "That's All" as theater of the absurd?
a. The characters have no names.
b. Nothing really happens.
c. There's no specific setting.
d. It's very short.

_____ **4.** Mrs. A's conversation suggests that she is essentially
a. mean and ill-tempered.
b. depressed and helpless.
c. bitter and angry.
d. lonely and superficial.

Name ________________ Date ________________ Class ________

Selection Test

(continued)

Analyze and Evaluate (30 points)

In the theater of the absurd, characters often exist anxiously in a meaningless world. What can be inferred about the unnamed woman's feelings toward Mrs. A? List evidence to document that inference.

Woman's Feelings	Evidence to Support Inference
5.	

BIG IDEA Connect (30 points)

Use a separate sheet of paper to answer the following essay question.

6. In a paragraph, discuss what Pinter implies about the quality of contemporary life in "That's All." Then relate his views to your own observations of human nature. Have you heard conversations somewhat like the one in the play? Does that conversation reflect the way most people talk, in your opinion? Explain your responses.

Name ______________________ Date ______________ Class __________

Open-Book Selection Test

Score

What We Lost (page 1280)

Recall and Interpret (60 points total; 10 points each)
Write the letter of the best answer.

_____ **1.** At the beginning of the poem, the speaker describes a woman
- **a.** writing.
- **b.** painting.
- **c.** sewing.
- **d.** singing.

_____ **2.** Lines 7 and 8 contain
- **a.** end rhyme.
- **b.** alliteration.
- **c.** simile.
- **d.** personification.

_____ **3.** The first half of the poem is set in a
- **a.** restaurant.
- **b.** theater.
- **c.** bedroom.
- **d.** kitchen.

_____ **4.** The child in the poem is the speaker's
- **a.** cousin.
- **b.** mother.
- **c.** daughter.
- **d.** sister.

_____ **5.** The tone can be best described as
- **a.** nostalgic.
- **b.** indifferent.
- **c.** scolding.
- **d.** passionate.

_____ **6.** What does the child do in response to the story she is told?
- **a.** She makes a drawing.
- **b.** She becomes agitated.
- **c.** She asks to hear another.
- **d.** She soon forgets it.

Name ______________________ Date ______________ Class __________

Open-Book Selection Test *(continued)*

Analyze and Evaluate (20 points)

In the boxes below, describe the voice in "What We Lost." Then describe techniques Boland uses that help create this voice.

Voice	Techniques That Create Voice
7.	

BIG IDEA Connect (20 points)

Use a separate sheet of paper to answer the following essay question.

8. Explain what you think Boland is saying about memory and language in this poem. Support your ideas with examples from the poem.

Name ______________________ Date ______________ Class __________

Selection Test

Score

A Mild Attack of Locusts (page 1286)

Recall and Interpret (48 points total; 8 points each)
Write the letter of the best answer.

_____ **1.** At the beginning of the story, Margaret cannot understand why she and Richard aren't bankrupt because
- **a.** Richard is lazy.
- **b.** their land is barren.
- **c.** their taxes are astronomical.
- **d.** the farmers complain constantly.

_____ **2.** Richard and Stephen, his father, react to the locust attack with
- **a.** frustration and rage.
- **b.** passive resignation.
- **c.** grim determination.
- **d.** panic and desperation.

_____ **3.** Margaret's job during the attack is to
- **a.** ring the alarm bell.
- **b.** call the neighbors.
- **c.** keep the workers supplied with tea.
- **d.** sweep locusts away from the porch.

_____ **4.** Although Stephen says all the crops are "finished," he continues to fight because
- **a.** he's in a rage.
- **b.** he hates locusts.
- **c.** he has to prove he can fight.
- **d.** the swarm might settle and lay eggs.

_____ **5.** After the attack, Margaret takes comfort in the fact that
- **a.** she has seen the locusts fanning their wings at dawn.
- **b.** they had set aside enough savings to survive a year.
- **c.** her husband and his father weren't killed.
- **d.** they have saved some of their crops.

_____ **6.** Lessing's use of the word *mild* in her title is an example of
- **a.** foreshadowing.
- **b.** oxymoron.
- **c.** understatement.
- **d.** satire.

Vocabulary Practice (12 points total; 4 points each)
Write the letter of the best answer.

_____ **7.** Which substance has the most **acrid** smell?
- **a.** smoke
- **b.** chocolate
- **c.** soap

_____ **8.** To be told that your health problems are **irremediable** would most likely make you
- **a.** uncertain.
- **b.** relieved.
- **c.** upset.

_____ **9.** An **imminent** storm would likely be
- **a.** extremely forceful.
- **b.** arriving soon.
- **c.** widespread.

Name ______________________ Date ______________ Class __________

Selection Test

(continued)

Analyze and Evaluate (20 points total; 5 points each)

In the course of the story, Margaret's emotions and feelings change. In each box on the left, note a dominant attitude that Margaret shows at various times in the story. In the corresponding box on the right, indicate how this attitude reflects the theme development in "A Mild Attack of Locusts."

Margaret's Attitude	Contribution to Theme Development
10.	
11.	
12.	
13.	

BIG IDEA Connect (20 points)

Use a separate sheet of paper to answer the following essay question.

14. How does "A Mild Attack of Locusts" illustrate some of the effects of colonialism?

Name ______________________ Date ______________ Class ________

Selection Test

Score

The Train from Rhodesia (page 1297)

Recall and Interpret (40 points total; 8 points each)
Write the letter of the best answer.

_____ **1.** The imminent arrival of the train makes the people at the station feel
- **a.** fearful.
- **b.** joyful.
- **c.** hopeful.
- **d.** discouraged.

_____ **2.** Gordimer uses the presence and activities of the dogs at the station to establish that
- **a.** visitors need to be very cautious.
- **b.** this is a place were resources are scarce.
- **c.** pets are held in high regard in this culture.
- **d.** trains are new enough to make animals fearful.

_____ **3.** Which of the following best describes the feelings of many of the white travelers toward the black merchants at the station?
- **a.** fear
- **b.** sympathy
- **c.** curiosity
- **d.** detached amusement

_____ **4.** The young wife is angry at her husband for buying the lion because she
- **a.** thinks he paid too much.
- **b.** wanted to do the bargaining.
- **c.** thinks her husband exploited the merchant.
- **d.** changed her mind about buying the lion.

_____ **5.** The theme of the story relates to the
- **a.** consequences of racial inequality.
- **b.** underdeveloped South African economy.
- **c.** inevitable tensions between newlyweds.
- **d.** improvements brought by new technologies.

Vocabulary Practice (20 points total; 5 points each)
Write the letter of the best answer.

_____ **6.** You might expect a **vendor** to
- **a.** repair your fan.
- **b.** shine your shoes.
- **c.** sell you a hot dog.

_____ **7.** A taxi that **careers** down the street is
- **a.** creeping.
- **b.** speeding.
- **c.** backing.

_____ **8.** A person who makes a **wry** face is
- **a.** satisfied.
- **b.** sleepy.
- **c.** displeased.

_____ **9.** The legs of the carved lion showed each **sinew**, or
- **a.** muscle.
- **b.** tendon.
- **c.** bone.

Name ______________________ Date ______________ Class __________

Selection Test

(continued)

Analyze and Evaluate (21 points total; 7 points each)

Gordimer uses the setting of the train station to symbolize the differences between the groups of people. In the boxes on the left, write words or phrases that describe the people in each group. In the box on the right, explain how the train stresses the difference between the groups.

10. The people at the station:	
	12. The role of the train:
11. The people on the train:	

BIG IDEA Connect (19 points)

Use a separate sheet of paper to answer the following essay question.

13. How does the woman's reaction to her husband's gift of the lion relate to the concepts of colonialism and postcolonialism in Africa? Why does she reject it?

Name ______________________ Date ______________ Class __________

Selection Test

Score

Dead Men's Path (page 1306)

Recall and Interpret (40 points total; 10 points each)
Write the letter of the best answer.

_____ **1.** Michael Obi's attitude toward his new position might best be described as
- **a.** enthusiastic.
- **b.** tentative.
- **c.** fearful.
- **d.** displeased.

_____ **2.** Before Michael Obi took his new assignment, Ndume School had been
- **a.** chaotic.
- **b.** highly regimented.
- **c.** unprogressive.
- **d.** very effective.

_____ **3.** The villagers continue to use the path through the school compound because
- **a.** it saves them time.
- **b.** they want to spite Michael Obi.
- **c.** it has sacred meaning for them.
- **d.** they think flowers are frivolous.

_____ **4.** The villagers tear up and trample the school grounds because
- **a.** they fear modern education.
- **b.** they hate Michael Obi.
- **c.** they think Nancy has bad taste.
- **d.** a fortune teller prescribed the action.

Vocabulary Practice (12 points total; 4 points each)
Write the letter of the best answer.

_____ **5.** A **pivotal** event is one of
- **a.** little value.
- **b.** importance.
- **c.** high emotion.

_____ **6.** A person's **denigration** of one's beliefs indicates that the person
- **a.** agrees with them.
- **b.** questions them.
- **c.** ridicules them.

_____ **7.** Mr. Obi thought that the villagers held **superannuated** beliefs, or
- **a.** mystical beliefs.
- **b.** old-fashioned beliefs.
- **c.** incredible beliefs.

Name ______________________ Date ______________ Class ________

Selection Test

(continued)

Analyze and Evaluate (20 points total; 10 points each)

Think about how a lack of understanding can cause conflict. In the chart, describe what is important to Mr. Obi and what is important to the villagers. Give details from the story that support your answer.

8. Important to Obi:	Supporting details:
9. Important to villagers:	Supporting details:

BIG IDEA Connect (28 points)

Use a separate sheet of paper to answer the following essay question.

10. In your opinion, does any one group or culture have the right to force its values on another? Put yourself in the place of the villagers in this story. How would you feel? Explain.

Name ____________ Date ____________ Class ____________

Open-Book Selection Test

Score

Telephone Conversation (page 1315)

Recall and Interpret (40 points total; 8 points each)
Write the letter of the best answer.

_____ **1.** This account of the telephone conversation is told from which point of view?
- **a.** first person
- **b.** second person
- **c.** third-person limited
- **d.** third-person omniscient

_____ **2.** The purpose of the phone call is to
- **a.** arrange for a loan.
- **b.** inquire about a job.
- **c.** answer a personal ad.
- **d.** ask about renting an apartment.

_____ **3.** This selection is an example of free verse because
- **a.** some parts include dialogue.
- **b.** it lacks a definite pattern of rhyme and rhythm.
- **c.** it discusses an issue of personal freedom.
- **d.** it leaves conclusions up to the reader.

_____ **4.** The woman receiving the call might best be described as
- **a.** nosy.
- **c.** bigoted.
- **b.** demanding.
- **d.** snobbish.

_____ **5.** The tone of this selection might best be described as
- **a.** militant.
- **c.** ironic.
- **b.** melancholy.
- **d.** vengeful.

Vocabulary Practice (20 points total; 5 points each)
Write the letter of the best answer.

_____ **6.** The **rancid** odor was probably coming from
- **a.** baking bread.
- **b.** the shampoo.
- **c.** rotting fruit.

_____ **7.** The **friction** was caused by the couple's mutual
- **a.** dislike for each other.
- **b.** good looks and intelligence.
- **c.** consent to work on the problem.

Name ______________________ Date ______________ Class __________

Open-Book Selection Test

(continued)

_____**8.** Martha **assented** to the proposal because
- **a.** she thought it was a good one.
- **b.** it was impracticable.
- **c.** no one told her about it.

_____**9.** The **revelation** of the villain's crimes
- **a.** ensured that they would succeed.
- **b.** led to his trial and imprisonment.
- **c.** proved that he was a genius.

Analyze and Evaluate (20 points total; 5 points each)
In the boxes, answer the questions.

10. What sort of person is the caller?	**11.** What parts of the poem support your opinion?
12. What sort of person is the woman?	**13.** What parts of the poem support your opinion?

Big Idea Connect (20 points)
Use a separate sheet of paper to answer the following essay question.

14. In this poem, what techniques does Soyinka use to ridicule racism?

Name ______________________ Date ______________ Class __________

Selection Test

Score

Two Sheep (page 1320)

Recall and Interpret (40 points total; 10 points each)
Write the letter of the best answer:

_____ **1.** At the start, the first sheep's certainty about his fate makes him
- **a.** frightened about his future.
- **b.** grateful for life.
- **c.** confused about his purpose.
- **d.** sad to be leaving.

_____ **2.** In contrast to the first sheep, the second sheep is more
- **a.** pessimistic.
- **b.** frightened.
- **c.** eager.
- **d.** frivolous.

_____ **3.** In giving the sheep human traits, the writer uses
- **a.** symbolism.
- **b.** myth-making.
- **c.** satire.
- **d.** anthropomorphism.

_____ **4.** By the end of the story, the first sheep has become
- **a.** angry and vindictive.
- **b.** silent and timid.
- **c.** morbid and resigned.
- **d.** a passionate crusader.

Using Vocabulary (15 points total; 5 points each)
Write the letter of the best answer.

_____ **5.** A **pall** cast over a room would likely evoke
- **a.** laughter.
- **b.** outrage.
- **c.** silence.

_____ **6.** The **barren** soil gave the farmer reason to
- **a.** despair.
- **b.** hope.
- **c.** rejoice.

_____ **7.** **Unperturbed** by the dense fog, the pilot
- **a.** sent a distress signal.
- **b.** landed safely.
- **c.** panicked.

Name ______________________ Date ______________ Class __________

Selection Test

(continued)

Analyze and Evaluate (20 points total; 10 points each)

Analyze Frame's use of anthropomorphism by noting, in the chart below, how each of the two sheep demonstrates specific human attitudes toward life and death.

8. First sheep:	**9.** Second sheep:

BIG IDEA Connect (25 points)

Use a separate sheet of paper to answer the following essay question.

10. Why is this fable a good example of literature for people in an age of globalization?

Name ______________________ Date ______________ Class ________

Open-Book Selection Test

Score

from **Tales of the Islands** (page 1329)

Recall and Interpret (50 points total; 10 points each)
Write the letter of the best answer.

_____ **1.** Where is the speaker in the poem?
- **a.** in a car
- **b.** on a train
- **c.** on a plane
- **d.** in a balloon

_____ **2.** "Roads as small and casual as twine" is an example of which literary device?
- **a.** personification
- **b.** oxymoron
- **c.** metaphor
- **d.** simile

_____ **3.** What is the rhyme scheme of the first four lines?
- **a.** *abab*
- **b.** *aabb*
- **c.** *abba*
- **d.** *abcd*

_____ **4.** Which of the following best describes the speaker's feelings in the poem?
- **a.** hopeful
- **b.** relieved
- **c.** panicky
- **d.** apprehensive

_____ **5.** What does the speaker think of in the last lines of the poem?
- **a.** nothing
- **b.** happiness
- **c.** hunger
- **d.** money

Vocabulary Practice (10 points total; 5 points each)
Write the letter of the best answer.

_____ **6.** The **precipice** was quite
a. dusty. **b.** steep. **c.** round.

_____ **7.** The **fidelity** Jonathan felt in his friendship with Sam made him feel
a. content. **b.** bored. **c.** nervous.

Name ______________________ Date ______________ Class ________

Open-Book Selection Test *(continued)*

Analyze and Evaluate (20 points total; 10 points each)

In the boxes below, list two images from the poem and say which senses the images appeal to.

Image	Senses It Appeals To
8.	
9.	

BIG IDEA Connect (20 points)

Use a separate sheet of paper to answer the following essay question.

10. Discuss the speaker's attitude toward the island. Why and for how long do you think he is leaving?

Name ______________________ Date ______________ Class __________

Selection Test

Score

B. Wordsworth (page 1333)

Recall and Interpret (36 points total; 6 points each)
Write the letter of the best answer.

_____**1.** B. Wordsworth's request is different from those of others who come calling in the narrator's neighborhood because it
- **a.** is spoken in broken English.
- **b.** is unreasonably demanding.
- **c.** doesn't involve a handout.
- **d.** is made in writing.

_____**2.** B. Wordsworth explains his overgrown yard by
- **a.** saying he's too old to care for it.
- **b.** telling a love story.
- **c.** saying he's been too busy.
- **d.** saying he loves nature.

_____**3.** The narrator's mother beats him because
- **a.** he skipped school.
- **b.** he gave B. Wordsworth money.
- **c.** he took money from her purse.
- **d.** he spent a day with B. Wordsworth.

_____**4.** B. Wordsworth makes his living by
- **a.** begging.
- **b.** selling poems.
- **c.** selling honey.
- **d.** performing calypsos.

_____**5.** The boy's language in the story can best be described as
- **a.** formal.
- **b.** very colorful.
- **c.** uneducated.
- **d.** high class.

_____**6.** B. Wordsworth tells the boy that poets are people who
- **a.** have a strong sense of rhythm.
- **b.** have large vocabularies.
- **c.** can cry for everything.
- **d.** let their gardens grow wild.

Using Vocabulary (24 points total; 6 points each)
Write the letter of the best answer.

_____**7.** Which word best characterizes a **hospitable** environment?
- **a.** sterile
- **b.** welcoming
- **c.** spacious

_____**8.** Seafarers used **constellations** to
- **a.** hoist their sails.
- **b.** secure their cargo.
- **c.** guide them.

Name ______________________ Date ______________ Class __________

Selection Test

(continued)

_____ **9.** You would most likely **patronize** a store that
- **a.** lowered prices.
- **b.** was a long distance away.
- **c.** had limited stock.

_____ **10.** Trying to **distill** the essence of her high school experience, the graduation speaker
- **a.** spoke for an hour.
- **b.** tried to be funny.
- **c.** told a short story.

Analyze and Evaluate (20 points total; 5 points each)

In the chart, list the aspect of each of the characters that is reinforced by the use of dialect.

Character	Quality
11. Narrator	
12. Mother	
13. B. Wordsworth	
14. Policeman	

BIG IDEA Connect (20 points)

Use a separate sheet of paper to answer the following essay question.

15. How does the title "B. Wordsworth," as well as incidents in the story, emphasize the global nature of poetry?

Name ______________________ Date ____________ Class ________

Selection Test

Score

from ***Imaginary Homelands*** (page 1340)

Recall and Interpret (60 points total; 10 points each)
Write the letter of the best answer.

_____ **1.** Where did Rushdie spend the early part of his life?
- **a.** London
- **b.** Scotland
- **c.** Pakistan
- **d.** Bombay

_____ **2.** When he sees his childhood house, Rushdie is surprised by its
- **a.** fence.
- **b.** owners.
- **c.** disrepair.
- **d.** colors.

_____ **3.** Rushdie wrote his novel *Midnight's Children* in order to restore
- **a.** the memory of his mother.
- **b.** the past to himself.
- **c.** a sense of hope to his children.
- **d.** faith in the goodness of people.

_____ **4.** According to the author, a book is justified by the
- **a.** awards it receives.
- **b.** author's intentions.
- **c.** quality of the writing.
- **d.** number of people who buy it.

_____ **5.** Rushdie believes that England's Indian writers should
- **a.** write poetry and plays primarily.
- **b.** visit South Africa and Bangladesh.
- **c.** remake the English language.
- **d.** separate themselves from Canadian writers.

_____ **6.** One advantage Rushdie thinks Indian British writers have is a kind of
- **a.** reliance on myth.
- **b.** ruthless independence.
- **c.** unified community.
- **d.** double perspective.

Name ______________________ Date ____________ Class ________

Selection Test

(continued)

Analyze and Evaluate (20 points total; 10 points each)

In the boxes below, describe a challenge Rushdie says Indian British writers face and a positive influence they are having on literature in English.

7. Challenge faced by British writers:	**8.** Positive influence on English literature:

BIG IDEA Connect (20 points)

Use a separate sheet of paper to answer the following essay question.

9. Discuss Rushdie's opinions on whether Indian British authors writing about India should be writing in English. Cite specific examples from the essay to support your ideas.

Name ______________________ Date ______________ Class __________

Selection Test

Score

Games at Twilight (page 1346)

Recall and Interpret (50 points total; 10 points each)
Write the letter of the best answer.

_____ **1.** The tension between the children and the mother at the start of the story is caused by the
- **a.** father's absence.
- **b.** mother's attitude.
- **c.** children's pets.
- **d.** evening heat.

_____ **2.** Saying that the birds "drooped, like dead fruit" is an example of
- **a.** a simile.
- **b.** irony.
- **c.** symbolism.
- **d.** an oxymoron.

_____ **3.** Which of the following best describes Ravi's position among the children in the story?
- **a.** bully
- **b.** leader
- **c.** trickster
- **d.** insignificant

_____ **4.** Ravi stays in the shed, with its "unspeakable and alarming animal life" because he
- **a.** falls asleep.
- **b.** is afraid of Raghu.
- **c.** wants to win the game.
- **d.** is embarrassed to give up.

_____ **5.** We know how Ravi feels at the end because
- **a.** Raghu forces him to tell.
- **b.** we can tell from his actions.
- **c.** the narrator explains his feelings.
- **d.** he tells his mother what he's feeling.

Vocabulary Practice (10 points total; 2 points each)
Write the letter of the best answer.

_____ **6.** To avoid speaking **stridently**,
- **a.** gesture more frequently.
- **b.** add more examples.
- **c.** soften your voice.

_____ **7.** When Bill learned that his computer was **defunct**, he was
- **a.** disheartened.
- **b.** relieved.
- **c.** excited.

_____ **8.** Which of the following occupations would most likely require a good deal of **temerity**?
- **a.** librarian
- **b.** ballerina
- **c.** race-car driver

Selection Test

(continued)

_____ **9.** A **fray** is most likely to occur at a
- **a.** theater performance.
- **b.** hockey game.
- **c.** picnic.

_____ **10.** One might expect to hear **lugubrious** music at a
- **a.** pep rally. **b.** funeral parlor. **c.** shopping mall.

Analyze and Evaluate (20 points total; 10 points each)

Although the story is told by a narrator and gives Ravi's perspective, we also learn about other characters through their words and behavior. In the boxes below, write character sketches of Raghu and Mira, identifying their most apparent traits and noting how those traits are revealed.

11. Raghu's character traits:	How those traits are revealed:
12. Mira's character traits:	How those traits are revealed:

BIG IDEA Connect (20 points)

Use a separate sheet of paper to answer the following essay question.

13. In what way is "Games at Twilight" an example of globalization that shows the connectedness of the world's people and cultures.

Name ______________________ Date ______________ Class __________

Open-Book Selection Test

Score

Elegy for the Giant Tortoises (page 1357)

Recall and Interpret (48 points total; 12 points each)
Write the letter of the best answer.

_____ **1.** In the poem's first stanza, the speaker lists things that are
- **a.** natural predators of tortoises.
- **b.** types of flightless birds.
- **c.** native to the European continent.
- **d.** extinct or in danger of extinction.

_____ **2.** The speaker tries to think of the giant tortoises as she moves through
- **a.** her house.
- **b.** a city.
- **c.** an aquarium.
- **d.** a laboratory.

_____ **3.** Which line contains a simile?
- **a.** 4
- **b.** 7
- **c.** 10
- **d.** 12

_____ **4.** Which stanza contains references to war?
- **a.** 1
- **b.** 3
- **c.** 6
- **d.** 8

Vocabulary Practice (12 points total; 3 points each)
Write the letter of the best answer.

_____ **5.** The flowers were **withering** from too much
a. sun. **b.** attention. **c.** soil.

_____ **6.** A person at the **periphery** of a group is
a. its leader. **b.** at its edge. **c.** one of many.

_____ **7.** A **lumbering** person might be carrying
- **a.** a baseball cap.
- **b.** a large boulder.
- **c.** an umbrella.

_____ **8.** An example of an **obsolete** form of technology is
a. the Pony Express. **b.** the computer. **c.** DVD players.

Name ______________________ Date ______________ Class ________

Open-Book Selection Test *(continued)*

Analyze and Evaluate (20 points)

In the boxes below, cite two examples of alliteration that Atwood uses in the poem. Then describe the effect of each example.

Alliteration	Effect
9.	

BIG IDEA Connect (20 points)

Use a separate sheet of paper to answer the following essay question.

10. In what way does this poem relate to the topic of globalization?

Name ______________________ Date ______________ Class __________

Selection Test

Score

Music Goes Global (page 1360)

Recall and Interpret (60 points total; 10 points each)
Write the letter of the best answer.

_____ **1.** According to the article, music is often used as a tool for
- **a.** social change.
- **b.** visual art.
- **c.** curing headaches.
- **d.** worker productivity.

_____ **2.** Femi Kuti, Ziggy Marley, and Max de Castro are
- **a.** Colombian pop stars from the 1950s.
- **b.** studio producers known for hits.
- **c.** a trio that plays techno music.
- **d.** the children of musical pioneers.

_____ **3.** Which technology does the author believe has most spurred the rise of global music?
- **a.** wireless laptops
- **b.** the Internet
- **c.** audiocassette tapes
- **d.** CD players

_____ **4.** According to the author, American musicians
- **a.** also contribute to global music.
- **b.** dominate music heard in Britain.
- **c.** should not record albums in Icelandic.
- **d.** sing about alienation and isolation.

_____ **5.** Many global musicians today
- **a.** are based in Tokyo and Kyoto.
- **b.** start performing songs when they are children.
- **c.** record albums in more than one language.
- **d.** prefer to write lyrics that are hard to understand.

_____ **6.** The author's tone can best be described as
- **a.** enthusiastic.
- **b.** outraged.
- **c.** ironic.
- **d.** anxious.

Name ______________________________ Date __________________ Class __________

Selection Test

(continued)

Analyze and Evaluate (20 points total; 10 points each)

In the boxes below, name two trends the author describes as happening in global music today. Then list countries where these trends are occurring.

Trends in Global Music	Where
7.	
8.	

BIG IDEA Connect (20 points)

Use a separate sheet of paper to answer the following essay question.

9. Discuss the author's attitude toward the globalization of music. Cite examples from the article to support your answer.

Name ______________________ Date ______________ Class ____________

Open-Book Unit Test

Score

Unit 1: The Anglo-Saxon Period and the Middle Ages, 449–1485

Part A. (40 points total; 20 points each)
Use a separate sheet of paper to answer TWO of the following essay questions.

1. Compare Beowulf and Sir Gawain as epic heroes. What do you think is each one's greatest talent or quality? In what types of societies might these particular abilities be most useful or appreciated?
2. Compare the speaker of *The Seafarer* with Chaucer's pilgrims in *The Canterbury Tales*. What motivates them to make their journeys, and how do the journeys reflect the power of faith?
3. Compare the Wife of Bath's view of women with that of the author of "Get Up and Bar the Door." How do the Wife of Bath and the wife in the ballad relate to the men in their lives?

Part B. (20 points; 5 points each)
Think about what the deaths that occur in many of these selections are intended to convey to the reader.

- **Select and circle the letter of ONE selection.**
- **In the boxes, answer the questions about any ONE death in that selection.**

a. *Beowulf*
b. "Sir Patrick Spens"
c. *Le Morte d'Arthur*
d. *Everyman*

4. Who dies?
5. How does he die?
6. What effects does the death have?
7. What lesson, moral, or idea about life is conveyed to the reader through this death?

Name ______________________ Date ______________ Class __________

Open-Book Unit Test

(continued)

Part C. (20 points total; 10 points each)

Many of the people and characters in these selections make critical errors of judgment that have serious consequences.

- **Select and circle the letter of ONE person or character below.**
- **In the box on the left, identify a mistake made by that person or character.**
- **In the box on the right, identify the consequences of that mistake.**

a. Grendel in *Beowulf*
b. Barbara Allan
c. King Arthur in *Le Morte d'Arthur*
d. Margery Kempe

Mistake:	Consequences:

Part D. (20 points)

Think about the struggles that are won and lost in these selections.

- **Select and circle the letter of ONE person or character below.**
- **Answer the questions in the boxes about that individual.**

a. Beowulf
b. King Edwin in *The Ecclesiastical History of the English People*
c. Gilgamesh
d. Sir John Graeme in "Bonny Barbara Allan"
e. Everyman

What is one of the main struggles faced by this individual?
Does he win or lose this struggle? ____Wins ____Loses
How does this reflect the characteristics of the Anglo-Saxon period or the Middle Ages?

Name ______________________________ Date ________________ Class __________

Open-Book Unit Test

Score

Unit 2: The English Renaissance, 1485–1650

Part A. (40 points total; 20 points each)

Use a separate sheet of paper to answer TWO of the following essay questions.

1. In several poems in this unit, the speaker attempts to make a convincing argument. Which speaker's argument do you find most convincing or effective? Which do you find least so? Why did reason and logic matter more to humanists in this period than to writers in the Middle Ages?

2. The court during the reign of Elizabeth I valued displays of wit, which Elizabeth encouraged and in which she gladly took part. Choose TWO of the courtiers' poems, and discuss their witty approaches to their subjects. Remember that wit means clever thought, not always humor.

3. Many selections in this unit deal with the temporary nature of human life and employ the motif of *carpe diem* ("seize the day"). Choose TWO of the selections to which this motif is relevant and explain how the motif is applicable to the feelings expressed by the writer.

Part B. (20 points)

Think about the effectiveness of the metaphors and similes in these selections.

- **On the line below, write the title of a selection containing an interesting metaphor or simile.**
- **In the top box, write that metaphor or simile.**
- **In the middle box, note the two things that are compared.**
- **In the bottom box, note two ideas that the metaphor communicates to the reader.**

Selection: ____

Metaphor or simile:
Compares . . .
Communicates the ideas that . . .

Name ______________________ Date ______________ Class __________

Open-Book Unit Test

(continued)

Part C. (20 points)

In many of these selections, a problem is presented and a solution is offered.

- **On the line below, write the title of ONE selection in which that occurs. Do not choose a selection you wrote about in Part B.**
- **In the boxes at the top, identify the problem and the solution.**
- **In the box at the bottom, give your opinion of that solution.**

Selection: ______________________________

Problem presented:	Solution offered:
Your opinion of solution:	

Part D. (20 points)

Think about the dramatic changes that Macbeth and Lady Macbeth undergo during *The Tragedy of Macbeth*. In the boxes, note characteristics to compare and contrast each character early in the play with the same character later in the play.

MACBETH	LADY MACBETH
Early:	Early:
Late:	Late:

Name ______________________ Date ______________ Class ________

Open-Book Unit Test

Score

Unit 3: From Puritanism to the Enlightenment, 1640–1780

Part A. (40 points total; 20 points each)
Use a separate sheet of paper to answer TWO of the following essay questions.

1. Which selection in this unit did you find most effective as a work of criticism? Explain your choice in a paragraph or two.
2. Which TWO of the selections in this unit do you think reflect the most heartfelt or sincere beliefs? Explain your choices in a paragraph or two.
3. All the selections in this unit were written over 200 years ago. Choose one that you think still speaks to modern readers. Choose another that you think is dated or difficult for modern readers. Explain your choices in a paragraph or two.

Part B. (20 points)
Think about the movement from strict monarchy to more democratic government that occurred during this period.

- **Choose ONE writer for whom obedience to authority is important.**
- **Choose ONE writer for whom a more democratic approach is important.**
- **Compare their views in one or two short paragraphs.**

Open-Book Unit Test

(continued)

Part C. (20 points)

Think about the events that marked British history during this period.

- **Choose TWO people from this unit who are strongly affected by important personal or historical events.**
- **Explain how and why they are affected in a paragraph or two.**

Part D. (20 points total; 10 points each)

Think about the various attitudes toward humanity that are reflected in these works.

- **Circle the letter of ONE individual below.**
- **In the top box, describe his or her attitude toward humanity.**
- **In the bottom box, write words or phrases from the selection that indicate this attitude.**

a. Bunyan, author of *The Pilgrim's Progress*
b. Pepys in *The Diary of Samuel Pepys*
c. The speaker in *A Modest Proposal*
d. Swift, author of *A Modest Proposal*
e. Gulliver in *Gulliver's Travels*
f. The king of Brobdingnag in *Gulliver's Travels*
g. Lady Montagu in "Letter to Her Daughter"
h. Johnson as seen in Boswell's *The Life of Samuel Johnson*

Description of attitude:
Words or phrases that indicate attitude:

Name ______________________ Date ______________ Class __________

Open-Book Unit Test

Score

Unit 4: The Triumph of Romanticism, 1750–1837

Part A. (40 points total; 20 points each)
Use a separate sheet of paper to answer TWO of the following essay questions.

1. The Romantics valued the individual over society, the natural over the artificial, and emotions over logic. Choose ONE selection from this unit that you think epitomizes, or sums up, this Romantic philosophy. Discuss that selection in terms of the three Romantic elements identified above.
2. The poets in this unit make liberal use of figurative language, such as similes, metaphors, vivid imagery, and symbols. Choose ONE figure of speech, such as the simile, and provide examples of that device from the work of two poets in this unit. Tell how the figures of speech enhance the poems.
3. Many poems in this unit begin as nature studies and become imaginative meditations on what the scene means to the poet. Choose ONE of the poems, and compare and contrast the reality of the image or event it describes with the imaginative meaning that image or event holds for the poet.

Part B. (20 points)
Several of the works in this unit address the situations of people who have little control over their lives and thus are exploited by others. Choose TWO such works, and discuss why their authors chose to present the situations of these powerless people. How were such lives important to Romantic beliefs about individuals and their rights?

Name ________________________ Date ______________ Class __________

Open-Book Unit Test *(continued)*

Part C. (20 points)
The excerpts from *The Diary of Fanny Burney* and *Pride and Prejudice* comment on social life during this period.

- **From each selection, choose ONE aspect of social life and describe it.**
- **Then discuss how social life today is the same or different.**

Part D. (20 points)
Think about the strong feelings expressed in many selections in this unit.

- **Choose ONE of the selections in which strong feelings are expressed.**
- **In the small boxes, note your choice, what the strong emotion is, and the object of that emotion.**
- **In the large box, answer the question.**

This individual	feels this strong emotion	about

Why does the individual feel this way, and why is this reaction so strong?

Name ______________________ Date ______________ Class __________

Open-Book Unit Test

Score

Unit 5: The Victorian Age, 1837–1901

Part A. (40 points total; 20 points each)
Use a separate sheet of paper to answer TWO of the following essay questions.

1. Several selections in this unit focus on the phenomenon of romantic love. Discuss TWO of these works, comparing and contrasting their tones and attitudes toward the subject.
2. The Victorian Age was a time of transition from old traditions to more modern views. Discuss which of the selections from the Victorian period in this unit seems the most traditional to you and which seems the most contemporary. Cite specific examples from the selections to support your ideas.
3. Choose TWO works from the unit that pay tribute to someone or something. Identify who or what is honored, and discuss possible reasons for the writer's, speaker's, or narrator's desire to do so.

Part B. (20 points total; 10 points each)
In this unit's selections, some characters embrace life, while others fear it.

- **On the lines at the top, write the names of ONE character who embraces life and ONE who fears it and the titles of the selections in which they appear. Do not choose characters from a selection you wrote about in Part A.**
- **In the boxes, explain your choices.**

4. Selection: ______________________

   Character who embraces life: ______________________

What makes you think that this character embraces life?

5. Selection: ______________________

   Character who fears life: ______________________

What makes you think that this character fears life?

Name ______________________ Date ______________ Class __________

Open-Book Unit Test

(continued)

Part C. (20 points total; 10 points each)

Several of the authors in this unit wrote in part to reform problems they saw in Victorian society. Choose TWO works from the unit that describe societal problems, and complete the boxes below.

- **Note the problems addressed by each selection.**
- **Discuss how the author makes those problems known and creates sympathy for the people suffering from them.**

6. Selection: ______________________

Societal problems:	How author creates sympathy:

7. Selection: ______________________

Societal problems:	How author creates sympathy

Part D. (20 points total; 10 points each)

Several selections in the unit make use of irony to express themes. Choose TWO selections that contain irony, and complete the boxes below.

- **Cite an example of the use of irony in each selection.**
- **Identify what type of irony is being used: situational or verbal.**
- **Describe the effect of this use of irony.**

8. Selection: ______________________

Example:	Type of irony:	Effect:

9. Selection: ______________________

Example:	Type of irony:	Effect:

Name ______________________ Date ______________ Class __________

Open-Book Unit Test

Score

Unit 6: The Modern Age, 1901–1950

Part A. (40 points total; 20 points each)
Use a separate sheet of paper to answer TWO of the following essay questions.

1. Several of the works in this unit focus on class differences resulting from discrepancies in wealth and power. Discuss TWO of these works, comparing and contrasting their ideas.

2. Choose TWO characters or speakers from this unit who experience the effects of war. Describe the effect war has on the mind of each character or speaker.

3. Several works in this unit express ideas about the function of art. Choose TWO such works, and compare and contrast their ideas.

Part B. (20 points total; 10 points each)
In the poems of this unit, several speakers express a sense of alienation from modern life. Choose TWO poems that feature such speakers, and complete the boxes below.

- **Note who each speaker is and what he or she describes.**
- **Describe the tone the speaker uses.**
- **Finally, describe what ideas about modern life are conveyed in the poem.**

4. Selection: ______________________

Speaker and subject:	Tone:	Ideas about modern life:

5. Selection: ______________________

Speaker and subject:	Tone:	Ideas about modern life:

Open-Book Unit Test

(continued)

Part C. (20 points)

Several of the works in this unit express optimism in the aftermath of a world war. Choose TWO such works, and write an essay addressing the points below. Do not use works you have chosen in response to previous questions.

- **Describe how each author handles the subject of war. What does the author focus on?**
- **Discuss how the author expresses optimism in the face of war.**

Part D. (20 points)

Choose TWO works from the unit that convey strong psychological portraits of characters or speakers. Write an essay addressing the following points:

- **What are each character's or speaker's main psychological characteristics?**
- **How does the author convey those characteristics? What literary devices does the author use?**
- **What effect did each work have on you?**

Name ______________________ Date ______________ Class __________

Open-Book Unit Test

Score

Unit 7: An International Literature, 1950–Present

Part A. (40 points total; 20 points each)
Use a separate sheet of paper to answer TWO of the following essay questions.

1. Several works in this unit focus on a character's or speaker's relationship with a parent or parents. Discuss TWO of these works, comparing and contrasting their moods and the attitudes the characters have toward their parents.
2. Choose two characters or speakers from this unit who mostly observe things happening to others. Describe the relationship each character has to the people observed. What are the feelings of the character or speaker toward those people?
3. Consider which works in this unit struck you as the most contemporary or reflective of the world we live in. Choose two such works and compare and contrast them, discussing what makes them seem contemporary in technique and subject matter.

Part B. (20 points total; 10 points each)
Although all the poems in this unit are contemporary, some use traditional forms and themes. Choose TWO poems that strike you as traditional, and complete the boxes below.

- **On the line at the top, write the name of the work.**
- **Note the work's traditional theme(s).**
- **Describe the work's traditional form.**
- **Say why you think the poet chose to use this traditional form.**

4. Selection: ______________________________

Traditional theme(s):	Traditional form:	Why poet chose this form:

5. Selection: ______________________________

Traditional theme(s):	Traditional form:	Why poet chose this form:

Name ______________________ Date ______________ Class ________

Open-Book Unit Test

(continued)

Part C. (20 points)
Several selections in this unit feature characters or speakers who address some aspect of British colonialism or postcolonialism. Choose TWO works from the unit that focus on this subject and write an essay addressing the following points:

- **How does the author address colonialism or postcolonialism?**
- **What is the tone of the work, or the author's attitude toward the subject?**

Part D. (20 points)
Choose TWO prose selections from the unit that refer to globalization and the worldwide use of the English language. Write an essay addressing the following points:

- **What are the authors' attitudes toward globalization?**
- **What do the authors say about the global use of the English language?**
- **Whose opinion do you agree with more and why?**

from *Beowulf*

Open-Book Selection Test (page 1)

Recall and Interpret

(66 points total; 6 points each)

1. d
2. d
3. c
4. a
5. d
6. b
7. a
8. a
9. a
10. d
11. c

Analyze and Evaluate (14 points)

12. Elements of both internal and external conflict are present in the scene in which Beowulf and his men go to slay the dragon. The external conflict is fairly obvious—Beowulf is going to fight the dragon that has been terrorizing his people and burning their homes. The internal conflicts (there are 3) are not so obvious. Beowulf is struggling with himself; he is old and weary and knows that this is probably the battle in which he might die, triumphant or not. His reputation is at stake. His men are struggling with their fear of death, of the dragon, and at the moment of crisis, they not only fail to rush to his aid, they run for their lives. Wiglaf, one of the men, is struggling with fear, too, but he does not run, he stands there, "miserable, remembering, as a good man must, what kinship should mean." His loyalty and inner resources enable him to assist the king in killing the dragon, which Beowulf could not have accomplished alone.

BIG IDEA Connect (20 points)

13. Answers will vary. Students might identify the following values; additional answers are likely. Support will vary; one example of support is given for each value; other support should be accepted.

- Religious devotion: ". . . he never / Dared to touch king Hrothgar's glorious / Throne, protected by God." (lines 82–84)
- Compassion: ". . . he'd go to that famous king, / Would sail across the sea to Hrothgar, / Now when help was needed." (lines 95–97)
- Love of adventure: "And they urged the adventure on." (line 100)
- Courage: "So Beowulf / Chose the mightiest men he could find, / The bravest and best . . ." (lines 101–102)
- Gratitude: "And then / They gave thanks to God for their easy crossing." (line 124)
- Good judgment: "The mounted officer / Answered him bluntly, . . . / I believe your words, I trust in / Your friendship.'" (lines 182–187)
- Responsibility; "My people have said, the wisest, most knowing / And best of them, that my duty was to go to the Danes' / Great King." (lines 228–230)
- Strength: "They have seen my strength for themselves . . ." (line 230)
- Bowing to fate: "Fate will unwind as it must!" (line 268)

from *Beowulf;* from *Gilgamesh: The Death of Humbaba;* from "The Battle of the Pelennor Fields" from *The Lord of the Rings: The Return of the King;* from *The Collected Beowulf*

Selection Test (page 3)

Recall and Interpret

(50 points total; 5 points each)

1. a
2. b
3. d
4. d
5. a
6. b
7. d
8. b
9. b
10. b

Analyze and Evaluate

(30 points total; 10 points each)

11. Théoden is a major character in the larger saga, but he is minor in this excerpt because he is taken out of major action by his horse falling on him. He becomes the point of conflict between Éowyn and the Dark Lord of Nazgûl. He is major in that he is the leader of the army.

12. The Dark Lord is a major character in that he exemplifies evil and is the "other half" of the conflict between Éowyn and himself over the life of Théoden.

13. Dernhelm, who is really Éowyn in disguise, exemplifies good and is a major character in this excerpt, which presents a conflict between good and evil. She conquers evil both by killing the Dark Lord's steed and by dealing the fatal blow to the Dark Lord himself.

BIG IDEA Connect (20 points)

14. All the authors use setting to grip the reader in a world that is supernatural and larger than life. The language they use to describe dangerous monsters and war settings makes readers understand they are in another world, of violence and fire pits, huge and horrible birdlike creatures and monsters like Grendel, evil beings and foul odors. These settings take the readers to times and places where characters are larger than life; that is, of epic proportions. The settings in these excerpts also create an understanding of the fear that almost disables many from being able to act. This understanding makes each hero's bravery, both physical and psychological, even more awe-inspiring.

A Brief History of Heroes

Selection Test (page 5)

Recall and Interpret

(40 points total; 4 points each)

1. d
2. c
3. a
4. a
5. a
6. d
7. b
8. d
9. c
10. d

Analyze and Evaluate

(40 points total; 2 points each)

11. Answers will vary. Possible answers:

a. Fighting
b. Soldier
c. Noble
d. Renaissance
e. All-around abilities
f. Intellect
g. Noble
h. Reasoning
i. Scientist, philosopher
j. Intellect
k. Leadership
l. Charisma, conviction
m. Upper classes
n. Unimportant
o. Decency
p. Unimportant
q. Varies
r. Varies
s. Commitment
t. Unimportant

BIG IDEA Connect (20 points)

12. Answers will vary.

Beowulf can be compared to the twenty-first-century hero in that he goes to a foreign place to assist a downtrodden people in their effort to overcome a monster. Although one might attribute this good deed to selflessness or humanity, it is more likely that Beowulf is looking for challenges to prove his physical strength and his prowess as a fighter, like the true hero of the Middle Ages that he is. Beowulf does not exemplify the education or intellect required of heroes from later periods, but he does demonstrate the physical courage and nobility required of the Medieval hero of whom the storytellers loved to tell.

Éowyn exemplifies the hero of the Middle Ages with one important difference: she is a woman. In a way she is like Carlyle's Great Man in that she has the conviction to challenge the Dark Rider in order to save Théoden. Her charisma inspires Merry, the hobbit, so that he is able to snap out of his frozen horror and come to her aid in killing the Lord of Nazgûl. Although she is a woman, she nevertheless embodies the hero of the Middle Ages in that she is a a proven soldier with great physical strength and of the noble class.

The Seafarer

Open-Book Selection Test (page 7)

Recall and Interpret

(60 points total; 6 points each)

1. a	**6.** b
2. c	**7.** a
3. b	**8.** b
4. c	**9.** d
5. d	**10.** d

Analyze and Evaluate

(21 points total; 7 points each)

Answers will vary. Possible answers:

11. The introductory description of the tale—"How the sea took me, swept me back / And forth in sorrow and fear and pain"—has a grievously nurturing quality; it is as if the sea, in a motherly fashion, claims the solitary speaker as her own and comforts him with a deeply mournful kind of rocking ('back and forth').

12. The descriptive phrase "whirled in sorrow, / Alone in a world blown clear of love" (lines 15-16) provides a stark and vast backdrop in which the only motion is that of hypnotically curling waves. Here the speaker is not just by himself but wildly, terribly, even perhaps somehow permanently alone. His description of the "world" of the sea as "blown clear of love" suggests not only distance from land but some kind of catapaulting motion, as if he and the ship had been launched away from humanity and its clamorous emotions. There is also the implication that this new world is purer, distilled, unruined; its devastating emptiness is oddly thrilling.

13. The descriptive phrase "my feet were cast / In icy bands, bound with frost" (lines 8-9) suggests some mythical permanence, as if the speaker were not just bound during his watch but endlessly or repeatedly.

BIG IDEA Connect (19 points)

14. Answers will vary but could include points similar to the following:

- Life is like a difficult sea journey, and everyone is a seafarer.
- Just as a seafarer longs for his or her home on land, the soul longs for heaven.
- Earthly joys are temporary; the joys of heavenly life are everlasting.
- Living a good and courageous life has its rewards in heaven.
- Everyone's true home is heaven.
- The things of the world are unimportant compared to eternal life in heaven.

from *The Ecclesiastical History of the English People*

Selection Test (page 9)

Recall and Interpret

(56 points total; 7 points each)

1. b	**5.** a
2. c	**6.** b
3. a	**7.** d
4. c	**8.** d

Vocabulary Practice

(12 points total; 3 points each)

9. a	**11.** c
10. b	**12.** b

Analyze and Evaluate (12 points)

Answers will vary. A model answer:

13. There is no description of what King

Edwin or Caedmon looked like, which details would encourage the reader to visualize them. Further, there is no omniscience, so the reader has no real access to the thoughts and/or feelings—the inner life, the heart—of either man. They are not characters per se, and the narrative is not sharply focused on them but, rather, more generally on their respective roles in history and the changes they underwent. This makes them somewhat two-dimensional for the reader. Details about them as people (details characteristic of biographical narrative) are missing. If such details were present, the text might be something other or more than a historical narrative.

BIG IDEA Connect (20 points)

14. Answers will vary. For either excerpt, students could note that

- it tells of real people.
- it describes real events.
- the people and events it describes existed in the past.

Students who discuss "The Anglo-Saxons Embrace Christianity" might say that the excerpt fails as a history because it lacks objectivity in that it

- reveals Bede's admiration for Edwin.
- makes Bede's own religious beliefs obvious.
- uses such terms as "the true God" and "wise advice."

Students who discuss "Caedmon" might say that the excerpt fails as a history because it lacks objectivity in that it

- never questions, or offers other explanations for, Caedmon's interpretation of his dream.
- reveals Bede's admiration for Caedmon.
- uses such words as "delightful" and "excellent" to describe Caedmon's verses.

from *The Canterbury Tales:* from *The Prologue*

Open-Book Selection Test (page 11)

Recall and Interpret

(49 points total; 7 points each)

1. c
2. d
3. a
4. b
5. b
6. d
7. d

Analyze and Evaluate

(36 points total; 4 points each)

Notes will vary and, because some traits are revealed in more than one place, line numbers will vary. Model answers:

8. Nun (Prioress): phoniness; 143–145; Character's actions
9. Monk: extravagance; 197–201; Character's appearance
10. Friar: ignores those in need; 247–252; Direct statement
11. Franklin: gluttony; 351–360; Character's actions
12. Skipper: cruelty; 409–410; Character's actions
13. Doctor: dishonesty; 435–437; Character's actions
14. Miller: dishonesty; 576–579; Character's actions
15. Summoner: drunkenness; 640–641; Character's appearance
16. Pardoner: dishonesty; 690–691; Character's actions

BIG IDEA Connect (15 points)

17. Answers will vary. Students could say that Chaucer's attitude:

is one of caution, distrust, or cynicism.

- He thoroughly approves of only the Parson.
- He does not criticize the Cleric, seeming to see him as sincere.
- He points out questionable characteristics in the Prioress, seeing

her as vain, overly concerned with the niceties of courtly manners, and too concerned with the welfare of her pets.
- He is openly critical of the motives and behavior of the Monk, Friar, Summoner, and Pardoner.

varies, depending on the character he is describing.
- He has a positive attitude toward those who honor their vows and live by Christian ideals, such as the Parson.
- He has a negative attitude toward those who are insincere in their Christianity, such as the Summoner and the Pardoner.

from *The Canterbury Tales:* from *The Pardoner's Tale*

Open-Book Selection Test (page 19)

Recall and Interpret

(54 points total; 6 points each)

1. a
2. d
3. c
4. c
5. d
6. b
7. a
8. a
9. b

Analyze and Evaluate

(24 points total; 8 points each)

Answers will vary. Possible answers:

10. Situational, because they swear to live and die for one another but will actually die because of one another

11. Situational, because the day will be anything but lucky

12. Situational, because the speaker expects to spend the evening celebrating instead of dying in agony

Dramatic, because the reader knows what the speaker doesn't—the wine is poisoned and they are about to die.

BIG IDEA Connect (22 points)

13. Answers will vary. Possible answers:
- You never know when you will meet death. The rioters, looking for Death, do not realize that the old man on the road may actually be Death.
- Greed (or any other significant character flaw) can be one's undoing. It is the rioters' greed that makes them such easy victims of Death. When they allow themselves to be ruled by greed, they take actions that result in their own deaths.
- Always be on the lookout for Death. This is what the tavern-knave's mother told him, and it is this advice that the three rioters ignore. When they discover the gold coins, they forget all about Death until they become his victims.
- Those who choose evil friends will suffer as a result. All three rioters die at the hands of those they foolishly trust.
- The love of money is the root of all evil. It is the uncontrolled love of wealth that leads the rioters to plan murder and to become its victims.

from *The Wife of Bath's Tale*

Open-Book Selection Test (page 15)

Recall and Interpret

(35 points total; 5points each)

1. b
2. d
3. b
4. a
5. d
6. c
7. d

Vocabulary Practice

(25 points total; 5 points each)

8. a
9. c
10. c
11. c
12. b

Analyze and Evaluate (20 points)

Answers will vary. A possible answer:

13. Of the friar's walks to purge the woods of fairies: "Women can now go safely up and down / By every bush or under every tree; / There is no other incubus but he..." (lines 52-54). The Wife is slightly irreverent about religion (even though the ending of her tale indicates that she is moral / religious), and this gibe at the holy friar, suggesting he himself is an 'incubus' and a threat to women's virtue, is meant to be funny and slightly lewd. The implication that predators on women's virtue have been lurking under trees and in bushes prior to this "purging" by the friar is, in the context of talk about fairies, somewhat darkly wry and comic.

BIG IDEA Connect (20 points)

14. The Wife of Bath uses humor throughout her story, even when referring to religious personages, but at the end of her story she makes point after point about the importance of God and the church. Most of these points are made by the old woman when rebuking the knight for his mean behavior and speech. She describes the importance of the lessons taught by the church, the source of noble and gentle behavior through the example given by Jesus. She preaches about gratitude. She speaks of the poverty that God chose and emphasizes that there is no shame in it. In fact, she says poverty often brings people to God.

The Roads Now Taken

Selection Test (page 17)

Recall and Interpret

(50 points total; 5 points each)

1. c
2. c
3. d
4. b
5. b
6. a
7. a
8. c
9. a
10. b

Analyze and Evaluate

(32 points total; 8 points each)

Answers will vary.

11. Not very important. This is a short article, not a vehicle for real information. The author provides little historical background.

12. Somewhat important. Chu gives a detailed definition of pilgrimages, as well as some historical examples of pilgrimages. He also gives some historical information related to pilgrimages.

13. Somewhat important. This is a lighthearted article, not a serious one, so the author doesn't try hard to persuade the reader of his point of view but merely presents his opinions. He does try to make pilgrimages sound inviting, however, so that in that sense he may persuade the reader to make a pilgrimage.

14. Important. This is a Time magazine article, after all; engaging the reader is of prime importance. Chu's use of popular individual and group sports as examples allows the reader to easily understand his points. At the beginning of the article, his informal language describing the predicament of the Benedictines is humorous.

BIG IDEA Connect (18 points)

15. That which is sacred to our time is commonly referred to as an individual's "passion." That is, if an individual feels passionately about something, that becomes the person's pilgrimage. For Lance Armstrong, the bicycle ride through France is his pilgrimage. That example fits well with Chu's definition of a pilgrim as someone with his "map in his heart." He also participates with hundreds of others in the ride along the trail; and other pilgrims can participate in the pilgrimage by watching and admiring those actively involved in the race, much like the mass worship that Chu cites in the football stadium. Further, in the bicycle race the individual participates in something larger than himself. Along the way, there is also plenty of time for him to deepen his self-understanding.

from *The Book of Margery Kempe*

Selection Test (page 19)

Recall and Interpret

(56 points total; 8 points each)

1. a
2. b
3. a
4. b
5. c
6. a
7. a

Vocabulary Practice

(15 points total; 3 points each)

8. c
9. a
10. b
11. b
12. c

Analyze and Evaluate

(14 points total; 7 points each)

13–14. Answers will vary. Possible answers:

suffers from guilt; revealed by
- her emotional suffering over her secret sin
- her belief that the sin is so horrible that she will suffer great criticism from her priest if she reveals it
- her belief that she gave in to the devil on several occasions

very religious; revealed by
- her penances
- her visions
- her beliefs about her visions
- her deep concern about sin

practical; revealed by
- the fact that her first rational act after her illness is to eat and drink
- her statements that she returned to a level-headed way of doing things

grateful; revealed by
- her feeling that Jesus Christ saved her
- her acknowledgment that her husband was always kind

sensitive or vulnerable; revealed by
- her inability to withstand the priest's criticism

BIG IDEA Connect (15 points)

15. Answers will vary. Students could say that Kempe blames
- herself for committing a significant sin and failing to confess it.
- her priest for being so harsh and judgmental that she was unable to confess her secret sin.
- the devil for encouraging her to fail to confess and for tempting her to be wicked.

from *Everyman*

Open-Book Selection Test (page 21)

Recall and Interpret

(56 points total; 7 points each)

1. d
2. a
3. c
4. b
5. b
6. a
7. d
8. c

Analyze and Evaluate

(24 points total; 8 points each)

Notes will vary. Possible answers:

9. Friends and Friendship:
- friends don't always keep promises
- there are some things friends can't or won't do
- friendship doesn't extend beyond death
- it's foolish to depend on friends for things they can't provide

10. Possessions:
- people spend too much time and energy on acquiring things
- possessions are temporary; they're "loaned" to people
- "You can't take it with you."
- love of possessions detracts from more important concerns

11. Good Deeds:

- people spend too little time and energy doing good deeds
- sin detracts from good deeds
- benefits of good deeds are lasting

BIG IDEA Connect (20 points)

12. Answers will vary. Model answer:

People who have lived a good life find death easier to deal with than those who haven't. This lesson is conveyed through the example of Everyman. He isn't prepared for death. He hasn't accomplished many good deeds. He hasn't concerned himself with God's wishes. As a result, Everyman is devastated by the idea of dying, knowing that he is threatened with eternal damnation.

Our lives are enriched by the things we do for others. This lesson is conveyed through the character of Good Deeds who, despite Everyman's neglect, remains steadfast and loyal to him when all others abandon him.

from *Sir Gawain and the Green Knight*

Open-Book Selection Test (page 23)

Recall and Interpret

(40 points total; 5 points each)

1. c
2. b
3. a
4. a
5. c
6. d
7. c
8. d

Vocabulary Practice

(10 points total; 5 points each)

9. b
10. a

Analyze and Evaluate

(30 points total; 10 points each)

Answers will vary. Possible answers:

11. Courage: Gawain shows his courage by honorinig his covenant with the Green Knight. He stands and take the Green Knight's feints and actual blow, and, perhaps most importantly, he is brave enough to admit his cowardice—loving his own life so much that he took the wife's sash to protect himself from harm; flinching under the first swing.

12. Humility: Gawain shows his humility when he admits his wrongdoing without hesitation. He confesses to taking the wife's sash and to flinching under the first swing. Earlier, when arguing that he should be the one to accept the knight's challenge, he shows his humility by professing to be the knight least worthy, the one who would be least missed if the Green Knight should fell him.

13. Loyalty: Gawain shows his loyalty to and respect for Arthur in the rather skillful way he obtrudes on the proceedings and offers to be the one to accept the knight's challenge; in reality, he is protecting Arthur.

BIG IDEA Connect (20 points)

14. Answers will vary. Possible answers:

Gawain feels ashamed and unhappy because he

- failed to live up to the ideals of knightly perfection.
- broke a promise (covenant) made with the Green Knight.
- lied about receiving the girdle.
- allowed his desire to live to win over his sense of honor.
- flinched when threatened.

The Green Knight is amused, forgiving, and sympathetic because

- he admires Gawain's reckless courage in being ready to fight so soon after having nearly lost his life.
- he believes that Gawain is a good and brave man who was tempted only by his love of life to behave dishonorably.
- Gawain confesses and apologizes for his misdeeds.
- Gawain reacts with such overwhelming guilt about what the Green Knight considers minor flaws in his character.

Answers

from *A Distant Mirror*

Selection Test (page 25)

Recall and Interpret

(50 points total; 5 points each)

1. c
2. a
3. b
4. d
5. a
6. c
7. a
8. a
9. a
10. d

Analyze and Evaluate

(30 points total; 10 points each)

11. Knights fought battles to give their lives purpose. They were willing to die for their cause, whatever that cause might have been. In part, the cause itself was not what mattered most. Many of them loved and admired valor for its own sake, which is why they made such excellent warriors. Don Pero Niño is the best example of a valorous knight. He remained standing and fighting even with multiple serious injuries.

12. The knights had to wear heavy armor, carry heavy weapons, ride a horse for long periods of time, receive heavy blows, continue to fight while seriously wounded, and were frequently killed. Don Pero Niño is the best example of a knight with stamina. Most men would not have been able to continue fighting with the number of serious injuries he sustained.

13. For a knight, dying in battle was an honorable death, and a good knight went into battle intending to fight until the fight was won or he was slain. A good knight never backed down or ran off. He charged ahead, even when doing so was guaranteed to be deadly. The 12 knights who tied their horses' reins together and rode into the heat of battle with Blind King John are an example of sacrifice and "brotherhood." Blind King John would likely have gone back into the fray without them. They elected to go with him, to follow their leader, probably anticipating a fatal outcome.

BIG IDEA Connect (20 points)

Answers will vary.

14. Based on Barbara Tuchman's article and on "Sir Gawain and the Green Knight," the term "Romantic" seems to be another way of expressing the idea of idealization. In the stories from the Middle Ages, as well as derivative later ones such as the musical "Camelot," good knights are depicted as working to right the wrongs of society, to protect women and children, and to protect the holiness of the Church. According to Tuchman, this is what the Church wished were true. In fact, the noblemen had little to do and so they headed off to battle for the thrill of engagement and to test their own mettle, not, according to Tuchman, out of devotion to a higher cause. This does not mean their motivations were totally selfish, however. "Romantic," in both cases (in "Sir Gawain and the Green Knight" and in Tuchman's article), seems to mean "in the name of something larger than the self," whether that be religion, country, love…or victory. The knights' "sword arm" may have been in the service of the church, but what they truly romanticized was valor.

from *Le Morte d'Arthur*

Selection Test (page 27)

Recall and Interpret

(35 points total; 5 points each)

1. b
2. a
3. c
4. d
5. b
6. c
7. b

Vocabulary Practice

(20 points total; 5 points each)

8. b
9. a
10. a
11. b

Analyze and Evaluate

(30 points total; 10 points each)

12–14. Answers will vary. Possible answers:

responsibility; demonstrated by
- efforts to safeguard Excalibur, even when dying
- concern for safety of his knights

wisdom; demonstrated by
- heeding Gawain's advice
- listening to councilors
- not being fooled by Bedivere's reports

courage; demonstrated by
- actions shown in battle
- calm attitude toward death

decisiveness; demonstrated by
- quick reactions to Gawain's warning
- quick agreement with Mordred's demands
- lack of hesitation in battle

physical strength; demonstrated by
- killing Mordred
- ability to survive, at least for a while, a serious wound
- prowess in battle

emotional strength; demonstrated by
- willingness to do what is necessary regarding Mordred
- attitude toward death
- insistence on safeguarding Excalibur despite being gravely wounded

BIG IDEA Connect (15 points)

15. Answers will vary. Possible answers:
Malory attaches the greatest level of importance to Arthur's death. This is shown by
- comparison with the scant attention he gives to the deaths of Mordred and other characters.
- the suggestion that there is little to hope for after Arthur's death except his return.

Arthur's death is portrayed as ill-fated and tragic.
- Despite all of his and others' efforts to avoid it, death catches him and all but a few of his followers.
- The battle that results in his death is caused by a twist of fate.

Arthur's death is noble.
- He is tended by queens.
- His grave is guarded by a bishop and a noble.

Arthur's death is mystical or magical.
- Malory suggests that Arthur might live on in some other form.
- Malory suggests that Arthur may one day return to rule.

Sir Patrick Spens, Bonny Barbara Allan, and Get Up and Bar the Door

Selection Test (page 29)

Recall and Interpret

(40 points total; 5 points each)

1. b
2. a
3. c
4. d
5. a
6. c
7. d
8. d

Vocabulary Practice (5 points total)

9. a

Analyze and Evaluate (15 points)

Answers will vary. Possible answer:
10. The refrain relies on Barbara Allan's name as the last two words of a stanza. This is the case in stanzas 1, 2, 4, and 6, and it also occurs in lines 2 and 8 of stanza 4. The ballad is clearly about tragic romance, and the repetition of Barbara Allan's name lends a sonorous knell-like quality to the young swain's ailing and death. He is haunted by her (thus, repeating her name). Even Barbara Allan herself refers to herself third person (stanzas 4 and 6) as if she has been thoroughly objectified. The changes in the refrain follow the plot of the poem—the young man falls in love, his men seek the object of his love to bring her to his sickbed, he claims his ailing is all for her, she brings up the slight he gave her, he sorrowfully makes a last request

that everyone be kind to her, he dies, she rues her own unforgivingness and plans to die, too. As is typical of a ballad, the refrain lends a musicality to the poem.

BIG IDEA Connect (40 points)

11. Answers will vary. Possible answers regarding troubles:

Sir Patrick Spens's problems are created by

- a king who orders him to sea without regard for conditions.
- Spens's sense of duty, which sends him to sea despite adverse conditions.
- Spens's failure to heed the advice of his men.

Barbara Allan's and John Graeme's problems are created by

- Graeme's insulting Barbara Allan.
- Barbara Allan's excessive pride.
- Graeme's inability to ask for forgiveness.
- both lovers' overreactions to difficulty in their relationship.

The married couple's problems are created by

- each one's unwillingness to give in.
- the rudeness, cruelty, and illegal behavior of strangers.

The most likely answer regarding whose troubles are least deserved:

Spens, because he neither creates nor wishes for the situation that leads to his death.

Spens, because his sense of duty to the king results in death.

Possible answers regarding which situations could be considered tragic:

Spens's troubles are tragic in that

- they result in his death and the death of all of his men.
- he acted honorably in following the king's orders.

John Graeme's troubles are tragic in that

- they result in his death from a broken heart.
- he doesn't seem to have meant any real harm by the behavior that caused Barbara Allan to reject him.
- the "punishment" is excessive for the "crime."

Barbara Allan's troubles are tragic in that

- they result in her death from a broken heart.
- she seems not to have realized the depth of Graeme's love for her.
- she has let herself be controlled by pride.

On Monsieur's Departure and **Speech to the Troops at Tilbury**

Open-Book Selection Test (page 31)

Recall and Interpret

(40 points total; 5 points each)

1. a
2. b
3. c
4. d
5. d
6. c
7. a
8. b

Vocabulary Practice

(20 points total; 5 points each)

9. b
10. a
11. c
12. c

Analyze and Evaluate

(20 points)

13. Answers will vary. A model answer:

Tone in poem: regret, sorrow

Words that establish tone: grieve, discontent, care, rue, cruel, etc.

Tone in speech: daring, courageous, proud

Words and phrases that establish the tone: honor, heart and stomach of a king, you have deserved rewards and crowns, noble, worthy, obedience, valor, famous victory, etc.

BIG IDEA Connect (20 points)

14. Answers will vary but should list examples of language and thought that demonstrate sacrifice and/or difficult action in both the

poem and the speech. Possible examples include:
From the poem:

- the contradictions in the first stanza (for example, "I grieve and dare not show my discontent") to describe how the speaker makes a supreme effort to hide her true feelings
- the similes to shadows and to snow, indicating her steadfastness though she feels powerless
- the request in the last three stanzas emphasized by the couplet, which indicates that what she is enduring is nearly unbearable
- The speaker is sacrificing love on the altar of duty.

From the speech:

- traveling to Tilbury to appear before the troops will bolster and inspire the soldiers
- not heeding the advice of those who urge her to avoid multitudes/crowds, choosing instead to go "amongst" her people
- emphasizing her inner strength and fortitude (heart and stomach of a king) over her outward (feminine/frail) appearance.
- claiming that she, too, is willing to die for England

The Lover Showeth How He Is Forsaken and Whoso List to Hunt

Open-Book Selection Test (page 33)

Recall and Interpret

(60 points total; 12 points each)

1. a
2. a
3. d
4. b
5. d

Analyze and Evaluate (15 points)

6. Notes will vary, depending on the image chosen. A model answer:
Image: "in a net I seek to hold the wind"
Feelings and ideas:

- attempting the impossible
- certain failure
- hopelessness of wanting what can't be had
- romantic view of beloved
- beloved is, by her nature, unattainable
- frustration of speaker

BIG IDEA Connect (25 points)

7. Answers will vary but could include points similar to the following:

Although the subject matter of unrequited love is the same in both poems, the attitudes of the speakers are very different. In "Whoso List to Hunt," the speaker feels wistful, hopeless, romantic, and sad. All of his efforts to win the heart of his beloved have failed. His beloved belongs to another, very powerful, man. Although the speaker has given up, he can't stop thinking about her. He does not seem to hold anything against his beloved. In "The Lover Showeth How He Is Forsaken," the speaker feels bitter and angry. He believes that he was betrayed by a lover who unfairly used him and cast him aside. He blames his lover(s) for inconstancy. He had believed in the signs of affection he received.

Sonnet 30 and Sonnet 75

Open-Book Selection Test (page 35)

Recall and Interpret

(60 points total; 6 points each)

1. b
2. a
3. a
4. d
5. a
6. c
7. b
8. c
9. d
10. d

Answers

Analyze and Evaluate

(20 points total; 10 points each)

11. Answers will vary but should suggest ideas similar to the following:

Problem or Question:

- The beloved rejects the speaker's love.
- How can indifference from a lover increase one's love?
- The beloved's indifference makes the speaker's love grow stronger.
- The stronger the speaker's love grows, the more uncaring the beloved becomes.

Solution

- Love can be so strong that it can cause nature to contradict itself.
- Love can have many strange effects.
- Love can change the world.

BIG IDEA Connect (20 points)

12. Answers will vary. Students could say that readers learn

- that love is often illogical and frustrating
- that love can change the way the lover sees the world
- that love can be overpowering
- that love can see beyond death
- that love recognizes what is good about the beloved
- that lovers believe their love will never die

Sonnet 31 and Sonnet 39

Open-Book Selection Test (page 37)

Recall and Interpret

(64 points total; 8 points each)

1. c
2. b
3. d
4. b
5. c
6. c
7. d
8. a

Analyze and Evaluate

(16 points total; 8 points each)

Answers will vary. Model answers:

9. Sonnet 31:

Moon; this is appropriate because the speaker is a rejected lover, and the moon has long been associated with love and romance

10. Sonnet 39:

Sleep; this is appropriate because the speaker is having trouble sleeping and wants relief from despair—sleep can bring it

BIG IDEA Connect (20 points)

11. Answers will vary.

Students who feel that Sonnet 31 is more meaningful or relevant could say that

- the tone is bitter, and unhappy people are often bitter.
- the speaker complains about how he has been treated, and this is a natural response.
- people who have suffered some disappointment often feel that they can spot similar suffering in another and tend to empathize with them.

Students who feel that Sonnet 39 is more meaningful or relevant could say that

- sleep really is a method of escape from unhappiness.
- depressed people often sleep more than normal.
- people who are worried or upset often find it difficult to fall asleep.
- sleep does refresh, and unhappy people need to be refreshed in order to cope.
- people who cannot fall asleep often find themselves unable to get a troubling situation off their minds.

Answers

The Passionate Shepherd to His Love

Open-Book Selection Test (page 39)

Recall and Interpret

(60 points total; 10 points each)

1. b
2. d
3. d
4. d
5. c
6. b

Analyze and Evaluate

(18 points total; 9 points each)

Answers will vary. Possible answers:

7. In the first three stanzas the shepherd offers natural, free, beautiful experiences, which reflect his unworldly, pastoral point of view.

8. In the third and fourth stanzas the shepherd offers fanciful, impractical, and sometimes expensive objects, which reflect his point of view of his beloved; he considers her perhaps too worldly for him, and strives to throw in gold and coral and amber—"riches" he thinks might persuade her to stay with him.

BIG IDEA Connect (22 points)

9. Answers will vary. Students could suggest that:

- the simple language and short lines are appropriate to a shepherd, who would probably not be educated
- the simple rhyme scheme and short stanzas reflect the sung or spoken nature of the poem, since the shepherd would probably not write the poem down
- the poem's simplicity reflects the shepherd's simplistic and naïve attitude towards love itself
- the shepherd is offering his love a simple, natural life in which to enjoy (and wear) nature's beauty

The Nymph's Reply to the Shepherd

Open-Book Selection Test (page 41)

Recall and Interpret

(60 points total; 10 points each)

1. c
2. a
3. b
4. b
5. d
6. c

Analyze and Evaluate (20 points)

Answers may vary. Model answers:

7. Raleigh's nymph sees love as a luxury of youth, not as something infinitely sustaining. Raleigh's view is realistic, but there is something jaded about his nymph and her logic. Raleigh himself held the favor of Queen Elizabeth (whom he flattered more effectively than Marlowe's shepherd does his nymph) for some time, but after he fell in love with and married one of her ladies-in-waiting, the queen turned on him and imprisoned him. This misfortune—how "true" love cost him pretty much everything—may have embittered him (and his nymph) about love.

BIG IDEA Connect (20 points)

8. Answers will vary. Students who think the nymph's reply is appropriate could say that

- her attitude toward love and relationships is far more realistic than the shepherd's is.
- she knows that life and relationships involve far more than frolicking in the fields.
- she is right to reject the silly gifts that the shepherd offers her.
- love cannot be bought, even if the shepherd were able to produce all that he offers the nymph

Students who think the nymph's reply is not appropriate could say that

- it is too harsh, negative, and mean-spirited.
- the shepherd, who is obviously very

much in love with her, deserves better treatment, even if his offer is rather ridiculous.
- the shepherd's offer was not meant to be taken literally.

Of Studies

Selection Test (page 43)

Recall and Interpret

(54 points; 9 points each)

1. b
2. a
3. c
4. b
5. d
6. d

Vocabulary Practice

(15 points; 3 points each)

7. c
8. c
9. b
10. b
11. b

Analyze and Evaluate (11 points)

12. A model answer:

"And therefore, if a man write little, he had need have a great memory; if he confer little, he had need have a present wit; and if he read little, he had need have much cunning to seem to know that he doth not."

BIG IDEA Connect (20 points)

13. Answers will vary but should reflect students' understanding that, according to Bacon, the three main purposes of studies are
- "delight," or to provide pleasure to people who pursue them.
- "ornament," or to make people's speech and conversation more effective.
- "ability," or to improve people's judgment and ability to conduct their affairs.

In addition, students should provide and defend a personal opinion based on their own experiences.

Sonnet 116 and Sonnet 130

Open-Book Selection Test (page 45)

Recall and Interpret

(40 points total; 8 points each)

1. c
2. d
3. d
4. b
5. d

Vocabulary Practice

(20 points total; 5 points each)

6. b
7. a
8. a
9. b

Analyze and Evaluate

(20 points total; 10 points each)

Answers will vary. A model answer is given for each sonnet.

10. Sonnet 116:
Metaphor: "it is an ever-fixed mark"
Compares love to landmark used as a navigational guide
Feelings and ideas suggested:
- love is constant and steadfast
- love is necessary for survival
- love helps and guides the beloved
- love can be depended on, especially in difficult times
- love is important during dark times

11. Sonnet 130:
Simile: "I think my love as rare / As any she belied by false compare"
Compares his beloved's appearance to that of any beautiful woman praised with exaggeration
Feelings and ideas suggested:
- love looks for the beautiful in the beloved
- love doesn't need to exaggerate the beloved's qualities
- lovers who praise their beloveds with exaggeration are lying about them and may not in fact find them beautiful

BIG IDEA Connect (20 points)

12. Answers will vary. A model answer for Sonnet 130: Shakespeare's Sonnet 130 is a good example of the kind of clever thinking and writing that Elizabethan writers and readers admired. In the first place, it uses the sonnet form expertly, following the rules for rhyme scheme, meter, and division of problem and solution. Just being able to play the sonnet game by its rules spoke well of the poet's intellect. But it is also cleverly arranged, taking the reader through a list of contrasts that seem to put the woman described down. Various body parts—eyes, hair, lips—are described, and several senses are appealed to, including sight, smell, and sound. Finally, the sonnet has an understated humor that would have appealed to Shakespeare's peers. It's a sweet little joke that does no harm to the woman described and in fact compliments her inner beauty.

Sonnet 73 and Sonnet 29

Open-Book Selection Test (page 47)

Recall and Interpret

(60 points total; 10 points each)

1. d
2. d
3. c
4. a
5. b
6. c

Analyze and Evaluate

(20 points total; 4 points each)

7. Line 5 compares the speaker, who feels pessimistic, to a man who is optimistic about his future.

8. Line 6 compares the speaker, who feels unattractive, to a handsome man.

9. Line 6 compares the speaker, who feels "all alone," to a man with many friends.

10. Line 11 compares the speaker, who suddenly feels happier, to a "lark at the break of day" that flies upward and sings "hymns at heaven's gate."

11. The final simile turns the poem sharply from complaint to grateful praise; it seems to change the poem's setting from the depths of dark despair to a paradise.

BIG IDEA Connect (20 points)

12. Answers will vary. A model answer: Humanism emphasizes the abilities and achievements of human beings. Humanists are optimistic that people have what it takes to learn, to grow, to change themselves and their world for the better. In both sonnets, this appreciation of individuals is clear. Sonnet 73 laments the passing of human life; after the speaker's death, "the sweet birds" of his creativity and uniqueness will no longer be heard; when his "fire" burns out, something special and important—a single human being—will be lost forever. This is why his friend's love for him increases as age comes: his friend knows that there is not much time in the world to appreciate this individual. In Sonnet 29, the friendship of a single, unique human being is prized above everything else that people tend to want: wealth, popularity, learning. The idea of humanism—that each person is valuable just because he or she is unique and individual—informs both sonnets' discussions of friendship.

Fear No More the Heat o' the Sun and Blow, Blow, Thou Winter Wind

Open-Book Selection Test (page 49)

Recall and Interpret

(40 points total; 8 points each)

1. a
2. b
3. c
4. b
5. b

Answers

Vocabulary Practice

(20 points total; 5 points each)

6. a
7. b
8. b
9. a

Analyze and Evaluate

(20 points total; 4 points each)

10. The speakers say that people expect to love, to learn, to work, and also to experience scorn, anger, and pain.
11. The speakers say that in the end, all hopes and pains must "come to dust"—everything in life ends in the grave.
12. The speaker expected that his friends would be grateful for the good things he had done for them (the "benefits forgot" of line 13) and remember their friendships with him.
13. The speaker got betrayal and ingratitude from his friends instead.
14. Both songs convey the sad message that life is not always what people expect it to be (life and friends may be kind, but also cruel). Even so, there is respite in self consolation and, finally, in the reprieve of death.

BIG IDEA Connect (20 points)

15. Answers will vary. A model answer: Both songs point out the fickle and even dangerous nature of life at court. In "Fear No More," the singers are sons of the king, and the person whose apparent death they mourn, though they do not know it, is their sister, who has been falsely accused of a terrible crime and has done desperate things to try to prove her innocence and gain her place at court again. In addition, the song itself lists some of the dangers or indignities of court life that death frees the youth from; namely, tyranny and censure. In "Blow, Blow," the singer is an attendant to a lord whose brother has betrayed him and taken away his power. The singer laments that courtly friendships cannot be trusted, that people who want power will trample on any previous friendships or obligations to get it. Both songs show that courtly life was hard to navigate successfully.

To be, or not to be, All the world's a stage, and Our revels now are ended

Open-Book Selection Test (page 51)

Recall and Interpret

(60 points total; 10 points each)

1. d
2. a
3. c
4. d
5. b
6. a

Analyze and Evaluate

(20 points total; 10 points each)

Answers will vary. Model answers for the three speakers (students will provide two):

7-8. Hamlet's voice is moody, despairing, fearful, etc. Word choice supporting this claim occurs throughout the speech and includes "end / The heartache and the thousand natural shocks / That flesh is heir to"; "the respect that makes calamity of so long life"; "the pangs of despised love"; "To grunt and seat under a weary life"; "the dread of something after death"; "thus conscience does make cowards of us all."

Jacques's voice is witty and worldly-wise, and also down-to-earth. He doesn't shy away from unpleasant details and facts about life. Word choice supporting this claim occurs throughout the speech and includes "the infant / Mewling and puking in the nurse's arms"; "the whining school-boy . . . creeping like a snail / Unwillingly to school"; "soldier . . . Seeking the bubble reputation / Even in the cannon's mouth"; "Sans teeth, sans eyes, sans taste, sans everything."

Prospero's voice is gentle but weary. His voice is mature and mindful that death is not far off. Word choice supporting this claim includes "We are such stuff / As dreams are made on, and out little life / Is rounded with a sleep"; "I am vexed"; "Bear with my weakness"; "My old brain is troubled"; "Be not disturbed with my infirmity."

BIG IDEA Connect (20 points)

9. Answers will vary. Possible answer: Humanists focus their attention on what humans are capable of and what human life is like in this world, rather than on an afterlife or other world. These speeches emphasize this aspect of life. The speakers are concerned with what life is like, good and bad, here and now. Hamlet worries about what he can and can't control in his life and whether it would be better to be done with life. Jacques outlines in gritty detail the earthy aspects of life, with its crying and dirt and illness, right up to the oblivion of senility. Prospero, too, is concerned with life in this world. After the pageant, he turns the audience's attention away from the world of make-believe and back to the real world, with its worries and exhaustions and, finally, its end.

The Tragedy of Macbeth, Act 1

Selection Test (page 53)

Recall and Interpret

(30 points total; 5 points each)

1. d

2. b

3. c

4. d

5. d

6. a

Vocabulary Practice

(20 points total; 5 points each)

7. b

8. a

9. c

10. a

Analyze and Evaluate

(20 points total; 10 points each)

Answers will vary. Possible answers:

11. Summary: The king and his sons thank Macbeth and Banquo for their service in battle.

Atmosphere:

- victorious, celebratory
- happy, joyous
- public, formal

Details:

- Duncan dressed in royal clothing
- brightly lit set
- use of celebratory music
- Duncan stands and moves with pride and dignity

12. Summary: Macbeth loses courage to perform the murder and is chided by Lady Macbeth. Macbeth decides to go ahead with the plan.

Atmosphere:

- private, secret
- anxious, worried, conflicted
- evil, dangerous

Details:

- dim lighting
- dark, heavy, luxurious draperies or wall hangings
- dark, somber costumes
- unsettling music
- Lady Macbeth moves decisively

BIG IDEA Connect (30 points)

13. Answers will vary.

Students could say that Lady Macbeth

- appeals to Macbeth's love for her.
- accuses him of cowardice.
- accuses him of unmanliness.
- encourages him to seize the present opportunity.
- compares her determination with his indecisiveness.
- rejects the possibility of their failure.
- presents him with a specific plan for the murder.

Answers

Students could say that Macbeth agrees because
- she is demanding that he do what he, deep down, wants to do.
- he fears seeming cowardly or unmanly.
- her plan will cast blame for the murder on Duncan's guards.

The Tragedy of Macbeth, Act 2

Selection Test (page 55)

Recall and Interpret

(30 points total; 5 points each)

1. b
2. d
3. d
4. c
5. b
6. c

Vocabulary Practice

(20 points total; 5 points each)

7. a
8. b
9. a
10. c

Analyze and Evaluate (20 points)

Answers will vary. Model answer:

11. In this act, sleep is a motif. The night of the murder is full of sleepers (innocents) and the sleepless (fretful, guilty, ghostlike). Macbeth, in preface to his crime, asks of the "merciful powers" to restrain in him the "cursed thoughts" that nature gives to him in "repose." That is, his dreams are terrifying when he does sleep—of the witches and their dark premonition. Alone before going to kill the king, he remarks in soliloquy that sleep is like death ("o'er the one-half world / Nature seems dead, and wicked dreams abuse / The curtained sleep"). After the murder, Macbeth fears that he may "sleep no more." Sleep is natural, dreams are natural, but the dreams and the deed of Macbeth are an abomination. All of the images of sleep he presents in the wake (no pun intended) of the murder—as a knitter of the "raveled sleeve of care," as the "Balm of hurt minds," etc.—are warm and nurturing…and lost to him. "Macbeth," he cries, remote from himself, "hath murdered sleep."

BIG IDEA Connect (30 points)

12. Answers will vary. Possible answers:
- He fully intends to murder Duncan.
- His commitment to this course of action makes him feel desperate.
- He knows that what he will do is wrong.
- He is not fully in his right mind.
- He knows he is not in his right mind.
- He has difficulty distinguishing between reality and fantasy.
- He is afraid.
- He is filled with the horror of the moment.

The Tragedy of Macbeth, Act 3

Selection Test (page 57)

Recall and Interpret

(45 points total; 5 points each)

1. d
2. b
3. c
4. a
5. c
6. a
7. b
8. a
9. b

Vocabulary Practice

(15 points total; 4 points each)

10. b
11. a
12. c

Analyze and Evaluate (20 points)

Answers will vary. A model answer:

13. Banquo's ghost at the banquet greatly disturbs Macbeth, alerting the other attendees that something is not right with him. The ghost's presence seems vengeful—Banquo has been murdered at Macbeth's bidding—but this vengefulness is deserved. Macbeth's vengefulness, in contrast, springs from his imagination (his fears of Banquo "stick deep," and every minute of Banquo's "being" is remarked to "thrust[] against" his heart—violent images, though Banquo does him no violence.). Macbeth has already imagined a dagger; his imagining of Banquo may not in fact be Banquo's purposeful haunting of him but a manifestation of his own guilt. Macbeth does seem like a victim (pitiable) at the banquet, and Banquo certainly is a victim when he is set upon and killed, but Banquo, who is noble and fearless and stoically accepting of fate, and Macbeth, who is ignoble, fearful, and impulsive, who attempts to master or defeat his own fate, do not appear to have anything in common (save, perhaps, initial rank) in life, and Macbeth and the dead Banquo do not have anything in common either.

BIG IDEA Connect (20 points)

14. Answers will vary. Students could say the statement indicates that Macbeth

- realizes that his actions have been horribly bloody.
- realizes that he can never set things right again, that there is no turning back.
- believes that he can never get rid of his guilt.
- believes that he might as well go forward.
- finds it increasingly easy to murder those who stand in his way.
- has gained a certain confidence in himself.
- is resigned to fate.

The Tragedy of Macbeth, Act 4

Selection Test (page 59)

Recall and Interpret

(35 points total; 5 points each)

1. d
2. b
3. c
4. d
5. b
6. b
7. c

Vocabulary Practice

(15 points total; 5 points each)

8. a
9. c
10. b

Analyze and Evaluate

(30 points total; 15 points each)

Answers will vary. Model answers:

11. This scene is after King Duncan's murder, which seemed to be the climax. However, in this scene, the action rises again as Macbeth's suspicion/fear that threats to him remain is corroborated by the apparitions. He is afraid of MacDuff and Fleance, and, after his visit to the witches, fully intends to take action to eliminate them ("the very firstlings of my heart shall be the firstlings of my hand"). The action is not "falling" yet, and it seems as if the climax of the play has not yet occurred.

12. Macbeth's reaction to the apparitions shows that his paranoia and capacity for violence are escalating. He is no longer appalled by shedding blood, is even eager to do it. The apparitions—which, it seems, tell him his own fears and intentions—encourage him to be "bloody, bold, and resolute," and to be "lion-mettled, proud, and take no care who chafes, who frets…" He has become a grotesque, a caricature, an obsessive.

BIG IDEA Connect (20 points)

13. Answers will vary. Possible answers:

- Edward heals, while Macbeth kills.
- He "solicits heaven," while Macbeth calls on witches.
- He has a "heavenly gift of prophecy," while Macbeth ties his fate to the prophecies of witches and apparitions.
- He lays his hands on people's sores to cure them, while Macbeth's hands drip, literally and figuratively, with his victims' blood.
- He brings peace, comfort, and health to

his people, while Macbeth brings fear, violence, and death.
- He is loved and admired, while Macbeth is feared and despised.
- He is a healer of "the evil," while Macbeth is, according to Malcolm, a "deadly grief" that must be cured.
- It is said that he will pass on the power of healing to his descendants, while Macbeth's legacy can only be evil.

The Tragedy of Macbeth, Act 5

Selection Test (page 61)

Recall and Interpret

(30 points total; 5 points each)

1. b
2. a
3. b
4. c
5. d
6. b

Vocabulary Practice

(25 points total; 5 points each)

7. b
8. c
9. b
10. c
11. a

Analyze and Evaluate

(21 points total; 7 points each)

Students should not be scored in terms of where they mark the bars but on how well their reasoning supports the judgments they make. Answers will vary.

12. Students who give significant importance to Macbeth's "tragic flaw" could make points similar to the following:
- his flaw is deep; witch's remark is sufficient to bring out overriding ambition in him
- once awakened, ambition directs all his actions; destroys his conscience and reason
- before taken over by desire to be king, he was known for loyalty and courage
- ambition leads him to take what is not rightfully his—the throne
- his actions bring disorder, suffering, and death
- achieving his ambition leaves him unpopular, unsatisfied, unfulfilled, friendless, a widower, and, finally, dead

Students who judge Macbeth's "tragic flaw" to be relatively unimportant could make points similar to the following:
- tragic flaw is just the means by which fate manipulates him
- errors in judgment are what make his flaw a tragic one

13. Students who give significant importance to Macbeth's "errors in judgment" could make points similar to the following:
- he rushes into action
- thinks he is unstoppable
- fails to consider he'll be likely suspect
- fails to realize Malcolm will find support
- kills people with too little cause
- fails to consider effects of conscience, which cause him to behave insanely
- instead of heeding conscience, he makes matters worse
- angers and alienates those who might have kept faith in him

Students who judge "errors in judgment" to be relatively unimportant could make points similar to the following:
- his immoral acts, not his mistakes, bring him down
- it's not an "error in judgment" to be a murderer and usurper

14. Students who give significant importance to "fate" could make points similar to the following:
- witches cast a spell
- prophecies are not suggestions but reflect what will be
- Macbeth's trapped by sorcery and powers of darkness

- witches arrange sorcery to trap him more completely
- even if first murder is result of free will, all that follows is a chain of events that are consequences of (fated by) that murder

Students who judge "fate" to be relatively unimportant could make points similar to the following:

- witches choose him because of his flawed character
- he does little to resist helping the prophecy along
- he may be destined to be king, but he himself chooses the means to throne
- it's his own actions that bring his downfall
- he chooses to ignore Banquo's warning about the witches and yield to temptation

BIG IDEA Connect (24 points)

15. Answers will vary. Possible answers:
Blind ambition leads to ruin.

- Macbeth is a beloved, trusted man until he is consumed by ambition.
- Ambition robs him of every decent impulse.
- In his search for power and position, he sacrifices everything that had given his life meaning before—a loving relationship with his wife, loyalty to his king, respect from his peers.
- Once begun on his quest for power, he sinks lower and lower into depravity.
- By abandoning his morality to achieve power and position, he guarantees disloyalty and rebellion.

Fate is determined by character.

- Macbeth brings on his own demise.
- It is flaws in his character that set the tragic chain of events into action.
- Not only is he ambitious, he is weak. That weakness makes him unable to resist temptation and his wife's prodding.
- His reaction to the witches' prophecy that he would be king is immediate and overwhelming.

The love of power corrupts.

- In his search for power and position, he sacrifices everything decent in his life—a loving relationship with his wife, loyalty to his king, respect from his peers.
- His craving for power overpowers his conscience and his reason.
- He allows himself to sink into complete immorality in his search to gain the throne and keep it.

Violence corrupts.

- At first, just contemplating murder fills Macbeth with fear and horror; planning it furthers his dread; committing it almost undoes him.
- The very next day, he kills two more men and seems not at all bothered.
- His murder of Banquo results in his seeing a ghost and behaving insanely.
- After Banquo's murder, violence has little if any horror for him. He orders the murder of an innocent woman and her children just because they are his enemy's family.

Throne of Blood

Selection Test (page 63)

Recall and Interpret

(60 points total; 10 points each)

1. c
2. d
3. d
4. b
5. b
6. c

Answers

Analyze and Evaluate

(20 points total; 10 points each)

Answers will vary. Possible answers:

7. Macbeth is motivated by ambition, pressured by his wife to act, and spurred by the witches' words. Macbeth is successful on the battlefield but fails in intrigue; he is a leader of men, not a good behind-the-scenes manipulator. His guilt and feelings of loyalty undo him.

8. Washizu is motivated largely by his wife. Washizu succeeds as long as Asaji is pushing him to act and directing his actions, but when she crumbles under the stress of guilt, he is without guidance. He looks to the forest spirit for guidance but is killed by his own men. He is a lesser leader than Macbeth.

BIG IDEA Connect (20 points)

9. Answers will vary. Possible answer: In the play, Macbeth and Lady Macbeth want to rule the kingdom for selfish reasons. Duncan is a good king and has honored, not harmed, them. They have no child to be their heir, so they don't act to secure the kingdom for their line. They just want the power. In the movie, on the other hand, other forces seem to be at work. Asaji seems to be in league with the forest spirit in propelling Washizu to power, and inheritance is part of the plan, too. Their ambitions seem more vast, more a part of some greater plan. This difference takes the stress off human action and reaction and the human-made catastrophe in the play. It adds a more mystical tone: perhaps Washizu and Asaji are not entirely masters of their own fates.

A Midsummer Night's Spectacle

Selection Test (page 65)

Recall and Interpret

(60 points total; 10 points each)

1. c
2. b
3. b
4. c
5. d
6. a

Analyze and Evaluate (21 points)

7. Answers will vary. Possible answers:

Facts

- outdoor performances of Shakespeare draw large crowds
- people drive for miles to see outdoor plays
- most Shakespeare festivals are thriving
- many people prefer to see the plays outdoors than indoors
- not all Shakespeare plays are equally popular
- sound systems are hard to handle outdoors

Opinions

- Americans can't get enough of Shakespeare
- people feel good about themselves when they see the plays
- plays are more honest and less phony when performed outdoors
- watching Shakespeare outdoors makes people New Yorkers

BIG IDEA Connect (19 points)

8. Answers will vary. Possible answer: When people sit outside, on the grass or in chairs, to watch a Shakespeare play, they are seeing the play very much as Shakespeare's original audiences saw it: without air conditioning, open to the weather, at risk of all kinds of interruptions and sound problems. The same themes, scenes, heroes, and villains that thrilled people when Shakespeare himself was onstage are seen by and speak to audiences today in the outdoor setting.

Answers

from *the King James Bible*

Selection Test (page 67)

Recall and Interpret

(40 points total; 10 points each)

1. a
2. c
3. d
4. d

Vocabulary Practice

(20 points total; 5 points each)

5. c
6. a
7. b
8. b

Analyze and Evaluate

(18 points total; 6 points each)

Answers will vary. Some possible answers:

9. Word choice: The excerpt relies on simple words that are mostly monosyllables, easy to read and understand.

10. Repetition: The repetition of nouns from sentence to sentence gives a sonorous, song-like quality to the prose. Repetition of "And" at the beginning and in the middle of sentences creates flow and continuity.

11. Arrangement of sentences: The syntax of the sentences is almost always very simple; there is little punctuation, and almost all sentences lack modifiers or complexity. They are structured in the "Subject-verb-object" style, with preponderant use of the verb "to be."

BIG IDEA Connect (22 points)

12. Answers will vary. Possible answers:

- God is the creator of heaven, earth, and all living beings.
- All of God's creations are good.
- People have authority over everything on earth.
- People were created in God's image.
- People lost their innocence through an act of disobedience.
- The loss of innocence was a tragedy.

Eve's Apology

Open-Book Selection Test (page 69)

Recall and Interpret

(40 points total; 10 points each)

1. c
2. c
3. b
4. a

Vocabulary Practice

(20 points total; 10 points each)

5. b
6. c

Analyze and Evaluate (20 points)

7. Answers will vary. Possible answers:

- The main strength of the argument is that it is logical. The speaker points out that it is foolish to blame Eve more when Adam was the one who was supposed to be far stronger than Eve. Adam had been granted dominion over all living things on earth and he was not tricked or fooled like Eve was.
- The main weakness of the argument is that it is emotional. The claim that Eve was motivated by good intentions doesn't make sense in light of the extreme degree of the sinfulness of her actions. There is no logical reason to believe that Eve was motivated by love and loyalty to Adam, and the speaker doesn't provide any evidence that this was indeed the case.

BIG IDEA Connect (20 points)

8. Answers will vary. Model answer:

Contrary to popular belief, Adam was more responsible than Eve for humanity's downfall. He, after all, was "lord and king of all the earth" (line 7). Adam was stronger than she, and she lacked the strength to stop him from something he wanted to do (line 24). Further, he did not rebuke her for eating the apple (line 29).

Answers

Song, A Valediction Forbidding Mourning, and Death Be Not Proud by John Donne

Open-Book Selection Test (page 71)

Recall and Interpret

(63 points total; 7 points each)

1. a
2. b
3. c
4. d
5. c
6. a
7. a
8. b
9. b

Analyze and Evaluate (15 points)

Answers will vary. One possible answer:

10. The very first line of the poem includes non-iambic feet in the meter: "Death, be not proud…". The effect creates a pause (caesura) after the first word of the poem, which gives the address more resonant gravity and also gives anthropomorphic Death a certain magisterial quality. This sets Death up for its "fall" as the poem progresses—Donne calls it "poor," a "slave to fate, chance, kings, and desperate men" (the non-iambic meter here, along with the hard consonants in the series, create slowness and emphasis).

BIG IDEA Connect (22 points)

11. Qualities will vary. Possible answers:

- Confidence; independence: The speaker urges his or her beloved not to be upset about the journey.
- Emotional restraint; pride: The speaker wants any conflict over their parting to be a personal matter. The speaker does not want the lovers' feelings obvious to others.
- Passion; intensity; capability of loving on a "higher plane": The speaker wants the lovers' souls to be so connected that their bodies need not even be near each other.
- Faithfulness; dependability; devotion: The speaker wants total devotion above all else.

Meditation 17

Open-Book Selection Test (page 73)

Recall and Interpret

(45 points total; 9 points each)

1. a
2. d
3. b
4. d
5. b

Vocabulary Practice

(12 points total; 4 points each)

6. b
7. a
8. c

Analyze and Evaluate

(24 points total; 4 points each)

Wording will vary. Possible answers:

9. God
10. mankind; humanity
11. individual; person; human; man or woman
12. death; soul
13. heaven; afterlife; next life; eternal life
14. possible ideas:
    - all people bound together
    - people are works of God
    - interests of the individual are interests of all
    - eternal life after death
    - death is will of God; therefore it is good
    - death unites people

BIG IDEA Connect (19 points)

15. Answers will vary. Possible answer: Donne is not entirely lucid at the beginning of the meditation. He hears the bell tolling and assumes it means someone has died. He expresses brief concern that the bell may signify his own death—that those near him have asked that it be rung without his knowing. He is clearly infirm, maybe bedridden, probably old—in a position to be ruminative. His expansive, humanist thinking and the conceit he presents, in which each man is a small part of a large whole, to which his life contributes and his death takes away from, indicates that he is tenderly, empathically, touching on his mortality—he seems almost to be looking down with God at man, as if he himself had already ascended somewhere. As he proceeds to the end of the poem, he remarks that the suffering and deaths of others are not only our own (in some sense), but they are prompts to us to contemplate our relationship to God, death, and humankind—through contemplation/ meditation, we, like the speaker, may "secure ourselves" and achieve peace before death. The pallid, febrile mood at the meditation's beginning changes, over its course, to a kind of righteous, magisterial glow at its end.

On My First Son

Open-Book Selection Test (page 75)

Recall and Interpret

(60 points total; 12 points each

1. c
2. a
3. b
4. d
5. d

Analyze and Evaluate (20 points)

Answers will vary. A possible answer:

6. The drama and extremism of this claim reflect the genre; an elegy strives to be poignant, to the speaker and the hearer/listener. In other words, Jonson, as a professional poet, can't help but employ (even exploit) his rhetorical skill to incite emotion in readers. On a personal level, the raw emotionalism of giving up on being a father may indicate how fresh the wound is to Jonson. The line itself suggests that the speaker/poet has no other (living) children, and that the loss of this only child is so great, even the chance that this could happen again is reason enough to 'give up.' All in all, this claim is not realistic. Time will pass, and it is likely that the speaker and his wife will have another child. The speaker here is still invested in life (he calls his son his "best piece of poetry," so concerns about fame are still apparently on his mind), which suggests that he will continue to strive to leave a legacy of work and blood.

BIG IDEA Connect (20 points)

7. Jonson's pride and arrogance are evident throughout the poem; it strives to be as much about him as it is about the dead child. He demonstrates possessiveness ("child of my right hand"), claims (presents a thesis) that perhaps his son's death is the result of his own sin ("too much hope of thee"), and notes the effect of his son's death on him personally ("could I lose all father now!"). Further, he remarks the possibility that he ("man" in general) might envy his son for having escaped the vagaries of life and aging—this remark, too, is more about the aging Jonson than it is about the boy. Most notably, Jonson calls his son his own "best piece of poetry," as if he had solely created the boy as he would a work of art.

Song: To Celia

Open-Book Selection Test (page 77)

Recall and Interpret

(60 points total; 15 points each)

1. b
2. b
3. a
4. c

Analyze and Evaluate (15 points)

Answers will vary. A model answer:

5. The title indicates that the poem is a "song," and many lyric poems were originally sung. The lilting, song-like quality is achieved by the use of short lines, an alternating rhyme scheme (in two octets), and the fancifulness and charm of lighthearted content paired with hyperbole—e.g., the speaker wants Celia to leave a kiss in a cup (cute), and he claims such a "drink" is superior to Jove's nectar (exaggeration). The wreath he sends to Celia is "rosy" (cute), and he claims to have hoped it would not wither next to her beauty (exaggeration). Even Celia's slight of the poet (sending the wreath back) occasions the light and charming conclusion that the wreath, which he would of course keep, now smells not like flowers but like the beloved herself (also an exaggeration). His use of the phrase "I swear" emphasizes the romantic willfulness that inspires this aromatic illusion.

BIG IDEA Connect (20 points)

6. Answers will vary. Possible answers:
- The wreath is energized, vitalized, or made to grow by Celia.
- Celia makes it impossible for the wreath to wither and die.
- Celia makes the wreath give off her own scent.
- Celia's effect on the wreath suggests that she is divine and that she has a powerful spiritual effect on the speaker.

To the Virgins, to Make Much of Time, Carpe Diem, To Hélène, and from *the Rubáiyát*

Open-Book Selection Test (page 79)

Recall and Interpret

(60 points total; 6 points each)

1. d
2. b
3. a
4. b
5. b
6. b
7. d
8. a
9. b
10. c

Analyze and Evaluate

(20 points total; 5 points each)

Answers will vary. A sample answer is given for each selection.

11. Lines 11-12: "the worse, and worst / Times still succeed the former," because it conveys the idea that the present, even if unpleasant, is accessible; the past is not. This is why we must seize the day no matter how good or bad it is relative to past days—it is the only day we have in our grasp.

12. Line 9: "Whilst we are talking, envious time doth slide," because of the personification of time as something that can envy the living and perhaps cheat them. No amount of time ever seems to be enough.

13. Line 13: "today won't come again," because it reminds readers that nothing stays the same and so everything must be enjoyed now.

14. Quatrain 38, line 3: "Unborn tomorrow and dead yesterday," because by personifying the days as things with short lives, the speaker stresses the shortness of human life, too.

BIG IDEA Connect (20 points)

15. Answers will vary widely. A possible answer:

These poems do seem to focus on the secular. Each one celebrates the enjoyable things of life—love, food, drink, and so on—ignoring the spiritual need. In fact, "Carpe Diem" and the quatrains actively encourage readers to turn away from their spiritual needs and questions such as "What will my life be worth in the end?" These poems do speak to the spiritual in humankind, but it is the human spirit—the passions—they seek to incite, not the holy spirit.

Answers

The Constant Lover and Why So Pale and Wan, Fond Lover?

Open-Book Selection Test (page 81)

Recall and Interpret

(56 points total; 8 points each)

1. d
2. c
3. c
4. a
5. b
6. d
7. b

Analyze and Evaluate

(20 points total; 10 points each)

Answers will vary. Possible answers:

8. "The Constant Lover": A shift in the rhyme scheme occurs in the third stanza. Here, Suckling introduces a major qualification to (shift in) his affection by starting with the conjunction "But…," and employs an *abab* rhyme scheme instead of the abcb scheme used in the previous and final stanzas. This speeds up the pace for him to deliver the punch line in the last two lines of the poem. The speed is maintained, and emphasis gained, by the repetition of a whole line (lines 12 and 13 are identical save the end punctuation), and this repetition links up the third and fourth stanzas.

9. "Why So Pale and Wan, Fond Lover?": The shift here occurs in the third stanza; stanzas 1 and 2 are comprised of rhetorical questions, questions with which the poet pelts/jabs the ailing lover. The last stanza is prescriptive rather than inquisitive; the poet admonishes the ailing lover to "Quit, quit…," and, in the last exclamatory line, curses the damsel over whom he's suffering if she does not, on her own, return the lover's love.

BIG IDEA Connect (24 points)

10. Answers will vary. Possible answers:

In "The Constant Lover," Suckling pokes fun at

- womanizers. (The speaker, who is a womanizer, is the chief object of Suckling's wit.)
- all shallow and short-lived romantic attachments. (The depth of the speaker's supposed feelings for the beloved are absurd in that they are based solely on her face.)

In "Why so Pale and Wan, Fond Lover?" Suckling pokes fun at

- the lovesick. (The subject of the poem, who is sick with unrequited love, is the chief object of Suckling's wit.)
- romantic love. (In the poem, romantic love makes a fool of the lover.)
- the idea of unrequited devotion. (In the poem, the speaker demands that the lovesick lover give up the woman immediately without regret.)

To Lucasta, Going to the Wars and To Althea, from Prison

Open-Book Selection Test (page 83)

Recall and Interpret

(52 points total; 13 points each)

1. c
2. d
3. b
4. b

Analyze and Evaluate (24 points)

5. Answers will vary. Possible answers:

- Because the speaker is honorable he must do the right thing and go to war even though it means leaving Lucasta, which seems on the surface to be dishonorable.
- It is honor that makes the speaker's love for Lucasta possible. If he were to choose to stay by her side instead of going to war, it would mean that he wouldn't love her because such a choice would be dishonorable and love without honor is impossible.
- Remaining with Lucasta would suggest a more shallow love than leaving her does.

Answers

BIG IDEA Connect (24 points)

Answers will vary. A model answer:

6. In the first stanza, the speaker associates liberty with love, intimacy, and romance. Basically, liberty is achieved by being with Althea. In the second stanza, liberty involves the freedom to drink and make toasts, revel and be carefree, have fun, and be in love. The third stanza associates liberty with freedom of speech, voicing one's opinions, and friendship. The final stanza connects liberty with innocence and love, spirituality, morality, goodness, and angels.

To His Coy Mistress

Open-Book Selection Test (page 85)

Recall and Interpret

(50 points total; 10 points each)

1. a
2. d
3. c
4. b
5. d

Vocabulary Practice

(10 points total; 5 points each)

6. b
7. c

Analyze and Evaluate (20 points)

8. Notes will vary. Some of many possible answers:

Lines 7 and 8:

- the speaker loves the mistress deeply
- sense of being outside of time or unaffected by it
- leisure
- self-indulgence
- romance

Lines 9 and 10:

- the mistress is incredibly stubborn
- the task ahead of the speaker is enormous
- sense of being outside of time or unaffected by it

Lines 11 and 12:

- slow growth
- the speaker loves the mistress deeply
- the speaker has a tremendous capacity for love
- sense of being outside of time or unaffected by it

Lines 15 and 16:

- the speaker finds the mistress extremely attractive
- the mistress is quite beautiful
- sense of being outside time or unaffected by it
- youthfulness

Lines 23 and 24:

- death and devastation
- isolation
- inability to escape fate
- eternity weighing down on the lovers
- sense of danger or impending doom
- necessity of seizing the moment

Lines 35 and 36:

- passion
- the mistress is greatly attracted to the speaker
- the mistress wants to give in to the speaker
- youthfulness

BIG IDEA Connect (20 points)

9. Answers will vary. Possible answers:

The lovers will make the sun "run" by moving forward themselves, by "seizing the day." Instead of standing by and watching the sun pass them by, they will force him to try to keep up with them. In a literal sense, this means that the lovers will stop wasting time, make the most of the time they have, or give in to their passion.

Answers

How Soon Hath Time and When I Consider How My Light Is Spent

Open-Book Selection Test (page 87)

Recall and Interpret

(60 points total; 12 points each)

1. a
2. c
3. c
4. d
5. b

Analyze and Evaluate (15 points)

Answers may vary. A model answer:

6. Time is personified in line 1 and called a "subtle thief." In line 2, Time appears to have a wing (i.e., to be personified as a bird). In line 3, the speaker's days appear to be personified as a bird; they "fly on". In line 4, a case of inverse personification appears; the speaker's productivity or growth is referred to as "bud" or "blossom."

BIG IDEA Connect (25 points)

7. Answers will vary. Students could say that the allusion helps to communicate that the speaker

- identifies with the servant who did wrong.
- views God as his master.
- views himself as God's servant.
- views his talent as a gift from God.
- fears he is doing wrong in God's eyes.
- suspects that he is misusing his talent or isn't fulfilling his potential.
- looks to Christianity to guide his everyday life.
- feels a responsibility to use his talent wisely and for the good of God.

from *Paradise Lost*

Open-Book Selection Test (page 89)

Recall and Interpret

(40 points total; 8 points each)

1. a
2. d
3. b
4. d
5. b

Vocabulary Practice

(20 points total; 4 points each)

6. a
7. b
8. a
9. a
10. b

Analyze and Evaluate

(20 points total; 5 points each)

The allusion's meaning is set; answers to what the allusion's adds to the poem will vary. Model answers:

11. Sinai / the mountain on which Moses received the Ten Commandments / allusion places the poem in the Judeo-Christian traditions and borrows authority from the book of Genesis

12. Sion hill / the hill in Jerusalem where the ancient Jewish temple was built / allusion traces history of Judaism and shows that author knows this sacred history

13. Siloa's brook / another reference to Jerusalem, the holy city / ties the poem to other works inspired by God

14. Aonian mount / the home of the Muses / this allusion places the poem in the western tradition, appealing to the ancient Greek muses

BIG IDEA Connect (20 points)

15. Answers will vary. Students could say that Satan prefers Hell to Heaven because

- to be in Heaven, one must serve God. Satan would rather burn in Hell than serve God (lines 261–263).
- in Heaven, only God is glorified and served. Hell is the only place where Satan can be glorified and served (line 39).
- if Satan didn't, he'd have to admit that he had done something wrong. He is too stubborn, willful, and proud to admit such a thing (lines 56–58; 106–116).
- God is in Heaven, and Satan hates God (line 58; 165–169).
- to be in Heaven, one must be good. Satan prefers to be evil (159 and 160).
- he equates Hell with freedom, Heaven with prison (258–260).

from *The Pilgrim's Progress*

Selection Test (page 91)

Recall and Interpret

(48 points total; 6 points each)

1. a
2. d
3. c
4. d
5. b
6. d
7. c
8. d

Vocabulary Practice

(12 points total; 4 points each)

9. a
10. a
11. c

Analyze and Evaluate

(20 points total; 10 points each)

12. Answers will vary. Possible answer:

The fair was founded thousands of years ago by three devils. These origins signify that the fair or what it represents, vanity, is a well-established part of human life. It also shows that vanity is sinful and poses a dangerous temptation to Christians. The town of Vanity is located on the way to the Celestial City. The only way to get to the Celestial City without going through the town is to die. This signifies that Christians must confront temptation and battle it. It shows that as long as there is life, there is temptation—the path to righteousness is treacherous.

BIG IDEA Connect (20 points)

13. Answers will vary. Possible answers:

- vanity is sinful: Vanity Fair, which symbolizes vanity, was created by three devils
- patience is a virtue: Faithful and Christian, who symbolize virtues, show great patience toward their persecutors
- goodness is rewarded: Faithful is taken into the Celestial City (Heaven)
- world is evil, filled with temptation: all worldly goods and concerns are shown as vain and sinful
- Being a good Christian can be difficult: Faithful and Christian (ideal Christians) are led into temptation, tormented, and tortured

On Her Loving Two Equally

Open-Book Selection Test (page 93)

Recall and Interpret

(45 points total; 9 points each)

1. c
2. d
3. c
4. d
5. a

Vocabulary Practice

(15 points total; 5 points each)

6. b
7. a
8. b

Analyze and Evaluate (20 points)

9. Answers will vary. For any example, "to maintain rhyme scheme" and "to add interest" are reasonable answers. Other possible answers:

- "powerful prove": to maintain meter
- "present is": to maintain meter
- "I for Damon sigh and mourn": to

emphasize sigh and mourn, which name the speaker's feelings, over Damon, which names the person she responds to.

- "when Alexis I do miss": to maintain meter; to emphasize miss (as opposed to Alexis)
- "One golden-pointed dart take back": to emphasize one and take back

BIG IDEA Connect (20 points)

10. Answers will vary. Possible answers:

- The poet is making fun of people who deliberately turn their lives into soap operas; young people who lack experience in love; people who play the field; or people who really don't understand what love is. The poem presents the speaker's situation as if it were a great tragedy. It isn't. She is simply infatuated with two men and can't make up her mind because she is afraid of what she will lose in doing so. If the speaker were truly in love with either man, she wouldn't be in this situation. Throughout the poem, the speaker emphasizes herself—her feelings, her reactions, her problems, her needs—and shows no concern whatsoever for either of the men for whom she supposedly cares so deeply. Romance is clearly a game to her; she didn't love either man until their attentions to her became a contest.
- The speaker is poking fun at romance, sentimentality, and/or works of literature that are romantic or sentimental. The speaker turns a small matter into a great tragedy. Her feelings for the two men will more than likely pass, despite her protestations of true love.

An Essay on Dramatic Poesy

Selection Test (page 95)

Recall and Interpret

(36 points total; 12 points each)

1. d
2. a
3. b

Vocabulary Practice

(10 points total; 2 points each)

4. c
5. e
6. b
7. a
8. d

Analyze and Evaluate (22 points)

9. The essay is set up as a dialogue among four friends, in which the context is much more informal than that of an authorial voice talking at the reader. Dryden uses a light conversational style, addressing the other friends (and the reader) in the first paragraph ("when [Shakespeare] describes anything, you more than see it, you feel it, too") and including first-person references ("I am apt to believe…"). The ease with which he traverses among subjects and ideas contributes to the engaging and entertaining aspect of the language.

BIG IDEA Connect (32 points)

10. Answers will vary. Possible answers:

- Admiration involves the intellect; love, the heart. Dryden found that Shakespeare's work affected his emotions much more strongly, and people tend to love books, plays, movies, and songs that touch the emotions.
- Shakespeare's subject matter often dealt with love; Jonson's did not. Perhaps it was easier for Dryden to respond with strong emotion to a writer who explored strong emotion in his work.
- Dryden finds Shakespeare's wit

(cleverness) superior to Jonson's and calls Shakespeare the "father of our dramatic poets."

from **The Diary of Samuel Pepys**

Selection Test (page 97)

Recall and Interpret

(40 points total; 8 points each)

1. b
2. a
3. c
4. b
5. d

Vocabulary Practice

(20 points total; 5 points each)

6. a
7. b
8. a
9. b

Analyze and Evaluate

(18 points total; 6 points each)

10–12. Answers will vary. Most details from the selection reveal Pepys's personality, character, or values in that he chose them for inclusion. Possible answers include the following:

- naturally calm: keeps his cool throughout the fire, even when his home is endangered
- values art and beauty: admires the clothing, ornaments, and music of the coronation ceremony
- favors rule by a monarchy: shows great admiration for the coronation celebration, is clearly pleased by the ceremony
- curious: keeps returning to observe the fire
- responsible: reports to the king about the fire and follows his orders to deliver a message to the mayor
- sympathetic: worries about those in danger, provides shelter for a friend, even pities the pigeons
- practical: makes a good suggestion to the king, organizes his household to protect his goods

BIG IDEA Connect (22 points)

13. Answers will vary. Sample answer:

Pepys's effort to stop the fire begins when he takes his boat and goes to Whitehall—"I to Whitehall…to Whitehall…." This repetition sounds like a muted rallying cry; this makes venturing there seem, to the reader, inspired and galvanizing. Whitehall is crowded, and Pepys gives everyone around him an account of the fire. Soon thereafter, he is called in for an audience with the King and the Duke of York, whom he has the temerity to advise. Interestingly, Pepys describes this daring—advising the King, whom he has been so remote from and invisible to during the crowning ceremony!—as a temperate and practical measure: "unless his Majesty did command houses to be pulled down, nothing could stop the fire." Pepys relays that, subsequently, the King and Duke seemed troubled, and the King commands Pepys to see the Mayor and tell him to do as Pepys has advised. That is all Pepys makes of his own role—he presents himself more as the bearer of instructions than the generator of them; here his modesty nearly eclipses his boldness and his confidence. In the preceding and successive portions of this section, he is concerned about the maid, whom his wife had recently fired, and whether she and her husband have lost their house, and concerned about others whom he mentions, one of whom he takes in. He appears to be a practical man with a humanist nature. For a diarist, he is remarkably unegocentric.

Answers

A Modest Proposal

Selection Test (page 99)

Recall and Interpret

(45 points total; 9 points each)

1. b
2. d
3. b
4. c
5. b

Vocabulary Practice

(15 points total; 5 points each)

6. c
7. a
8. b

Analyze and Evaluate (20 points)

Answers will vary. Possible answers:

9. • greed; narrator shows utter disregard for human values in search of solution to economic problems
   • cruelty; narrator shows staggering cruelty in suggesting plan to slaughter babies
   • indifference; narrator shows exaggerated degree of indifference to the poor by being interested in their problems only as they affect or pertain to the rich
   • ignorance; narrator knows nothing of human heart and soul.

BIG IDEA Connect (20 points)

10. Answers will vary. Possible answer:

The speaker's main point is that the poor children of Ireland should be put to practical use and that an ideal way to do this is to feed them to the rich. Swift's main point is that the English exploitation of Ireland is deplorable and inhumane—so much so that the Irish would not be much worse off if they were slaughtered than they are under English domination. Swift communicates his views through satire, sarcasm, understatement, hyperbole, irony, and tone. He deliberately shocks the reader into recognizing what he sees as a serious problem. Although only a lunatic would take the speaker's ideas seriously, Swift suggests that those ideas are not very far removed from the current reality.

from *Gulliver's Travels*

Selection Test (page 101)

Recall and Interpret

(50 points total; 5 points each)

1. d
2. a
3. d
4. c
5. a

Vocabulary Practice

(10 points total; 5 points each)

6. a
7. b

Analyze and Evaluate

(20 points total; 10 points each)

8. Swift parodies travel books and articles from the eighteenth-century, which "delighted" in describing exotic places and people. Swift mocks not only the self-satisfied air of such journeys, but emphasizes the suspicion and hostility with which most natives, even those imagined, greet foreign visitors/travelers. Swift writes "I felt above a hundred arrows discharged on my left hand . . . and besides, they shot another flight into the air, as we do bombs in Europe."

9. Swift parodies the legalistic style of governmental edicts by enumerating the nine articles that the "mighty Emperor of Lilliput," who is described in exhaustive hyperbolic terms ("whose dominions extend five thousand blustrugs . . . monarch of all monarchs . . . "), issues aloud and in detail to Gulliver. These edicts are meant to contain and control him, despite his size and the obvious fact that he must choose to abide by them; that is, the governmental edicts themselves are not effective unless Gulliver chooses to honor them.

BIG IDEA Connect (20 points)
Answers will vary. Possible answer:
10. Gulliver is a model, or representative, Englishman who has studied hard and achieved some status. He thinks well of his powers of reasoning. Yet in Brobdingnag, during his conversations with the king, he refuses to acknowledge the king's criticisms of the British. He does not learn to see himself and his people more objectively; instead, he illogically rejects the evidence and turns the blame for the difference of understanding back on the king, whose thinking is far more rational.

Epigrams and from *An Essay on Man*

Open-Book Selection Test (page 103)

Recall and Interpret

(45 points total; 9 points each)

1. d
2. c
3. a
4. c
5. b

Vocabulary Practice

(15 points total; 5 points each)

6. c
7. a
8. b

Analyze and Evaluate

(21 points total; 7 points each)
Paraphrases will vary. Possible answers:
9. Education has a great deal of influence on people.
10. Hope is an essential part of human nature.
11. The honest man is more noble than anyone else, including those with superior intellect and power.

BIG IDEA Connect (19 points)
12. Answers will vary. Possible answers:
- The speaker has an attitude of fascination and curiosity because humans are full of contradictions and there is much to discover about them.
- The speaker is respectful of humans because they are creatures of God and possess many attributes of greatness.

from *The Rape of the Lock*

Open-Book Selection Test (page 105)

Recall and Interpret

(50 points total; 10 points each)

1. d
2. c
3. a
4. b
5. a

Vocabulary Practice

(10 points total; 5 points each)

6. b
7. c

Analyze and Evaluate (20 points)

8. Answers will vary. A possible answer: Pope gently makes fun of two social customs: coffee and fashion. In the first example, he describes the wealthy young men and women having coffee as if they were in a temple in a faraway land, before an altar, taking part in a special ceremony. The elaborate description shows how the young people have lost their sense of what matters and what is trivial. Throughout the excerpt, Pope pokes fun at the young people's obsession with fashion. What could be a worse catastrophe than for Belinda to spill coffee on her "rich brocade"? Belinda's reaction to the loss of a lock of hair is also exaggerated: Pope compares it to the death of a woman's husband or her lapdog (that these are presented as equally tragic is also satiric), and the Baron compares his obtaining the hair to a great victory, even remarking that dying for her hair would not deject him—leaving her behind is worse. Pope is reminding readers to consider what really matters, and what is truly trivial.

BIG IDEA Connect (20 points)

9. Answers will vary. Possible answers:
- Image: the young people tussling together despite their voluminous clothing / Effect: the image brings the scene to life with sounds: fans smacking people, dresses rustling, hoops breaking—it is a touch of very physical comedy, and the young people seem to enjoy the melee
- Image: Belinda throwing snuff at the Baron to make him sneeze / Effect: the image of the proud, stylish Baron with his "high dome" and his watery eyes squeezed shut as he sneezes adds humor and brings him down from heroic status
- Image: Belinda drawing a flimsy hairpin to attack the Baron / Effect: the image reinforces the idea that Belinda, though pretty, is petulant and vain, and reinforces the silliness of this drama

Letter to Her Daughter

Selection test (page 107)

Recall and Interpret

(36 points total; 6 points each)

1. a
2. b
3. c
4. b
5. c
6. b

Vocabulary Practice

(24 points total; 6 points each)

7. c
8. a
9. c
10. b

Analyze and Evaluate

(21 points; 7 points each)

Answers will vary. Possible answers:

11. builders and parents (or mothers); buildings and daughters (or children)

12. Likenesses:

Builders and parents
- create and follow plans
- value beauty
- make mistakes
- make inappropriate plans
- place beauty above practicality

Buildings and daughters
- can be built "inappropriately"
- can be ruined by their builders
- are the results of the plans of others

13. Daughters (children) should be raised to fit their station in life.

BIG IDEA Connect (19 points)

14. Answers will vary. Students might find Montagu
- practical or sensible; she advises her daughter to raise her daughter in a way that will help her deal with her station in life.
- bossy; she gives much seemingly unasked for advice.
- opinionated; she has many strong opinions and declares them as fact.
- confident; she has strong opinions, gives advice freely, and clearly finds herself more intelligent than most people.
- intelligent; her letter is well-written, persuasive, and entertaining.
- self-assured; she clearly thinks that her opinions are worth sharing, that she has a clearer view of how things are and should be than others do, and that she has done things right in her life.

Answers

from *The Spectator*

Selection Test (page 109)

Recall and Interpret

(42 points; 6 points each)

1. d
2. c
3. b
4. c
5. a
6. b
7. d

Vocabulary Practice

(12 points; 4 points each)

8. b
9. b
10. a

Analyze and Evaluate

(24 points; 12 points each)

Answers will vary. Model answers:

11. Sir Richard Steele, "Sir Roger de Coverley": Steele's liveliness and enjoyment in "performing" (hearing himself talk or write) are evident in his style. His voice is much more flamboyant than that of Addison, and his habits of diction and syntax more personalized. For example, he delights in elegantly phrased understatement: "his singularities are . . . contradictions to the manners of the world only as he thinks the world is wrong." His style is meant to titillate and excite (this gives the subject matter the "spin" of gossip), and is based more on evasive, sly delivery than on actual content. This approach is evident in how he describes Sir Roger's failed romance: "It is said he keeps himself a bachelor by reason he was crossed in love by a perverse, beautiful widow of the next county to him." Steele puts entertainment above edification. Ironically, his poking fun directly at someone seems better intended and less condescending than Addison's mockery of country manners. (Steele seems to "identify" with Sir Roger, to some degree.)

12. Richard Addison, "Country Manners": Addison's serious, reserved, and sensible temperament do temper his prose. His syntax is more forthright and more direct, than Steele's: "The first and most obvious reflections which arise in a man. . .are upon the different manners. . . ." He even troubles himself to clarify: "By manners, I do not mean morals, but behavior and good breeding. . . ." Addison is more edifying than entertaining. He himself is not funny—his delivery is not comic—though he does entertain with anecdotes about the ridiculous lengths Sir Roger will go to in order to observe rank while arranging seating and making toasts, and the ridiculously obeisant gestures Will Wimble musters ("when we are going out of the hall, he runs behind me . . ."). Ironically, Addison's generalized examination of country manners makes him seem much more condescending and snobby than Steele's specific examination of Sir Roger makes Steele seem.

BIG IDEA Connect (22 points)

13. Answers will vary. Possible answers:

- The essays are entertaining. Sir Roger is an interesting character, and the narrator's account of the frustrations of dealing with country manners is amusing.
- The style makes the essays easy to read. Much eighteenth-century work is much more difficult to read, while these essays are straightforward and accessible.
- The authors are witty and opinionated. Blandness and neutrality do not often make for very interesting writing. Luckily, both of these pieces are filled with opinions and judgments.
- The essays suggest appropriate ways to behave. Since the authors are clearly quite respectable, people could feel comfortable about following their advice.

Answers

from *A Journal of the Plague Year,* from *The Demon in the Freezer,* from *History of the Peloponnesian War,* and from *The Plague*

Selection Test (page 111)

Recall and Interpret

(35 points total; 5 points each)

1. b
2. b
3. c
4. c
5. c
6. b
7. a

Vocabulary Practice

(15 points total; 5 points each)

8. a
9. b
10. b

Analyze and Evaluate

(20 points total; 5 points each)

Answers will vary. Model answers:

11. All three are appalled by the suffering they are describing and feel pity for those who suffered during the plague. All three try to describe the collective reaction to the plague.

12. Defoe was re-imagining events that felt not remarkably distant from him; the plague in London occurred when he was a child. It was part of the culture in which he grew up. His narrator is divided between recording events and recording the individual (his own) reaction to them—he is part of the story, and he provides the reader a lens through which to see it. He is equal parts audience and actor. He has an irrepressible, very real, almost indulgent and childlike sense of curiosity about how the city will deal with plague, and cannot help but edge up on the stage to get close to the action. He is given to description and tacitly assigning "roles" (such as the mourner, the buriers, the watcher).

13. This writer is concerned with the effect of the plague on morality. He reports not only on the disease of the body but on the disease of the soul—on people who give up, or refuse to give aid, or take advantage of the crippled city. He is more devoted to chronicling what is real than to personalizing it. He is a reporter, a chronicler, not an imaginative narrator culling his imagination for content. The facts and phenomena of the plague are his business.

14. Camus wholly imagined (fictionalized) his plague, which may explain why the writing itself and the psychological examination of the plague's impact are more the focus than the details of illness or facts. This narrator focuses on the psychological damage endured by the plague's survivors and those exiled by quarantine from ones they love. He is examining what happens to the human spirit, to hope, to love, not factually reporting or really participating in the plague. Camus chooses a doctor as his narrator—a man of science, a man given to observing and investigating—someone who strains to be objective, slightly remote, and philosophical.

BIG IDEA Connect (20 points)

Answers will vary. A model answer:

15. Yugoslav "medical authorities" had been vaccinating the Yugoslavian population "relentlessly" for more than thirty years when the Pilgrim unwittingly brought the disease back to the country. This thorough vaccination program and the decades without any incidents left the country ignorant of the possibility that smallpox might reappear. This probably explains why Ljatif M. was misdiagnosed as a case of allergic reaction to penicillin. Once the "waves" of the epidemic started, the governmental/cultural structure of Yugoslavia contributed to containing it. As the article explains, the "authoritarian Communist government," under the rule of Josip Broz Tito, "mobilized the Army" and "imposed strong measures to stop people from traveling and spreading the virus." Villages were closed, roadblocks were put up, people quarantined, and so on. Without a tractable population, a population agreeable to being told what to do, these measures would probably not have worked. As the article notes, the epidemic was ended by a "military crackdown" . . . and "vaccination for every citizen"—no small feat.

Death by Mosquito

Selection Test (page 113)

Recall and Interpret

(60 points total; 12 points each)

1. b
2. d
3. a
4. b
5. c

Analyze and Evaluate (20 points)

6. Causes include:
- substituting less effective pesticides for DDT
- drug-resistant malarial strains
- severely stricken nations are those that cannot afford antimalarial treatment
- the sense that malaria will never be wiped out discourages efforts

BIG IDEA Connect (20 points)

7. Countries in which many people suffer from malaria have smaller, weaker work forces. Not only people who are ill but the people caring for the ill are removed from the work force. The nation can't produce what it needs for use or sale at the same rate. Thus, the weakened economy forces the nation and citizens to cut back on expenses because they have less money. They are less likely to be able to afford antimalarial drugs, pesticides, and nets. At this point, one-third of many Africans' wages are spent on malarial treatments. This money is not being put back into circulation for goods or services that might improve the economy.

from *A Dictionary of the English Language* and Letter to Lord Chesterfield

Selection Test (page 115)

Recall and Interpret

(40 points total; 5 points each)

1. b
2. d
3. d
4. c
5. d
6. b
7. a
8. a

Vocabulary Practice

(20 points total; 4 points each)

9. b
10. d
11. c
12. e
13. a

Analyze and Evaluate

(20 points total; 10 points each)

Answers will vary. Possible answers:

14. Johnson's style:
- formal diction
- precise diction
- long sentences
- parallelism
- logical, straightforward argument
- understated tone of righteous indignation
- polite language
- use of sarcasm
- use of irony

15. Johnson's qualities:
- wit
- intelligence
- courage; willingness to take risks
- strong sense of right and wrong; moral indignation
- pride
- logic
- honesty
- sarcasm
- bitterness

Answers

BIG IDEA Connect (20 points)

16. Answers will vary. Model answer:

The definitions convey Johnson's beliefs that patrons are arrogant fools whose patronage must be purchased with flattery, the relationship between patron and writer is unequal, and the patronage system is fundamentally flawed. He seems to feel that patrons are willing to help only popular or established writers, who are least in need of their help. They are not interested in helping struggling writers and do not seem to be interested in art at all. They do not consider a writer's skill and only support writers whom they believe will add to their fame or reputation through association. Finally, patrons are worthless to established writers; the patronage they offer comes too late to be of use and results only in burdening the recipient.

from *The Life of Samuel Johnson*

Selection Test (page 117)

Recall and Interpret

(48 points total; 8 points each)

1. a
2. d
3. b
4. a
5. c
6. c

Vocabulary Practice

(15 points total; 3 points each)

7. a
8. b
9. c
10. b
11. a

Analyze and Evaluate

(20 points total; 5 points each)

Answers will vary. Possible answers:

12–13. Johnson is . . .; as revealed by . . .

- witty: quick, witty reply to Boswell's apology for being from Scotland
- opinionated: many opinions appear in this excerpt
- contradictory, complex: real opinions could seldom be figured out from his expressions and arguments
- messy, shabby, uncouth: was untidy in dress and appearance
- independent, unconventional: does not seem to care about what others might think
- loyal: threatens to do harm to one critical of the royal family
- good conversationalist: inspires Boswell to record his words verbatim
- pious, religious: was a devoted Christian
- prejudiced: scorned Scotland and its people
- self-assured: puts Boswell in his place when he questions his judgment of Garrick's treatment of him
- sarcastic: makes sarcastic comments about his friend Derrick
- narrow-minded: held narrow views on religion and politics
- proud: Boswell says he loved praise but was too proud to seek it
- conscientious: always wrote what he believed to be the truth

14–15. Boswell is . . . as revealed by . . .

- fair: notes Johnson's good and bad qualities
- insecure: is very nervous about meeting Johnson
- competent: organized all of his notes and observations into an interesting biography
- easygoing: Johnson's meanspirited jabs do not anger him
- determined: manages to become a friend of Johnson's despite a rocky first encounter

Answers

BIG IDEA Connect (17 points)

16. Answers will vary. Most students will choose "balanced," but any choice is acceptable if well-supported. A model answer for "balanced" follows:

Boswell's biography of Johnson is balanced for many reasons. Although Boswell clearly admires Johnson, he notes several of Johnson's flaws and, in fact, discusses his uncouth nature in great detail. Boswell makes no attempt to conceal his admiration for Johnson or his personal involvement in the man's life. He also allows Johnson to speak for himself without comment.

from *Samuel Johnson*

Selection Test (page 119)

Recall and Interpret

(60 points total; 12 points each)

1. a
2. c
3. d
4. d
5. d

Analyze and Evaluate

(18 points total; 6 points each)

Answers will vary. Possible answers:

6-7.
- unstable
- unsure of moral rectitude
- felt weakness of mind and character
- felt a lack of inner strength
- wanted to be calmer, braver, less impetuous, less "wayward"

8. Boswell tried to change his traits by observing older men that he admired and writing about them. He encouraged himself in his journals to be "like Father, grave . . . composed" or "like the Duke of Sully" and congratulated himself when he succeeded: "Fancied myself like Burke, and drank moderately."

BIG IDEA Connect (22 points)

9. It was a world limited to the important and intellectual men of London and to the places they frequented without women, taverns, and clubs. Boswell records many witty discussions and serious contemplations of current problems, so it was a world in touch with the city and its needs. The men he listened to were mostly conservative as well, so it was not a world that generated radical new ideas; rather, tradition was important. The Whigs and the Tories were the two main political parties. Boswell's father was a Whig; Boswell's sympathies, tellingly, lay with the Tories. He was said to have his own "romantic" Toryism.

Elegy Written in a Country Churchyard

Selection Test (page 121)

Recall and Interpret

(48 points total; 6 points each)

1. b
2. d
3. c
4. c
5. c
6. b
7. b
8. c

Vocabulary Practice

(15 points total; 3 points each)

9. e
10. a
11. c
12. d
13. b

Analyze and Evaluate (17 points)

14. Answers will vary. Students could say the epitaph suggests that Gray valued

- nature ("rests his head upon the lap of earth").
- generosity ("Large was his bounty").
- sincerity ("his soul sincere").
- simplicity and friendship ("He gained from Heaven ('twas all he wished) a friend").

- honesty, modesty, and straightforwardness ("No farther seek his merits to disclose, / Or draw his frailties from their dread abode").
- traditional Christian religious beliefs ("The bosom of his Father and his God").

BIG IDEA Connect (20 points)

15. Answers will vary. Model answer:
In the first stanza, the image of the plowman herding his flock at dusk is a stark and lonely one; he is "weary" and the cattle are "lowing" and moving "slowly." Not only does this image evoke isolation and loneliness, the last line reveals that the plowman's disappearance leaves the speaker entirely alone . . . except for darkness. The implication here is that the speaker has been unseen by the plowman (alone) and, in contrast to the plowman, who is going "homeward," is left out in the darkness—truly alone/isolated/abandoned by life and the comfort of living creatures. The vastness of the empty darkening meadow contributes to this sense that the speaker is alone with dusk/darkness and his own lonely thoughts. The first three lines of the stanza cleverly set the reader in a position of empathy with the speaker—watching with him, unselfconscious—then neatly separates the reader from the speaker, inducing the reader to see how alone the speaker is (he is without even the reader!) and to feel an impotent compassion for him.

John Anderson, My Jo; To a Mouse; and Auld Lang Syne

Open-Book Selection Test (page 123)

Recall and Interpret

(54 points total; 6 points each)

1. c
2. b
3. b
4. b
5. a
6. d
7. d
8. c
9. b

Vocabulary Practice

(10 points total; 5 points each)

10. b
11. a

Analyze and Evaluate

(18 points total; 9 points each)

Wording of answers may vary. Possible answers:

12. Like the efforts of animals that behave by instinct, the well-planned effort of humans can come to nothing. This leaves the planners with grief and pain instead of the joy they had looked forward to.

13. As children, the two of us ran together among the hills and picked flowers and were carefree. Since those easy, early days, we have both traveled widely, aged, and taken on the burden of adult cares.

BIG IDEA Connect (18 points)

14. Answers will vary. Possible answers:
Changing the dialect to Standard English might result in the loss of the following qualities:

- sound: the rhyme scheme and rhythm would be disrupted.
- message: ideas in the poem would no longer reflect the language of a Scots farmer-philosopher and might no longer seem fresh and new.
- tone: with the loss of the unique Scots dialect, the tone might seem preachy rather than subdued and sensible.

from *A Vindication of the Rights of Woman*

Selection Test (page 125)

Recall and Interpret

(40 points total; 8 points each)

1. b
2. b
3. c
4. b
5. a

Answers

Vocabulary Practice

(20 points total; 4 points each)

6. a
7. a
8. a
9. b
10. a

Analyze and Evaluate

(20 points total; 5 points each)

Answers will vary. Possible answers:

11. women's education

12. Women should be encouraged to learn and to grow to their full potential in all areas.

13–14. Possible evidence:

- a well-rounded woman is a more mature and capable wife and mother;
- a physically strong woman is better able to function in all areas;
- romantic love often goes away as people get older;
- respect lives on after romantic love dies;
- a woman who is dependent usually does not have respect for herself, nor is she respected by others.

BIG IDEA Connect (20 points)

15. Answers will vary. Possible answer:

Wollstonecraft voices concern that women are taught that their looks are all that they have to offer. They are taught to dress for male attention and to trade on their looks, otherwise acting helpless and in need of care. Unfortunately, age often diminishes their beauty and leaves them with nothing but bitterness. In some ways, things have changed today. Most girls and women in our society are encouraged to get an education, play sports, and excel in the business world. Also, marriage today is viewed as only one aspect of a woman's life. However, some things have not changed for the better since Wollstonecraft's day. Our society still places high value on women being attractive to the opposite sex, dressing well, staying fit, and looking young. Our society's obsession with good looks have led to sad consequences for many women, such as lowered self-esteem or problems with eating disorders.

Raising Their Voices

Selection Test (page 127)

Recall and Interpret

(60 points total; 12 points each)

1. d
2. c
3. d
4. c
5. d

Analyze and Evaluate

(20 points total; 5 points each)

6-9. Possible answers include

- difficulty of acquiring basic and specialized education
- difficulty getting loans without a male advocate
- men in business prefer to work with and speak to men
- people are not used to women working outside the home
- few role models to follow
- centuries of tradition are against it

BIG IDEA Connect (20 points)

10. The Romantics stressed the importance of the individual over that of the group or the state. Romantic poetry is marked by the word "I," as each poet expressed his particular feelings. Romantic impulses in the west added to the growing idea of individual freedom and opportunity for self-definition. This impulse is the same impulse that is on the rise among some men and women in Arab nations.

from *The Diary of Fanny Burney*

Selection Test (page 129)

Recall and Interpret

(48 points total; 6 points each)

1. c
2. b
3. d
4. a
5. d
6. a
7. c
8. d

Answers

Vocabulary Practice

(10 points total; 2 points each)

9. c
10. e
11. d
12. a
13. b

Analyze and Evaluate (21 points)

14. Answers will vary. Model answer:

Burney shows her wit in saying that the heroine of her novel is "a young lady whom I think I have some right to make free with." It's witty because it cleverly understates Burney's right, as the creator of Evelina and Evelina's "life," to do with Evelina as she pleases. These words convey the idea that Burney does not take herself or her novel too seriously, but is very proud of both and very excited and happy about what is happening to the book and herself.

BIG IDEA Connect (21 points)

15. Answers will vary. Possible textual examples may include:

- Burney states that she has not pretended "to show the world what it actually *is*, but what it *appears*. . . ."
- Burney describes her emotional responses to events and ideas in great detail ("I am so much in love with . . . ," "I grinned irresistibly. . . .").

A Poison Tree, The Lamb, and The Tyger

Open-Book Selection Test (page 131)

Recall and Interpret

(60 points total; 6 points each)

1. a
2. a
3. d
4. c
5. b
6. b
7. d
8. a
9. c
10. d

Analyze and Evaluate

(20 points total; 10 points each)

Answers will vary. Possible answers:

11. "A Poison Tree": ll. 1–2; "The Lamb": ll. 5–8, 15–18

12. "A Poison Tree": ll. 3–4; 5–8, 9–16; "The Tyger": ll. 3–4, 6–8, 9–10, 11–12, 14, 15–16, 17–20, 21–24

BIG IDEA Connect (20 points)

13. Answers will vary. Students could say that Blake views innocence as good and experience as evil, offering the following proof: To show that innocence is good, Blake says that the lamb is "meek and mild." It is described in terms of childlike wonder and innocence ("clothing of delight / softest clothing, wooly bright," "tender voice"). Like its maker, the lamb is as innocent as a child.

To show that experience is evil, Blake explores the ill effects of festering anger in "The Poison Tree." In "The Tyger," he implies that the tyger is not only strong; it is evil. It was made in a furnace and it seems to have defeated the "stars" in battle. He implies that even its maker is amazed and upset by how the Tyger turned out (ll. 12–12, 24). Students may disagree with these views saying that all experience is not bad, and that one should try to strike a balance—to maintain some innocence and goodness in face of necessary experience.

Answers

London, The Chimney Sweep from *Songs of Innocence,* and The Chimney Sweep from *Songs of Experience*

Open-Book Selection Test (page 133)

Recall and Interpret

(60 points total; 6 points each)

1. b
2. d
3. a
4. d
5. b
6. d
7. c
8. c
9. b
10. d

Analyze and Evaluate

(28 points total; 7 points each)

Answers will vary. Possible answers:

11. "London": Stanza 2 is very general and inclusive; the poet refers to "every Man" and "every Infant's cry" and "every voice." These are not actual people whom the poet hears while out walking; he cannot hear everyone, obviously. Instead these are ideas he is having, conclusions he is drawing, about the collective plight of people and families (among the poor) in London. The repetition of 'every' creates momentum that indicates how overwhelming the misery is to the observer-poet.

12. "The Chimney Sweeper" from *Songs of Experience:* Stanza 2 is an explanation (it starts out "Because . . .") the sweep gives the poet for why he was made to become a sweep. The stanza as a unit suggests that the child's innocence and joy were punished in some way—that his innocence was perhaps not bearable and caused the world (or his parents) to turn him into a sweep. They "taught" him to suffer and grow up, or they thought his innate joy would equip him to deal with the dark reality of being a chimney sweeper.

13. The movement from stanza 2 to stanza 3 in "London" is from the general ideas of the poet (internal) to the literal and particular (external) sweeper's cry and soldier's sigh he hears. He is, literally, seeing and hearing the manifestations of his ideas, and presenting them for the reader as evidence of the ideas he has put forth in the preceding stanza.

14. The movement from stanza 2 to stanza 3 in "The Chimney Sweeper" from Songs of Experience is from a literal condition (wearing "clothes of death" and "sing[ing] notes of woe") to a more abstract condition: the sweep's apparent happiness allows his parents to remain ignorant. A surprising comment here is that the young sweep sees their worship as a kind of ignorance, too—they are praising a God who "makes up a heaven of our misery." The movement from stanza 2 to 3 is also one from flat explanation to critical comment. The sweep says "our" misery, so he sees himself as part of a miserable collective in this stanza (moving from his individual plight in stanza 2).

BIG IDEA Connect (12 points)

15. Answers will vary. A possible answer: The Romantics highly valued the unspoiled innocence of nature. In "London" the city is a place where nature has been carefully controlled or eliminated, and the people suffer because they lack its healing influence. In both poems titled "The Chimney Sweeper," children represent the innocent and natural, but adults corrupt and destroy this innocence by forcing children to do heavy, sometimes fatal industrial work. The second poem in particular shows the destruction not only of the child's body but of his natural innocence.

from *Pride and Prejudice*

Selection Test (page 135)

Recall and Interpret

(42 points total; 6 points each)

1. a
2. d
3. b
4. b
5. d
6. a
7. c

Vocabulary Practice

(18 points total; 6 points each)

8. a

9. c

10. b

Analyze and Evaluate (20 points)

11. Answers will vary. A possible answer: Mrs. Bennet accuses Mr. Bennet of having "no compassion on [her] poor nerves," to which Mr. Bennet replies that, rather, he has "a high respect for [her] nerves." He goes on to say that, "They are [his] old friends," adding that he has "heard [her] mention them with consideration these twenty years at least." From this exchange, the reader can tell that Mrs. Bennet has long been given to melodrama and perhaps a little hypochondria; she uses her symptoms to motivate and manipulate Mr. Bennet. His end of the exchange indicates that he has a high tolerance for her exaggerations, and tends to "vex" her with a lively and affectionate mockery. He indulges her. He clearly has the humor and self-confidence to undertake action only when her underlying concern is a valid one—i.e., to call on Mr. Bingley and facilitate a meeting between his marriageable daughters and Bingley.

BIG IDEA Connect (20 points)

12. Answers will vary. A possible answer: The careful social hierarchies and niceties of the Enlightenment period play a large role in the novel, as Mrs. Bennet tries to bring her girls to Mr. Bingley's attention without acting improperly. Mr. Bennet's calm, rational approach to the marriage problem is also characteristic of that period. But the emphasis on the importance of love and beauty, and the fact that individual desire governs whom one will love, move the novel towards classification with those of Romanticism.

The World Is Too Much with Us; It Is a Beauteous Evening, Calm and Free; My Heart Leaps Up, and Composed upon Westminster Bridge, September 3, 1802

Open-Book Selection Test (page 137)

Recall and Interpret

(60 points total; 10 points each)

1. b

2. d

3. b

4. b

5. a

6. a

Vocabulary Practice

(10 points total; 5 points each)

7. a

8. b

Analyze and Evaluate

(10 points total; 5 points each)

Answers will vary. Model answers:

9. "The holy time is quiet as a Nun / Breathless with adoration; the broad sun / Is sinking down in its tranquillity" (lines 2-4): The first break allows the reader to imagine how quiet the time and nun are—the image is still, poised, until the reader moves to line 3, which infuses the stillness and quiet with mood and causation (the adoration causes and infuses stillness). The break at the end of line 3 allows the reader to feel the "breathlessness" of the nun and time as the line catches up with itself and, at its end, like the sun mentioned, "sinks" to the next line.

10. "Listen! the mighty Being is awake, / And doth with his eternal motion make / A sound like thunder—everlastingly" (lines 6-8): Line 7 ends on an internal rhyme and an accented syllable; the effect is like a pair of crashing waves. The enjambed line continues down to reveal the simile ('like thunder,' which describes this sound). The caesuras in these lines (after 'Listen!' and after 'thunder') create a pause like that between waves, and the iambic final word of line 8, "everlastingly," has a repetitive and wavelike onomatopoeia that emphasizes this effect—a big crashing thunder of waves followed by the repetitive smaller lapping of receding or waves. The mighty Being, God, in the "gentleness of heaven," stirs the "thunder" of the sea the poet observes.

BIG IDEA Connect (20 points)

11. Answers will vary. A sample answer: "The World Is Too Much with Us" is a sonnet that presents a problem in the first eight lines, or octet. The problem is that people become so involved with making money for basic survival and then for luxuries that they no longer respond to the natural world or have much contact with it. They are too caught up in "getting and spending" to pay attention to the natural world. The last six lines, or sestet, present a comment on this problem: the speaker thinks that it would be better to live in earlier times, when modern sensibilities and problems had not dulled people's ability to be "in tune" with nature.

Lines Composed a Few Miles Above Tintern Abbey

Open-Book Selection Test (page 139)

Recall and Interpret

(48 points total; 8 points each)

1. a
2. c
3. c
4. b
5. b
6. a

Vocabulary Practice

(12 points total; 6 points each)

7. b
8. a

Analyze and Evaluate

(20 points total; 10 points each)

Answers will vary. Model answers:

9. The diction here is indicative of the poet's mood and the larger meaning of the poem; he comes to this place to lose himself, lose his self consciousness, and be part of nature as the orchard tufts are. The image itself is notable because the poet, like an orchard tuft, does not, at his present age, see himself as the center of the universe; he is one of many, he is just a man. When he was a boy, a "glad animal," he felt more like a god, more unique, as if perhaps nature was his kingdom. Now he is simply "lost in" his reverie of nature, not acting on it.

10. The alliteration before the underlined portion is onomatopoeic—the "fretful stir" and "fever" of the world are unpleasant things the poet seeks to remove himself from, at least temporarily. The underlined portion indicates diction with a deeper meaning. These 'trappings' of the world "hang upon" him like heavy coats or drunken guests—they weigh him down. That it is his heart that they seem to hang upon suggests that they do more than immobilize him; they depress him. They make his heart, as it were, heavy, even slow down or muffle its "beatings." He is more alive and free when he is alone in nature. The world of humanity is stifling, maybe even suffocating.

BIG IDEA Connect (20 points)

11. Answers will vary. Possible answers:

- Disagree: While small kindnesses are important, it is better to do great things. There are advances to be made in every field. Someone who conquers a disease has had a far more important effect on a vast number of people than someone who does "unremembered acts of kindness." Even Wordsworth himself made a lasting impression on many people over the ages with his poetry, not with the smaller acts he may have performed.
- Agree: Only a small percentage of people are able to do great things. For the rest, simply being kind is a noble contribution to the good of the world.

Sometimes a kind word or act might have a larger effect than one might anticipate and could even save a person who is in trouble.

from *The Journals of Dorothy Wordsworth*

Selection Test (page 141)

Recall and Interpret

(40 points total; 10 points each)

1. b
2. a
3. c
4. c

Analyze and Evaluate

(36 points total; 6 points each)

Answers may vary. Possible answers:

5. a walk in the Lake District on a stormy spring day

6. The day is wild and windy. The wind stirs up waves on the lakes.

7. A huge patch of bright yellow daffodils seems to be dancing in the wind.

8. The wind is so strong that it is frightening; the drifting boat suggests the danger.

9. The flowers and their beauty bring her great joy.

10. Journal writers have a lot of freedom. They can use as many words and as much space as necessary to describe their observations, thoughts, and feelings. They don't have to worry about rhyme or rhythm, but still want their writing to sound good. Poets have more restrictions. They usually use fewer words to convey ideas and must pay attention to rhyme and rhythm. Both however, can use literary language, such as imagery, to help readers experience with all their senses the scene being described. Each can use personification, simile, and metaphor to help describe a topic.

BIG IDEA Connect (24 points)

11. Answers will vary. Students should point out that admiration of nature is a chief characteristic of Romantic writing and that Wordsworth's journal focuses on observations of nature, which in turn inspire her creative thoughts.

Kubla Khan

Open-Book Selection Test (page 143)

Recall and Interpret

(60 points total; 12 points each)

1. a
2. d
3. d
4. d
5. b

Analyze and Evaluate (20 points)

Answers will vary. A model answer:

6. The consonants/sounds of "*d*" (damsel, dulcimer, maid, played, deep, delight) and "*s*" (damsel, dulcimer, Abyssinian, singing, symphony, song, such) appear in most of the lines cited. The exception is a line that refers directly to the poet: "Could I revive within me"; because this line does not include the lyric, alliterative use of "*d*" and "*s*", it assumes a certain blunt or unmusical weight—important to shift the reader's focus from the lyrical vision/description back to and from the speaker. The line also refers to a state in which the vision is not present and needed to be revived.

BIG IDEA Connect (20 points)

7. Answers will vary. A sample answer: The pleasure dome incorporates many natural elements—the river, the gardens, the forests—in keeping with the Romantic emphasis on nature as teacher, comforter, and inspirer. The dome also involves a mysterious past, with "forests ancient as the hills" and a cavern where "ancestral voices" can be heard. The poem deals with the idea that the poet, or artist, is a sacred person whose role in society is critical.

Answers

The Rime of the Ancient Mariner

Open-Book Selection Test (page 145)

Recall and Interpret

(45 points total; 9 points each)

1. c
2. a
3. c
4. a
5. d

Vocabulary Practice

(15 points total; 5 points each)

6. a
7. b
8. b

Analyze and Evaluate

(21 points; 7 points each)

9.-11. Answers may be in any order.

- Lines 33-40, in which a description of the bride is interjected by the poet, indicating that the wedding guest's focus has been diverted. The wedding guest then beats his breast, but cannot tear himself away.
- Lines 224-229. Part IV opens with the wedding guest blurting out his fear of the Ancient Mariner and remarking some of his more ghostly, severe features (glittering eye, skinny brown hand).
- Line 345, where the wedding guest again blurts out his fear, directly after hearing the horrifying description of how the dead men mutely rose up to sail the ship.

BIG IDEA Connect (19 points)

12. Answers will vary. A sample answer: After the crew has died, and the mariner has reached the point of utter despair, he witnesses beautiful, lively sea creatures ("water snakes") swimming around the ship. Moved by their beauty, he cries, "Oh happy living things!" and a "spring of love gushe[s]" from his heart. This blessing the beauty of the sea creatures and acknowledging the simple right that nature's creatures have to exist wins him the help of the saints, and the dead albatross falls from his neck. His appreciation of nature is the beginning of his salvation.

from *In Patagonia*

Selection Test (page 147)

Recall and Interpret

(60 points total; 12 points each)

1. a
2. b
3. b
4. b
5. d

Analyze and Evaluate

(20 points total; 10 points each)

Answers will vary. Model answers:

6. Davis sacked towns and pillaged gardens to get the supplies his crew needed. / He was, on the one hand, willing to commit crimes to get what he needed, especially against native peoples. On the other hand, he wanted his crew to have the food and water necessary for health and survival.

7. Davis grieved for his crew when they suffered because of the worms and from scurvy and prayed for them. / He recognized the humanity of the sailors and had not led them into harm on purpose; he was sorry for what befell them.

BIG IDEA Connect (20 points)

8. Answers will vary. A sample answer: Coleridge would have disapproved of both actions, in keeping with the Romantic respect for primitive cultures, which were considered to be closer to nature and thus both more innocent and wiser than civilized people, and with the Romantic respect for living things. He might have considered worm infestation a natural and just consequence of the mass-clubbing of the defenseless birds. Certainly much of what befalls the mariner and his shipmates has an air of divine (or natural) justice.

from **The Introduction to *Frankenstein***

Selection Test (page 149)

Recall and Interpret

(40 points total; 10 points each)

1. c
2. d
3. b
4. a

Vocabulary Practice

(20 points total; 5 points each)

5. b
6. b
7. b
8. a

Analyze and Evaluate (20 points)

Answers will vary. A model answer:

9. Shelley indicates that her novel began with the words "It was on a dreary night of November," which immediately establishes a grim and gloomy setting for her tale and suggests that something ominous or worthy of note occurred and will be revealed later. Her diction, as she describes the dream that inspired the novel, suggests horror (see underlining): "the <u>pale</u> student of <u>unhallowed</u> arts kneeling beside the <u>thing</u> he had put together. I saw the <u>hideous</u> <u>phantasm</u> of a man stretched out . . . show signs of life and stir with an <u>uneasy</u>, half-vital motion." She uses very dramatic language, including "quench forever," "hideous corpse," "horrid thing." All of the action described is punctuated by word choice to imbue the scene with a strange and supernatural creepiness.

BIG IDEA Connect (20 points)

Answers will vary. Possible answer:

10. The idea that invention must have material, no matter how shapeless and disorganized, to draw on is in keeping with the Romantic approach to art. Romantic art was reactive: first, a writer experienced something intense—an emotion, a setting, an event—and then later considered the experience and shaped it into something new. This is what Wordsworth means when he speaks of poetry coming from emotions recalled and considered after they are experienced. Shelley could not write her ghost story at first because she had no material to draw on. Not until she listened to a conversation on reanimating corpses was she able to react to the idea and conceive a story.

She Walks in Beauty and from ***Childe Harold's Pilgrimage***

Open-Book Selection Test (page 151)

Recall and Interpret

(45 points total; 5 points each)

1. b
2. d
3. b
4. c
5. b
6. a
7. d
8. d
9. d

Vocabulary Practice

(10 points total; 5 points each)

10. a
11. b

Analyze and Evaluate (20 points)

Answers will vary. Sample answers:

12. Lines 10-13. The poet juxtaposes the shore that man has "marked" with "ruin" with the continuously rolling ocean that ships "sweep over . . . in vain." Man cannot control the ocean; his control "stops with the shore."

13. Lines 37-38. The poet juxtaposes the "empires" on the shore and how, over time, they have changed—been built, sacked, and/or rebuilt—while the ocean stayed the same.

Answers

BIG IDEA Connect (25 points)

14. Answers will vary. Possible answers might include the following:

- from "Childe Harold's Pilgrimage": the woods, the shore, the ocean, nature, swimming, water, storms
- "She Walks in Beauty": night, clear skies, stars and starlight, a woman's eyes, dark hair, smiles, innocence
- Students should be specific in their comparison of what they find beautiful to what Byron finds beautiful.

Ozymandias

Open-Book Selection Test (page 153)

Recall and Interpret

(60 points total; 12 points each)

1. a
2. b
3. a
4. c
5. b

Vocabulary Practice

(20 points total; 5 points each)

6. a
7. c
8. a
9. b

Analyze and Evaluate (10 points)

10. When the sculpture was first made, Ozymandias's intention seems to have been to make other men who were rulers or leaders feel small compared to him—they were meant to "despair," their sense of their own "mightiness" dwarfed by his greatness. By the time the traveler sees the sculpture, nothing remains of Ozymandias's empire, and little remains of his sculpture. Its message at this time is a lesson to those who aspire to power and greatness—the sculpture shows how the desire for power leads to ruin.

BIG IDEA Connect (10 points)

11. Answers will vary, but might include points similar to the following:

- Power never lasts; it is temporary.
- What was once awe-inspiring often becomes humorous or ironic.
- Artistic power (in the form of the sculpture) outlives political power.
- Nature is more powerful than humankind.

Ode to the West Wind and To a Skylark

Open-Book Selection Test (page 155)

Recall and Interpret

(56 points total; 7 points each)

1. c
2. d
3. b
4. d
5. a
6. a
7. d
8. a

Analyze and Evaluate

(24 points total; 8 points each)

Answers will vary. Model answers:

9. "O wild West Wind, thou breath of <u>Autumn's being</u>" (line 1): The diction here presents personification. Shelley could have personified Autumn just by use of the phrase "breath of Autumn." The end-word 'being' allows the rhyme scheme *aba* for the first stanza and suggests that the breath is more than just breathing; it is somehow the essence of Autumn.

10. "(Driving sweet buds <u>like flocks</u> to feed in air)" (line 11): This description animates the buds, suggesting, via simile, that they are sheep. This adds to the sense that they are alive and creates the implied metaphor that the wind is a shepherd.

11. "The sea-<u>blooms</u> and the <u>oozy woods</u> which wear / the sapless foliage of the ocean, know" (lines 39-40): The repetition of the vowel sound here has a lulling effect like the subterranean world under the ocean (onomatopoeia). The implied metaphors link Part 3 of the poem to Shelley's conjuring of a world parallel to that on the land in Part 2 (i.e., there are "blooms" and "woods" and "sapless foliage" under the ocean).

BIG IDEA Connect (20 points)

12. The poem starts out as an address of the West Wind and a song of praise for its power and beauty (Parts 1-3). The wind is personified and referred to with a deferential third-person pronoun ("thou"). In Part 4, there is a major shift: the poet introduces a condition and makes a request—as if to God—that the West Wind save him from the tribulations of life ("Oh, lift me as a wave, a leaf, a cloud!"). This leads into Part 5, the conclusion, in which the poet continues his "prayer," opening stanzas one, three, and four of this part with imperatives that are pleading ("Make me thy lyre;" "Drive my dead thoughts. . . ;" Scatter . . . ashes and sparks, my words among mankind"). In Part 5, the poet's prayer takes on a certain grandeur: he wishes to be the instrument of the wind, so that his poems may reach and move many people.

La Belle Dame Sans Merci and When I Have Fears That I May Cease to Be

Open-Book Selection Test (page 157)

Recall and Interpret

(60 points total; 10 points each)

1. c
2. d
3. c
4. a
5. a
6. d

Vocabulary Practice

(15 points total; 5 points each)

7. b
8. a
9. a

Analyze and Evaluate (10 points)

10. The content of the poem has the trajectory of a sad love story—the palely loitering knight has been seduced by a beautiful and troubled maiden, kissed and comforted her only to "awaken" alone and cold to find that he is one of many whom she has thus seduced . . . all sentenced to suffer without her as she continues her mythical course. Thus, the poem presents a dramatic and fully rendered episode or story; the poet, by allowing the speaker to ask of the knight-at-arms what ails him, opens the door to the knight's dramatization of what has befallen him. The beautiful woman is "without mercy" for her lovers, though she herself seems tortured and suffering too. The lady and the knight are both sad, forlorn, and beautiful, and love leads to sorrow, both of which are elements of a standard ballad.

BIG IDEA Connect (15 points)

11. Answers will vary, but opinions should be supported. Answers might include points similar to the following:

- Keats has a positive attitude toward nature and art, but not toward humankind.
- He finds art more interesting and powerful than life.
- He is afraid that he will not achieve anything with his life.
- He loves and is inspired by the natural world.
- Love seems irresistible to Keats. He longs for it in "When I Have Fears That I May Cease to Be" and shows it to have been irresistible to the knight and other ghostly men in "La Belle Dame Sans Merci."
- Love is both positive and negative to Keats; great desire for it dogs humans, having it moves them, and losing it haunts them.

Answers

Ode on a Grecian Urn

Open-Book Selection Test (page 159)

Recall and Interpret

(40 points total; 8 points each)

1. d
2. a
3. c
4. a
5. c

Vocabulary Practice

(20 points total; 10 points each)

6. c
7. a

Analyze and Evaluate

(20 points total; 10 points each)

Answers will vary. Model answers:

8. Apostrophe is a poetic figure of speech in which an idea, inanimate object, or absent person is directly addressed. Keats uses apostrophe throughout the poem; he addresses the urn, calling it a "still unravished bride of quietness," and referring to it as "thou."

9. One example of elevated diction appears in lines 38-39, where the poet says "And, little town, thy streets forevermore / Will silent be. . . ." The syntax is inverted so the verb comes at the end, and Keats uses the formal "thy" instead of "your." In common language, Keats might have said (less poetically), "And, little town, your streets will be silent forever."

BIG IDEA Connect (20 points)

Answers will vary. Possible answer:

10. When he says that "unheard" melodies are sweeter than those he can hear, Keats is literally saying that he can imagine music more beautiful than real musicians can produce. Real musicians are limited by their abilities and the weaknesses of their instruments. The imagination can conjure up perfect melodies, on the other hand. The Romantics venerated imaginative powers as the greatest of human abilities and sought to free their imaginations from earthly limitations, to honor them and to follow them.

To Autumn, Haiku for Four Seasons, To John Keats, Poet, at Springtime, and Untying the Knot from *Pilgrim at Tinker Creek*

Open-Book Selection Test (page 161)

Recall and Interpret

(48 points total; 6 points each)

1. d
2. a
3. c
4. d
5. b
6. c
7. a
8. c

Vocabulary Practice

(10 points total; 5 points each)

9. c
10. b

Analyze and Evaluate

(24 points total; 6 points each)

Answers will vary. Possible answers:

11. a butterfly hovering over an orchid; delicate
12. tall hollyhocks strain toward the sun during the summer rains; hopeful
13. a crow silhouetted on bare branch; stark
14. winter sun plays trick with shadows; mysterious

BIG IDEA Connect (18 points)

15. Answers will vary. Possible answer: Dillard clearly has affection for nature and is moved by nature, and this susceptibility and emotional reaction are classically Romantic. She goes out "to catch the new season" and is dismayed, at first, that she seems to have missed it. Nature moves her with its fascinating patterns, schedules, and events. And she draws life lessons from what she observes, so nature is a teacher to her, as it was to the Romantics. However, Dillard also has the more rational, scientific mind of those in the Enlightenment. She knows the habits of snakes and can identify them by their discarded skins. She measures and observes and records. She sees both sides of nature—its imaginative, Romantic side, and its down-to-earth, this-is-how-things-work side.

from *In Memoriam A.H.H.*; Crossing the Bar; Tears, Idle Tears

Open-Book Selection Test (page 163)

Recall and Interpret

(42 points total; 6 points each)

1. a
2. d
3. b
4. c
5. d
6. b
7. a

Vocabulary Practice

(20 points total; 5 points each)

8. c
9. b
10. a
11. c

Analyze and Evaluate (18 points)

Answers will vary slightly. A model answer:

12. The phrases "ring in. . ." and "ring out. . ." are used as a refrain in section 106 of the poem. They are apt because bells are a mournful (ring out) or celebratory (ring in) sound and symbol, a symbol of death (funeral) and life (marriage, congregation). This whole section gathers momentum from the rhythm of this repetition and the juxtaposition of ringing out the bad/sad/old with the good/hopeful/new. The poet wants to mourn his friend but also celebrate his life and the life ongoing—of the poet and of society as a whole—in his absence.

BIG IDEA Connect (20 points)

Answers will vary. A model answer:

13. The speaker of the poem "In Memoriam A.H.H." remarks on the value of a conscience in section 27, line 8, the value of rest that is earned (that follows struggle) in section 27, line 12, and the value of extending oneself to love others despite the risk of loss or rejection (section 27, lines 15-16). He is very earnest and modest, implying that he himself is not the "fuller minstrel" (section 106, line 20), and considering himself "an infant crying in the night…crying for the light" (section 54, lines 18 and 19). All-in-all, the speaker seems optimistic about humankind's capacity to be moral/good. He seems also earnest and modest; he believes in love and the struggle to be good (to others), the individual's ability to be self-actualized and continue to grow, and his own ability to be strong enough to bear grief and mourning without wallowing in it.

Ulysses

Open-Book Selection Test (page 165)

Recall and Interpret

(50 points total; 10 points each)

1. d
2. b
3. a
4. b
5. c

Vocabulary Practice

(10 points total; 5 points each)

6. b
7. c

Analyze and Evaluate (20 points)

Answers will vary. Sample answers:

8. Line 70 uses assonance: "To strive, to seek, to find, and not to yield." This line is an interesting example because the vowel sounds are alternating (long i, long e, long i, long e); all occur within accented monosyllabic words; and the words in which they occur are linked as a series of infinitives. The interior two "items" present a logical pair (to seek, to find), offsetting the flanking 'items,' the last of which is unique in that it is introduced by an accented negative—NOT to YIELD. The items ascend in order of emphasis/weight. The effect is galvanizing, momentous, and powerful.

9. Line 44 includes an example of consonance (and alliteration) used to vivify an image: "There lies the port; the vessel puffs her sail." The use of l and s here emphasizes the onomatopoeia of sailing, a breezy word comprised of breezy consonants. Use of the active verb 'puffs' (as if the ship were active rather than passive in the face of wind) further emphasizes the motion/image of the ship.

BIG IDEA Connect (20 points)

10. Ulysses expresses here how the self is created by experience—"I am a part of all that I have met." This sentiment implies that self improvement can be achieved through will and the exercise of will. That we can choose which experiences to expose ourselves to, and thereby change (improve) ourselves, is qualitatively Victorian. Ulysses also values motion and activity (as opposed to leisure), which is made clear when he says, "How dull it is to pause, to make an end, / To rust unburnished, not to shine in use!" This sense that being useful has personal, moral, and social value is also typically Victorian.

Sonnet 43, Love Is Not All: It Is Not Meat nor Drink, and Simone de Beauvoir to Nelson Algren

Open-Book Selection Test (page 167)

Recall and Interpret

(60 points total; 10 points each)

1. a
2. c
3. b
4. c
5. d
6. c

Analyze and Evaluate

(18 points total; 6 points each)

Answers will vary. Sample answers:

7. Barrett Browning's Sonnet 43: Barrett Browning repeats the phrase "I love thee" throughout the poem, and the repetition creates a tone or effect similar to that of a pledge, as if the author were swearing her love. The repetition nicely opens into the variation in the last line "I shall but love thee better after death," adding emphasis and resonance to this line.

8. St. Vincent Millay's "Love is not All...": Lines 3 and 4 contain the repetition of words representing a cycle: "[Love is not] a floating spar to men that sink / And rise and sink and rise and sink again". The effect here is to connote how cyclical the ups and downs of love are.

9. Beauvoir's Letter to Nelson Algren: Beauvoir writes to Algren: "I am happy to be so bitterly unhappy because I know you are unhappy, too, and it is sweet to have a part of the same sadness." The repetition here is meant to create a syntactical connection/mirror of the writer's mood and the recipient's mood. Lovers often strive to recognize themselves in the beloved, and/or assure themselves of an answering gaze. Beauvoir here tautologically creates this "mirroring."

BIG IDEA Connect (22 points)

10. Answers will vary but will include the following points and/or points similar:

Differences:

- Browning expresses her love in abstract terms (Being, Grace); Millay uses more mundane references (food, shelter, illness); de Beauvoir focuses on one personal experience of love (Algren)
- Browning's sonnet is straightforward, earnest, and passionate; Millay's sonnet is worldly and realistic; de Beavoir's letter is intensely passionate, familiar, and earnest

Answers

- Browning and Millay choose to use the sonnet form, while de Beauvoir uses the letter form.
- Browning's sonnet is consistent in its message from start to finish; Millay's sonnet starts with disclaimers and ends with an assertion of love; de Beauvoir's letter begins with a description of her journey home and becomes more and more focused on how much she loves Algren

Similarities:

- The audience for all three pieces is the beloved (the "you").
- All three works assert the primary importance of love as a basic need.
- All three works express a passionate, intense love for the beloved.
- Millay and de Beauvoir express nuanced descriptions of love (as not the same as food or drink and as both pain and pleasure).

In My Life

Open-Book Selection Test (page 169)

Recall and Interpret

(60 points total; 10 points each)

1. a
2. c
3. c
4. d
5. c
6. d

Analyze and Evaluate

(20 points total; 10 points each)

Answers will vary. Possible answers:

7. end rhyme; recall/all, you/new; before/more; makes the lines easier to remember and emphasizes points

8. alliteration; lovers, living, life, loved; points up connections between past and present, adds coherence

BIG IDEA Connect (20 points)

9. Answers will vary but should include the following points and/or points similar:

- Lennon ascribes importance to both current love and to memories of previous loves.
- He does not want to diminish previous loves by forgetting them.
- He wishes to preserve the memory of old loves by stopping to think about people and things from his history.
- He does not want to think of love as something totally new, because doing so would erase the meaning of his memories of his earlier life.
- Memories serve to enrich his current love by making it seem even more valuable.
- His viewpoint is optimistic, because he believes that memory enhances one's current life and loves.

What Is Love?

Selection Test (page 171)

Recall and Interpret

(60 points total; 6 points each)

1. d
2. b
3. a
4. b
5. d
6. d
7. b
8. a
9. b
10. c

Analyze and Evaluate

(20 points total; 10 points each)

Answers will vary. Possible answers:

11. swaying, almost falling down, acting silly and melodramatic; the connotation is that people in love observe an embarrassing kind of hyperbole.

12. darkness, doubt, a cloud; the connotation is meant to suggest something subtle and even poetic because it is some inherently poetic emotionalism in him and all of us that leads us to doubt that love is purely biological or scientific.

BIG IDEA Connect (20 points)

13. Answers will vary but could include points similar to the following:

- Gray's tone throughout the article is humorous.
- The opening allusion to the Cole Porter song sets the humorous, playful tone.
- He cites other song titles to create a humorous effect such as, "writing the book of love," "Love is still in the air," and "looking for love in all the wrong places."
- He also makes a point of saying that love was once the provenance of poets and songwriters who "would be in a fine mess without it"—again creating a playful tone.
- He describes the effects of love in a funny, dramatic way, noting that people will buy almost anything for the promise of love and that people in love look "helplessly loopy and self-besotted."
- Gray seems to stay in a "gray" area about love; he introduces enough cultural evidence to suggest that he believes "love is real," though he seems to cotton to the idea that there are scientific/biological impulses toward it.
- Overall, Gray's attitude is that science doesn't threaten to rob love of its mystery and/or appeal, as the last line makes clear.

Pied Beauty and Spring and Fall: To a Young Child

Open-Book Selection Test (page 173)

Recall and Interpret

(60 points total; 10 points each)

1. b
2. d
3. b
4. a
5. a
6. c

Analyze and Evaluate (18 points)

Answers will vary. A model answer:

7. Hopkin's notion of "sprung rhythm" involved metrical feet containing a stressed syllable and any number of unstressed syllables. Even a stressed monosyllable could constitute one foot. So, in effect, the rhythms of the poem were "springing" (into accented syllables) and "falling" (into unaccented syllables). An interesting example of this is the first line—"Margaret are you grieving". The rhythms of the poem are supposedly more like spoken language—a departure from the formality of iambic and structured meter.

BIG IDEA Connect (22 points)

8. Answers will vary. Possible answer:

- In "Spring and Fall," Hopkins expresses the belief that change, as the passing of time, is the "blight man was born for." The speaker in this poem addresses a child who is crying over the falling of autumn leaves. The speaker tells her that as she gets older, she'll become "colder" or more resigned to the notion of change as aging and moving toward death. In other words, she'll become aware of her mortality. Hopkins's tone in this poem is sad and elegiac, as he depicts change as an inevitable process of decay.
- In "Pied Beauty," Hopkins suggests that some things possess a beauty so unique that it is "past change." Most of the poem is a catalogue of such things, which include "rose-moles," "finches' wings," and other searingly original, "dappled things." Although he does not devote much attention to the notion of change, Hopkins suggests that some things are so dazzling that they go beyond the usual notions of decay and death in their very beauty. The tone of this poem is exuberant and celebratory, praising God for creating so much beauty.

Answers

Jabberwocky

Open-Book Selection Test (page 175)

Recall and Interpret

(60 points total; 10 points each)

1. b
2. d
3. c
4. b
5. b
6. b

Analyze and Evaluate

(20 points total; 5 points each)

Answers will vary. Possible answers:

Nonsense verbs:

7. gyre: move quickly
8. whiffling: moving quickly, with menace

Nonsense adjectives:

9. frumious: menacing, ferocious
10. tulgey: thick and leafy

BIG IDEA Connect (20 points)

11. Carroll's poem has an epic hero like Beowulf and Sir Gawain—a son who undertakes a quest to slay a monster. Beowulf and Sir Gawain were in the service of royalty, someone whom they had pledged to protect and serve, whereas the son in Carroll's poem undertakes his quest to serve his father. Like the epic heroes, the valorous character in "Jabberwocky" succeeds, and is welcomed home a hero (a "beamish boy"). Ironically the last stanza of Carroll's poem is the same as the first; not much changes in the "world" just because the Jabberwocky has been slain. The hero of "Jabberwocky" is not as impressive as Sir Gawain or Beowulf; he is a little comedic (he stands in "uffish" thought; his "vorpal blade" goes "snicker-snack"). In one regard, Carroll is satirizing the drama and seriousness of these old knightly stories.

Jabberwocky

Selection Test (page 177)

Recall and Interpret

(60 points total; 10 points each)

1. b
2. d
3. a
4. a
5. c
6. c

Analyze and Evaluate

(20 points total; 10 points each)

Answers will vary. Possible answers:

7. Coleman's childhood world was lonely and isolating:

- She was born and raised as an African American child in a predominantly white community in South Central Los Angeles during the 1950s and 1960s.
- There were few Black bookstores in her city, and she did not know about them until she was an adult.
- She was considered unattractive by her peers, family members, and the outside world.
- She was considered unattractive due to racial difference and the color of her skin.

8. Coleman found solace in the world of books:

- She considered the library her "Wonderland."
- She loved the forbidden world of adult literature.
- She read everything she could find including her parents magazines and the complete works of Shakespeare.
- She felt liberated by the imaginative works of writers like Carroll.
- These works gave her a sense of possibility beyond racial discrimination and stereotyping and gave her a sense of belonging.

Answers

BIG IDEA Connect (20 points)

9. Answers will vary but should include the following points and/or points similar:

- Coleman states that in her readings of Alice, she "rewrote" the character as herself. In other words, she pictured herself in the book, experiencing Alice's adventures.
- In these imaginings or projections of herself as Alice, Coleman also imagined transforming her skin color, as well as her size and shape, the way Alice does.
- The central appeal of the books lay in their spurring the young Coleman to imagine a better life than the one she was experiencing—one free from racism in particular.
- The books gave her a sense of belonging to a world in which she was not judged arbitrarily and harshly and in which she belonged intellectually and creatively.
- The positive experience she had reading Carroll has lasted into adulthood, as Coleman states that he has had an influence on her own work.

from *Jane Eyre*

Selection Test (page 179)

Recall and Interpret

(50 points total; 10 points each)

1. a
2. c
3. d
4. b
5. a

Vocabulary Practice

(10 points total; 5 points each)

6. c
7. a

Analyze and Evaluate

(20 points total; 10 points each)

Answers will vary. Possible answers:

8. physical description: a black pillar with a grim face on top like a mask, stony, large features, harsh and prim, a great nose, large teeth; personality: imposing and frightening, powerful, intimidating, hard, like a wolf

9. physical description: about 36 or 37 years of age, stout, square-shouldered, strong, robust, low-browed, large chin, eyes devoid of truth, flaxen haired; personality: strong and willful, not accommodating, used to being in charge and getting things done, imposing

BIG IDEA Connect (20 points)

10. Answers will vary but could include points similar to the following:

- The selection shows children in different states according to their class.
- As an orphan in the care of Mrs. Reed, Jane is treated poorly, like a servant, rather than as a valued child.
- Jane is expected to clean the nursery and perform other household tasks to assist Bessie.
- Jane is at the mercy of her caretakers. She recalls being punished severely and unfairly.
- Jane's state contrasts with Mrs. Reed's children, who are treated with more care. Eliza and Georgiana are left to pamper themselves if they wish rather than having to do chores.
- Mr. Brocklehurst's descriptions of Lowood suggest that other poor children are treated badly in Victorian England. Although he is proud of the school, the children seem to be treated harshly and are given only rudimentary clothing and care.

Answers

My Last Duchess

Open-Book Selection Test (page 181)

Recall and Interpret

(50 points total; 10 points each)

1. d
2. a
3. b
4. c
5. b

Vocabulary Practice

(10 points total; 5 points each)

6. c
7. b

Analyze and Evaluate (20 points)

Answers will vary. Possible answers:

8. how speaker sees himself: the speaker in "My Last Duchess" sees himself as a shrewd, sensitive nobleman

what monologue reveals: that the speaker is a proud, jealous, ruthless man

lines that convey true character:

- lines 13–15 reveal the speaker's pride and jealousy;
- it bothers him that the duchess was pleased by the presence of others besides himself;
- he felt his "nine-hundred-years-old name" should have been more impressive to his wife;
- he "gave commands," which may mean he had his wife killed, or at least banished, so that "all smiles stopped together"

BIG IDEA Connect (20 points)

9. Answers will vary but could include points similar to the following:

- The duke appears to be calm and comfortable at the end of the poem, telling his listener to notice a work of art, directly after revealing what a monster he is.
- One can conclude from earlier lines that the duke has probably killed his last duchess out of jealousy, but rather than showing remorse, the duke intends to marry another woman for her dowry.
- Browning emphasizes the duke's horrifying rationality by having the duke relate his thoughts in rhymed couplets, whose regularity points up the duke's madness.
- The rhymed couplets also add a sense of finality to everything the duke says and does, which is chilling in the face of his being a murderer.
- The influence of realism is evident throughout "My Last Duchess, because the subject matter itself is realistic.

from *Oliver Twist*

Selection Test (page 183)

Recall and Interpret

(50 points total; 10 points each)

1. d
2. b
3. b
4. d
5. a

Vocabulary Practice

(10 points total; 5 points each)

6. a
7. a

Analyze and Evaluate

(20 points total; 5 points each)

Answers will vary. Possible answers:

8. A hungry boy who does not know what a Board is.

9. A man who seems to be in charge of the workhouse

10. The workhouse

11. Oliver is told by Mr. Bumble that he is to appear before the board.

BIG IDEA Connect (20 points)

12. Answers will vary but could include points similar to the following:

- Dickens uses realistic characterization to create sympathy in his own times for Oliver and the other poor people.
- Oliver is portrayed as frightened, starving, and at the mercy of the powerful board members and other adults.
- He is terrified at the sight of the gentlemen and cries when they ask him questions.
- The board members are depicted as relentlessly cruel, rich men who exploit their power over the poor.
- The board members show no compassion toward Oliver, call him a fool, ask him cruel questions such as whether or not he understands he is an orphan, and put him up for hire when Oliver shows a bit of defiance.
- These characterizations point up the differences between the poor and the rich and show how the poor were mistreated in Victorian England.

Dover Beach

Selection Test (page 185)

Recall and Interpret

(50 points total; 10 points each)

1. b
2. c
3. b
4. a
5. c

Analyze and Evaluate

(30 points total; 15 points each)

Answers will vary.

6. The meter is very subtle in the first stanza, as the speaker describes the calm, peaceful moonlit water. It is mindful of lapping waves, regular, but not emphatic.

7. In the beginning of the last stanza, the meter is uneven with pauses, as if the speaker is choking up. As the stanza moves along, the meter begins to pound, "nor love, nor light, / Nor certitude, nor peace, nor help for pain;" The meter, combined with the imagery, contributes to our understanding of the last line "Where ignorant armies clash by night."

BIG IDEA Connect (20 points)

8. Answers will vary. A possible response:

The main theme of "Dover Beach" is the speaker's belief that there was a time, in ancient days, when people shared a common faith and certain values. At that time, the "Sea of Faith" was at high tide, full and universal. Now, the speaker says, the tide of that Sea of Faith has ebbed, leaving the shoreline bare. In the absence of some universal faith, Victorians are in chaos, living at a time when "ignorant armies clash by night," because no one can agree on any one set of values or beliefs.

To an Athlete Dying Young and When I Was One-and-Twenty

Open-Book Selection Test (page 187)

Recall and Interpret

(56 points; 8 points each)

1. b
2. a
3. b
4. d
5. c
6. a
7. d

Analyze and Evaluate

(20 points total; 10 points each)

Answers will vary. Possible answers:

8. "To an Athlete Dying Young":

Musical elements:

- tight, four-line stanzas, almost like a ballad
- rhythm is very regular, like the lines of a song
- regular rhyme scheme (aabb) contributes to same impression

Reinforce tone:

- it is better to die young, before your fame fades—is very rational (as opposed to emotional)
- regular rhyme and rhythm support logic

9. "When I Was One-and-Twenty":
Musical elements:
- very regular and tight, like a rhythmic song with a regular beat and rhyming lines

Reinforce tone:
- regularity reinforces the "wise man's" practical advice about not giving your heart away too easily

BIG IDEA Connect (24 points)

10. Answers will vary. Possible answer:

The poems take different views on the issue of youth: one suggests that youth is the best age; the other says youth is wasted on the young who don't have wisdom to make wise choices. "To An Athlete Dying Young" celebrates the strength and speed of the youthful runner. The athlete is considered "smart" for dying young, before fame fades. In "When I Was One-and-Twenty," the young man does a foolish thing because he's inexperienced. At twenty-one, he's not inclined to listen to advice ("No use to talk to me").

Students' personal responses will vary, depending on their own life experiences and observations.

The Darkling Thrush, The Man He Killed, and "Ah, Are You Digging on My Grave?"

Open-Book Selection Test (page 189)

Recall and Interpret

(54 points total; 6 points each)

1. a
2. c
3. b
4. d
5. d
6. d
7. c
8. d
9. a

Analyze and Evaluate

(21 points total; 7 points each)

Answers will vary. Possible answers:

10. "The Darkling Thrush": There is situational irony in the bird's joyous song. The poem has a desolate setting (a grim wintry evening at the end of a tired century) in which the speaker and "every spirit upon earth" is "fervorless," yet , in the midst of all that gloom, the aged thrush puts forth a joyous song, suggesting reason for hope

11. "The Man He Killed": The poem is ironic in a number of ways. The use of "quaint" to describe horrific war is verbal irony. Two ordinary men who have no personal grievance with each other facing each other in deadly combat suggests situational irony

12. "Ah, Are You Digging On My Grave?": The irony is found mostly in the general situation. A voice from the grave asks who is digging and it is only her forgetful dog, suggesting the bitter irony—no one cares what happens to people after they die.

BIG IDEA Connect (25 points)

13. Answers will vary, depending on the student's opinion. Possible answer:

Hardy is a "meliorist." While the settings and situations in all three poems are bleak and depressing, it is not a totally hopeless world. The bird in "The Darkling Thrush" pours out a joyful song even in the midst of wintry gloom and end-of-century exhaustion, suggesting that there's reason for hope. In "The Man He Killed," the speaker is remorseful about killing, suggesting the possibility that people might realize the futility of war. The first speaker in "Ah, Are You Digging On My Grave?" must be shocked at the indifference shown to her death, but the poem is mainly meant to be humorous—not an indication of people's true loyalty to lost loved ones.

Answers

A Cup of Tea, Village People, The Parable of Lazarus and the Rich Man, and from the Qur'an

Selection Test (page 191)

Recall and Interpret

(54 points total; 6 points each)

1. a
2. b
3. d
4. b
5. c
6. d
7. c
8. d
9. a

Vocabulary Practice

(6 points total; 2 points each)

10. a
11. c
12. b

Analyze and Evaluate

(20 points total; 10 points each)

Answers will vary. Possible answers:

13. Rosemary brings home a beggar. Her motives are selfish and self-serving. The result is that Rosemary becomes more jealous and insecure.

14. The narrator assists a needy old woman. The narrator is altruistic. The result is that the narrator feels satisfaction and her kindness is repaid.

BIG IDEA Connect (20 points)

15. Answers will vary but could include points similar to the following:

- Both selections express sympathetic attitudes toward the poor and a certain amount of contempt for the rich.
- In "Lazarus," the man who is rich in life is punished by going to hell and being tormented. When he appeals to Abraham, Abraham tells him that he already received good things in life, so now he has to pay.
- Conversely, the beggar Lazarus, who suffered from poverty in life, is rewarded by being sent to heaven in the afterlife.
- The Qur'an encourages people to give alms to the poor and destitute and for the freeing of slaves (who are presumably poor).
- The Qur'an also says that people who conceal their riches on earth will receive a shameful punishment in the afterlife.
- However, the Qur'an differs from "Lazarus" in that the wealthy will not necessarily suffer after dying, as those who give wealth for the cause of God in life will be rewarded and have nothing to fear.

Down and Out in Europe

Selection Test (page 193)

Recall and Interpret

(60 points total; 10 points each)

1. c
2. b
3. b
4. a
5. a
6. d

Analyze and Evaluate

(20 points; 10 points each)

7. Big Sid is probably homeless, because he suffers from mental illness. He is currently living on the streets of London with occasional forays to other parts of England. His situation indicates that Europe needs to address the problems of mental illness better in order to help people like him from becoming homeless.

8. Christelle is probably homeless because she can't afford to pay for rent and support her daughter and herself without a job. She is living in a Paris shelter and looking for a job. Her situation indicates that the tight job market in many European countries and lack of resources for single women with families have led to increased numbers of single mothers who are homeless.

BIG IDEA Connect (20 points)

9. Answers will vary but could include points similar to the following:
- European countries have traditionally given benefits to the unemployed and homeless. German, French, and British citizens all receive money for unemployment or homelessness.
- The author concludes the article by noting that giving money to the poor will not solve the problem.
- He notes that European governments should work with local authorities to come up with solutions.
- He notes that government agencies should also work with volunteer groups to solve the problem.
- He also points out that governments face the challenge of finding better ways to take care of people with mental, psychological, and abuse problems.

Miss Youghal's *Sais*

Selection Test (page 195)

Recall and Interpret

(56 points total; 8 points each)

1. d
2. c
3. b
4. d
5. b
6. a
7. c

Vocabulary Practice

(8 points total; 2 points each)

8. c
9. c
10. c
11. a

Analyze and Evaluate

(18 points total; 6 points each)

Answers will vary. Possible answers:

12. Strickland: Because of Strickland's secretive nature, it might have been hard for him to tell the story of his deception. If he did, we'd learn more about why and how he got himself into Indian organizations and rituals and just how he felt about Miss Youghal. We might have learned some of what he would have put into that book that was worth suppressing.

13. Mr. Youghal: Mr. Youghal's account might have had more surprise and suspense. He didn't know about Strickland's true identity or his daughter's feelings until the end. The story might have been more of a farce, since he was so out of touch with what was happening.

14. General: The general would have had to tell the story as a flashback from the time he learned of Strickland's engagement. His jovial nature and sense of fun might have made the story more outrageous. He most likely would have put more emphasis on the father's lack of insight.

BIG IDEA Connect (18 points)

15. Answers will vary somewhat. Possible answer:

The narrator is a worldly man. He is a British official, apparently, who has lived in India for quite a while. He's a bit sarcastic or ironic, because he calls Strickland's idea about knowing the local culture an "extraordinary idea," when it's clear he knows that's what makes Strickland effective. He is clearly a friend of Strickland's (he's asked to get him some special cigars), which is why he knows all these details and what makes him a good narrator.

Shooting an Elephant

Selection Test (page 197)

Recall and Interpret

(50 points total; 10 points each)

1. a
2. c
3. b
4. a
5. c

Answers

Vocabulary Practice

(10 points total; 2 points each)

6. a
7. a
8. c
9. b
10. c

Analyze and Evaluate (20 points)

Answers will vary. Possible answers:

11. The elephant symbolizes the old ways of life in Burma. A phrase describing the elephant is "suddenly stricken, shrunken, immensely old, as though the frightful impact of the bullet had paralyzed him without knocking him down." This phrase indicates that the elephant is old and vulnerable and conveys the idea that both the elephant and the old ways of life it symbolizes are dying.

BIG IDEA Connect (20 points)

12. Answers will vary but could include points similar to the following:

- In this statement, Orwell sums up his experience as an officer for the British Empire in Burma.
- The statement suggests that when a nation rules over another people tyrannically, as Britain did in Burma, the rulers also lose their freedom to act according to their own wishes.
- The thought occurs to him because he realizes then that he will have to shoot the elephant to please the crowd, even though he doesn't want to.
- He knows that he has to act against his own wishes in order not to lose face or the appearance of authority with the people he supposedly rules over.
- Since the appearance of authority is crucial to maintaining his power, the "white man"—Orwell—must act in accordance with the crowd's wishes rather than his own.
- Orwell sees this moment as emblematic of the experiences of Britain in occupied territories such as Burma.

The Soldier

Open-Book Selection Test (page 199)

Recall and Interpret

(60 points total; 15 points each)

1. a
2. d
3. b
4. a

Analyze and Evaluate

(20 points total; 10 points each)

Answers will vary. Possible answers:

5. Image: "In that rich earth a richer dust concealed"

Mood It Expresses: The image conveys a sense of warmth and a melding of the body with the earth. The image creates a mood of sensuousness that continues after death.

6. Image: "an English heaven"

Mood It Expresses: The image represents a kind of eternity that is comforting to the speaker and creates a mood of calmness and acceptance.

BIG IDEA Connect (20 points)

7. Answers will vary but could include points similar to the following:

- The speaker's attitude toward war is patriotic, and he is resigned about dying for his country.
- Lines 1–3 exemplify this sentiment.
- He says that if he should die, he hopes that his death will preserve a place for England in the country he dies in.
- His attitude puzzles me—he strikes me as naïve and patriotic in an unthinking way, given that war can be truly awful for those who are fighting it.

Dreamers

Open-Book Selection Test (page 201)

Recall and Interpret

(48 points total; 12 points each)

1. a
2. b
3. c
4. c

Vocabulary Practice

(12 points total; 4 points each)

5. b
6. b
7. a

Analyze and Evaluate (20 points)

Answers will vary. Possible answers:

8. The dreamers are the soldiers on the battlefield. They dream continually of going home to England and resuming their daily, sometimes pleasant, sometimes boring, lives. Sassoon uses this title somewhat ironically, as the word *dreamers* implies a kind of boyish dreaminess or indulgence in fantasy, whereas the fantasy the soldiers pine for is their old reality. This use of the title points up the horror of the soldiers' lives.

BIG IDEA Connect (20 points)

9. Answers will vary but could include points similar to the following:

- Sassoon uses opposing images of the battlefield and home to show the horrors of war.
- Throughout the poem, he asserts that soldiers continually dream of mundane things and long to return to them—often futilely.
- The images he uses to describe the battlefield are grim. For example, he speaks of "death's gray land," "foul dugouts," and "ruined trenches." All of these images express disgust and hopelessness.
- The images he uses to describe home suggest cheer and cleanliness—"firelit homes, clean beds, and wives," for example. Even things that weren't entirely pleasant, such as "spats," take on an air of impossible wonder in the context of the grim trenches.
- By contrasting such images, Sassoon emphasizes how the mundane becomes a much-longed-for goal among the soldiers.

Dulce et Decorum Est

Open-Book Selection Test (page 203)

Recall and Interpret

(48 points total; 12 points each)

1. d
2. c
3. a
4. b

Vocabulary Practice

(12 points total; 4 points each)

5. c
6. b
7. a

Analyze and Evaluate (20 points)

Answers will vary. Possible answers:

8. The first verse paragraph in the poem consists of lines 1 through 8. The main idea of this paragraph is that soldiers marching in the war are extremely fatigued and weary with pain. This main idea is supported by details such as the soldiers' moving "like old beggars under sacks" and being "drunk with fatigue."

BIG IDEA Connect (20 points)

9. Answers will vary but could include points similar to the following:

- Owen believes the statement *Dulce et decorum est pro patria mori*, meaning "It is sweet and honorable to die for one's country," is a lie.
- Throughout the poem he invokes

images of the horrors of war.

- These images include "bent double, like old beggars under sacks," "coughing like hags," "limped on, blood-shod," and "clumsy helmets." They all suggest that war is a grim, demoralizing, exhausting activity.
- The images of the dying man further express Owen's disgust with fighting. These images include "white eyes writhing in his face" and "froth-corrupted lungs." Such images graphically convey the horror of combat and undermine the notion of a sweet and honorable death.
- The images show how dying violently is the opposite of peaceful.

from *The Great War and Modern Memory*

Selection Test (page 205)

Recall and Interpret

(60 points total; 10 points each)

1. a
2. c
3. d
4. b
5. b
6. a

Analyze and Evaluate (20 points)

Answers will vary. Possible answers:

7. firing trench—used to position soldiers to fire at the enemy line
communication trench—connected the three trench lines
"sap"—thrust out into No Man's Land; provided access to observation post, listening post, grenade-throwing post, or machine gun position.

BIG IDEA Connect (20 points)

8. Answers will vary but could include points similar to the following:

- Fussell's tone is informative, detached, and admiring. He seems to marvel at the ingenuity and complexity of the trenches.
- He describes the trenches in a mostly straightforward manner, beginning with descriptions of their enormous length.
- He talks about how soldiers who fought in the trenches transformed them in their minds. Then he describes the structure and kinds of trenches.
- Although he describes the horrors of war, his focus is on the mechanics of how World War I was actually fought, and his tone remains detached and even optimistic throughout the piece.
- He also focuses on the soldiers' resourcefulness in maintaining humor about and distance from the situation they are in. For example, he notes that the British soldiers identified sections of trench by London place and street names.

The Lake Isle of Innisfree and **When You Are Old**

Open-Book Selection Test (page 207)

Recall and Interpret

(60 points total; 10 points each)

1. c
2. b
3. c
4. a
5. b
6. d

Analyze and Evaluate

(20 points total; 10 points each)

Answers will vary. Possible answers:

7. The structure of this poem is three stanzas of 4 lines each, or 3 quatrains. The rhyme scheme is *abab cdcd efef*. The effect of the rhyme scheme is a musical forward movement.

8. The structure of this poem is also three quatrains, however the rhyme scheme is *abba cddc effe*. This rhyme scheme creates a more closed and circular structure than the alternating lines of rhyme.

BIG IDEA Connect (20 points)

9. Answers will vary but could include points similar to the following:

- In "The Lake Isle of Innisfree," Yeats creates contrasts between different times of day and between the city and the countryside.
- He contrasts images of night "all a glimmer" with midday, or "noon a purple glow." All of these images convey a sense of peacefulness and lightness.
- The peaceful images of the countryside contrast sharply with the dreary images of the city. At the end of the poem, the speaker stands on "pavements gray," which are the opposite of the lovely and inviting countryside.
- In "When You Are Old," Yeats uses contrasting images of age and youth, as well as physical beauty and inner beauty.
- The speaker of "When You Are Old" pictures his beloved as an old woman. Her aged face contrasts with the "soft look / Your eyes had once."
- The speaker says that although she is now admired by many, she should remember that he was the one man who loved her for her inner beauty or "pilgrim soul" rather than her physical beauty.
- The opposing descriptions of age and youth create a tension in the poem and reinforce the idea that beauty doesn't last.
- The opposites also underscore how different the speaker is from the woman's other admirers.

Sailing to Byzantium and **The Second Coming**

Open-Book Selection Test (page 209)

Recall and Interpret

(48 points total; 8 points each)

1. b
2. b
3. a
4. c
5. a
6. d

Vocabulary Practice

(12 points total; 3 points each)

7. c
8. a
9. c
10. a

Analyze and Evaluate

(20 points total; 10 points each)

Answers will vary. Possible answers:

11. The structure of this poem is four eight-line stanzas, which are numbered with Roman numerals. Each stanza also has a set rhyme scheme of *abababcc*. This very regular structure creates a stately effect and imparts a formal feeling that enhances the meaning of the poem.

12. The structure of this poem is two stanzas. The first stanza has eight lines; the second has 14 lines. The structure creates an effect of imbalance, since one stanza is much longer than the other one. In addition, Yeats is playing with the structure of the sonnet, which is traditionally 14 lines long. This poem is a sonnet whose structure has expanded and exploded, conveying a sense of chaos.

BIG IDEA Connect (20 points)

13. Answers will vary but could include points similar to the following:

- The mood of "Sailing to Byzantium" is nostalgic and elegiac, whereas the mood of "The Second Coming" is terrifying and foreboding.
- The mood of neither poem is happy or celebratory.

- In "Sailing," Yeats employs several images to express the feeling of aging and becoming an old person. For example, he uses "a tattered coat upon a stick" and "dying animal" to describe an old man's body.
- He contrasts these images of aging with images of permanence, such as "hammered gold and gold enameling," that the speaker wishes he could become instead of human.
- In "The Second Coming," Yeats presents images of destruction, such as "blood-dimmed tide," to create a mood of terror.
- These images are enforced by images of monstrosity, such as "moving its slow thighs," and death, such as, "desert birds," which are probably vultures.
- The overall mood created by these images is one of menace and threat.

Preludes

Open-Book Selection Test (page 211)

Recall and Interpret

(50 points total; 10 points each)

1. d
2. c
3. a
4. b
5. b

Vocabulary Practice

(10 points total; 5 points each)

6. b
7. c

Analyze and Evaluate

(20 points total; 10 points each)

Answers will vary. Possible answers:

8. Image: broken blinds and chimney-pots
Sense: sight
Feeling: loss, despair

9. Image: yellow soles of feet
Sense: touch and sight
Feeling: sadness, melancholy

BIG IDEA Connect (20 points)

10. Answers will vary but could include points similar to the following:

- Throughout the poem, Eliot uses descriptions from urban life to convey a sense of alienation and despair.
- The images are generally drawn from working-class life.
- Images such as "burnt-out ends of smoky days" and "grimy scraps" convey a sense of decay and industrial garbage.
- Details such as "stale smells of beer" and "dingy shades" also express a sense of dirtiness and of never being clean.
- Other details, such as "a lonely cab-horse steams and stamps," convey the sense of loneliness and alienation frequently found in Modernist poetry.
- All these details together create a bleak picture of modern life.

The Rocking-Horse Winner

Selection Test (page 213)

Recall and Interpret

(48 points total; 6 points each)

1. d
2. a
3. c
4. d
5. d
6. c
7. d
8. b

Vocabulary Practice

(12 points total; 3 points each)

9. a
10. c
11. a
12. c

Answers

Analyze and Evaluate
(20 points total; 10 points each)
Answers will vary. Possible answers:
13. Paul sits on his rocking horse, riding with such frenzy that it frightens his sisters. This action foreshadows that riding the rocking horse will have disastrous consequences.
14. Paul's uncle Oscar says that Paul's ability to predict the outcome of the races makes him nervous. This statement foreshadows that Paul's uncanny talent will lead to his death.

BIG IDEA Connect (20 points)
15. Answers will vary somewhat.
- Students may say that D. H. Lawrence was critical of those who are greedy and who value material possessions above love and family.
- Students may or may not agree with his views, depending on personal experience.

Araby
Selection Test (page 215)

Recall and Interpret
(45 points total; 5 points each)

1. a
2. a
3. c
4. d
5. b
6. a
7. d
8. b
9. b

Vocabulary Practice
(15 points total; 5 points each)
10. a
11. c
12. b

Analyze and Evaluate (20 points)
Answers will vary. Possible answers:
13. The narrator's epiphany occurs at the end of the story, when he's at the bazaar and it's shutting down. He gains the insights that he has acted out of vanity and that the world has chastised him for doing so.

BIG IDEA Connect (20 points)
14. Answers will vary but could include points similar to the following:
- Joyce uses both traditional and innovative literary techniques in "Araby."
- The structure of the story is traditional in its use of chronological order.
- The story is Modernist in that Joyce emphasizes the internal life and thoughts and feelings of the narrator.
- Although dialogue is a traditional technique, Joyce makes it innovative by using dashes rather than quotation marks. In addition, the dialogue is sparse and interspersed with long passages of action or the narrator's observations.
- The story is also traditional in that it is a love story, with a boy trying to win the heart of a girl.
- However, the story is Modernist in that its lack of a happy ending and in its ending with the narrator grappling with new insights into himself and the world, alone.

from A Room of One's Own
Selection Test (page 217)

Recall and Interpret
(35 points total; 5 points each)

1. a
2. d
3. a
4. d
5. c
6. d
7. c

Vocabulary Practice
(25 points total; 5 points each)

8. c
9. b
10. a
11. c
12. b

Answers

Analyze and Evaluate (20 points)

Answers will vary. Possible answers:

13. Woolf argues that it would have been impossible for a woman in the sixteenth century to have written the plays of Shakespeare, because social and economic conditions would have prevented a woman from doing so. She supports her argument by citing a professor who notes that women were married very young, whether they liked it or not, and were thus occupied with housework and child-rearing, which kept them from artistic pursuits. She also supports her argument by imagining the life of Shakespeare's sister, who, with the same talents and ambitions as Shakespeare, would have ended up committing suicide because society would have thwarted her genius so thoroughly.

BIG IDEA Connect (20 points)

14. Answers will vary. Possible answers:

- working class, immigrants, lesser-educated people
- Woolf would state that other people in society are responsible for this repression, not the repressed group itself.

from *Mrs. Dalloway*

Selection Test (page 219)

Recall and Interpret

(50 points total; 10 points each)

1. a
2. b
3. c
4. c
5. d

Vocabulary Practice

(10 points total; 2 points each)

6. a
7. b
8. a
9. c
10. c

Analyze and Evaluate (20 points)

Answers will vary. Possible answers:

11. "She sliced like a knife through everything; at the same time was outside, looking on. She had a perpetual sense, as she watched the taxi cabs, of being out, out, far out to sea and alone; she always had the feeling that it was very, very dangerous to live even one day." The passage reveals that Mrs. Dalloway is introspective, quick, and an observer of herself and her surroundings. She feels loneliness constantly and a sense of anxiety or mild fearfulness. The passage also shows her to be intelligent and sensitive.

BIG IDEA Connect (20 points)

12. Answers will vary but could include points similar to the following:

- Clarissa thinks this, because she is unhappy with her own tendency to please others. She berates herself for doing things to elicit certain responses from other people rather than to please herself.
- Clarissa is a complex and self-reflective character. She tends to worry about what others will think, and she does try to please others.
- However, she also seems to be genuinely kind. She looks after friends who are not well, and she wishes to cheer them up.
- Woolf reveals Clarissa's character primarily through stream-of-consciousness passages that show what Clarissa is thinking or seeing at particular moments.
- Woolf also reveals her character through Clarissa's actions—going shopping, talking with Hugh, etc.

Answers

Be Ye Men of Valor

Selection Test (page 221)

Recall and Interpret

(48 points total; 8 points each)

1. a
2. b
3. d
4. b
5. b
6. c

Vocabulary Practice

(12 points total; 3 points each)

7. a
8. c
9. c
10. c

Analyze and Evaluate

(20 points total; 10 points each)

Answers will vary. Possible answers:

11. Appeal to Logic: Churchill says that in the air battles, British fighters are downing German fighters at a rate of three or four to one.
Appeal to Emotion: He says it would be foolish to lose heart or courage now.

12. Appeal to Logic: Churchill mentions that British bombers are inflicting damage on Nazi oil refineries.
Appeal to Emotion: He says that if the Germans invade Britain, the fight will be "for all that Britain is, and all that Britain means."

BIG IDEA Connect (20 points)

13. Answers will vary. Possible answers:

- Students should recognize that Churchill was appealing to emotions.
- His style includes loaded language and propaganda to instill pride and fear in the hearts of his listeners.
- Students will probably agree that this choice was effective.

The Demon Lover

Selection Test (page 223)

Recall and Interpret

(40 points total; 5 points each)

1. a
2. c
3. d
4. a
5. d
6. c
7. c
8. d

Vocabulary Practice

(20 points total; 4 points each)

9. a
10. b
11. c
12. b
13. a

Analyze and Evaluate (20 points)

Answers will vary. Possible answers:

14. The flashback shows Mrs. Drover as a teenager talking to a soldier, whom she is engaged to. Her fiancé tells her that they will be together sooner or later. She feels a little scared of her fiancé and is not terribly upset when he is reported missing in the war. The flashback has the effect of setting up later events in the story. It foreshadows the return of Mrs. Drover's fiancé as the "demon lover" and creates suspense in the story.

BIG IDEA Connect (20 points)

15. Answers will vary. Possible answers:

- Suspense is an anticipation of the outcome of events, especially as they affect a character for whom the reader has sympathy.
- Suspense generally induces a feeling of anxiety.
- Bowen uses suspense at the end of the story as the main character, Mrs. Drover, attempts to leave her house.
- Sights, smells, and sounds all begin to frighten her as she searches for a taxi.
- The eerie description of the taxi waiting for her also adds to the suspense.
- The suspense reaches a pinnacle as she

enters the taxi and realizes the driver has not asked her where she is going.

Musée des Beaux Arts and **The Unknown Citizen**

Open-Book Selection Test (page 225)

Recall and Interpret

(48 points total; 8 points each)

1. b
2. c
3. a
4. d
5. b
6. b

Vocabulary Practice

(12 points total; 4 points each)

7. b
8. c
9. a

Analyze and Evaluate

(20 points total; 10 points each)

10. Example: The torturer's horse scratches its behind on a tree.
Type of irony: dramatic

11. Example: The speaker says that the citizen "had everything necessary to the Modern Man."
Type of irony: verbal

BIG IDEA Connect (20 points)

12. Answers will vary but could include points similar to the following:

- Auden expresses dissatisfaction with modern life in the poem.
- He uses verbal irony throughout the poem to show how devoid of meaning and emotional satisfaction modern life can be.
- He portrays the citizen as a perfectly, absurdly average person who does everything "right" and causes no disturbance in society.
- In lines such as "He was found by the Bureau of Statistics to be / One against whom there was no official complaint," Auden shows how banal modern life is when its tenets remain unchallenged.
- The questions the speaker asks in line 28 indicate that the citizen was probably not happy or free and that modern life made it difficult for him to be so because it dismissed such notions as unimportant.

A Shocking Accident

Selection Test (page 227)

Recall and Interpret

(42 points total; 7 points each)

1. c
2. b
3. c
4. a
5. d
6. a

Vocabulary Practice

(15 points total; 3 points each)

7. c
8. a
9. c
10. b
11. c

Analyze and Evaluate

(20 points total; 10 points each)

Answers will vary. Possible answers:

12. Character: Jerome
Round or Flat?: round
Static or Dynamic?: dynamic
Function in story: Jerome is the main character in the story. His actions and thoughts propel the story's action.

13. Character: Jerome's aunt
Round or Flat?: flat
Static or Dynamic?: static
Function: Jerome's aunt serves as a constant in the story, as her behavior regarding the death of Jerome's father remains consistent. She provides the situation that will "test" Sally, Jerome's fiancée.

BIG IDEA Connect (23 points)

14. Answers will vary but could include points similar to the following:

- Greene satirizes several aspects of British society, using humor to make those aspects seem foolish.
- At the beginning of the story, the author mocks the British school system's hierarchical nature, as the narrator describes how certain students aspire to become "crusaders" as they advance through school.
- Greene also shows the callousness of students in their reactions to Jerome's father's death.
- He also satirizes the snobbishness of British society, as Jerome's aunt speaks belittlingly of Italy as an uncivilized country.
- He mocks the tendency to memorialize authors by writing their biographies.
- He also satirizes the predictability of middle-class life in Britain, as Jerome "in the course of time" becomes an accountant and engaged to someone who dreams of nothing but having babies.

Fern Hill and Do Not Go Gentle into That Good Night

Open-Book Selection Test (page 229)

Recall and Interpret

(48 points total; 8 points each)

1. c
2. b
3. c
4. a
5. c
6. d

Vocabulary Practice

(12 points total; 3 points each)

7. c
8. a
9. a
10. b

Analyze and Evaluate

(20 points total; 10 points each)

Answers will vary. Possible answers:

11. Assonance: "Old age should burn and rave at close of day"
Consonance: "Curse, bless, me now with your fierce tears"

12. Assonance: "In the sun that is young once only"
Consonance: "And green and golden I was huntsman and herdsman"

BIG IDEA Connect (20 points)

13. Answers will vary but could include points similar to the following:

- The two poems suggest Thomas's belief in the sanctity of living, natural things.
- In "Fern Hill," this belief is expressed through his celebration of the innocence and imagination of youth. The boy who revels in the joys of nature is not yet aware of his mortality and so enjoys life in a full, spontaneous way.
- The speaker of "Do Not Go . . ." encourages his dying father to rage against death, to assert his strength and dignity, as wise, good, wild, and grave men do. He celebrates the vitality of living.

Not Waving but Drowning

Open-Book Selection Test (page 231)

Recall and Interpret

(60 points total; 12 points each)

1. d
2. b
3. b
4. c
5. d

Analyze and Evaluate

(20 points total; 10 points each)

Answers will vary. Possible answers:

6. The dead man; lines 3, 4, 9, 11, 12
7. "They"; lines 5–7

Answers

BIG IDEA Connect (20 points)

8. Answers will vary but could include points similar to the following:
There is a sense of detachment conveyed by the poem, a bleak comment on a person's life. In death, the speaker is able to say that he was not "larking," he was drowning. He was always cold, not just at the time that he drowned. The poem could be said to convey the hopelessness that the British felt as a result of the loss of the empire, unemployment, and economic depression. The speaker's detached sadness is also expressed by quoting the words of other people, who misunderstand the dead man's actions.

At the Pitt-Rivers

Selection Test (page 233)

Recall and Interpret

(45 points total; 9 points each)

1. b
2. d
3. d
4. a
5. c

Vocabulary Practice

(15 points total; 5 points each)

6. a
7. b
8. b

Analyze and Evaluate

(20 points total; 10 points each)
Answers will vary. Possible answers:

9. Example: "If they're attractive they have lots of blokes after them and if they're not they don't."
Translation: If they're good-looking, lots of guys pursue them, if they're not, that doesn't happen.

10. Example: "So I reckoned I must have made a mistake."
Translation: So I thought I must have made a mistake.

BIG IDEA Connect (20 points)

11. Answers will vary but could include points similar to the following:

- The love story the speaker observes is traditional in that
  - it seems to involve a traditional manner of courtship
  - the two people are in love and display affection toward one another
  - the woman is glowing with happiness
  - they meet regularly
- The love story is nontraditional in that
  - the man is much older than the woman
  - they choose to meet at an odd location (the Pitt-Rivers)
  - the story does not have a happy conclusion (It is clear that the two people split up at the end, and that the woman is very unhappy about this.)

Follower, Mnemonic, and Photograph from *Running in the Family*

Open-Book Selection Test (page 235)

Recall and Interpret

(60 points total; 10 points each)

1. b
2. b
3. c
4. b
5. d
6. a

Analyze and Evaluate

(21 points total; 7 points each)
Answers will vary. Possible answers:

7. The speaker ruminates about the past by thinking of his father and how he used to follow his father everywhere on the farm. He realizes that his father's presence still means much to him, as his father "keeps stumbling / Behind me, and will not go away."

8. The speaker in "Mnemonic" gains some insight into the man his father was by thinking about the past. He realizes that even painful memories are sweet and thinks about how his father acted tenderly toward him.

9. The speaker looks for and finds evidence of his parents' being perfect for one another. The photograph shows him how they were joined in their sense of fun.

BIG IDEA Connect (19 points)

10. Answers will vary but could include points similar to the following:

- The tone of "Follower" is nostalgic and a bit sad. The speaker recalls how as a boy he worshiped his father and saw him as heroic and skilled.
- The first five stanzas of the poem recall those memories of his father in detail.
- However, in the last stanza the speaker realizes that even though he is now grown, his father's spirit still haunts him, reminding him of the past.
- The tone of "Mnemonic" is nostalgic and melancholic. The speaker recalls how he looked up to his father, who was both stern and loving.
- The speaker seems to admire his father and forgive him for hurting him on occasion. He chooses to focus on how his father showed him tenderness.
- The tone of "Photograph" is wry and nostalgic. The speaker is looking for evidence of how well suited his parents were to each other. Although he finds this evidence, he expresses a bit of sadness and implies that they did not stay together too long.
- He seems to admire his parents and their sense of fun and playfulness.

Wind

Open-Book Selection Test (page 237)

Recall and Interpret

(45 points total; 9 points each)

1. a
2. a
3. c
4. a
5. c

Vocabulary Practice

(15 points total; 5 points each)

6. b
7. c
8. a

Analyze and Evaluate

(20 points total; 10 points each)

Answers will vary. Possible answers:

9. Wind; lines 3, 15
10. Fields and skyline; line 13

BIG IDEA Connect (20 points)

11. Answers will vary. Possible answer:

- The poem suggests that nature is powerful and uncontrollable by human beings.
- At the end of the poem, the people are huddled fearfully inside, isolated from each other, unable to communicate through reading or thought, aware of the power of nature, hoping the house will survive the windstorm.
- Hughes uses several literary devices, including personification, metaphor, and simile.
- For example, he uses personification to express the wind's power in line 15, saying that the wind "flung a magpie away."
- He uses simile in line 8 to compare the light to "the lens of a mad eye," also expressing nature's power.

Answers

That's All

Selection Test (page 239)

Recall and Interpret

(40 points total; 10 points each)

1. c
2. d
3. b
4. d

Analyze and Evaluate (30 points)

5. Answers may vary but should resemble the following:
Woman's Feelings: At best, she is indifferent toward Mrs. A.
Evidence:

- She never told Mrs. A she was going to the butcher on Thursday, which suggests she didn't want to maintain contact with Mrs. A.
- She "doesn't come in so much," which suggests that her visits are fairly rare.

BIG IDEA Connect (30 point)

6. Answers will vary. Possible answers:
Pinter shows with the conversation between Mrs. A and Mrs. B that much of modern life is banal, superficial, and trivial. Students will agree or disagree with Pinter, depending on the quality of communication in their own social groups.

What We Lost

Open-Book Selection Test (page 241)

Recall and Interpret

(60 points total; 10 points each)

1. c
2. b
3. d
4. b
5. a
6. d

Analyze and Evaluate (20 points)

Answers will vary. Possible answers:
7. The voice is quiet and somewhat sad and rueful. The many old names of fabrics create a feeling of nostalgia. Images such as "the quiet sweat of wax" create a feeling of stillness and somberness. Images of darkness, such as "fields are dark already," give the voice sadness.

BIG IDEA Connect (20 points)

8. Answers will vary but could include points similar to the following:

- Boland seems to be saying that memory is frail and language can get in the way of memory by supplanting other ways of communicating.
- She expresses that memory is frail by noting that the child in the poem will soon forget the story she is told and that "the frail connections have been made and are broken."
- She follows this assertion with the statement that "legend has become language, / is becoming silence" and goes on to say that language was once a host of other things, including her grandmother's love letters and lavender and various sewn items.
- In these lines, Boland expresses the idea that there are many ways of communicating love and that these old ways have largely been lost as language has supplanted traditions.
- She suggests that we have lost our ability to relate to each other by focusing on language, which cannot suffice alone.

A Mild Attack of Locusts

Selection Test (page 243)

Recall and Interpret

(48 points total; 12 points each)

1. d
2. c
3. c
4. d
5. a
6. c

Vocabulary Practice

(12 points total; 4 points each)

7. a
8. c
9. b

Answers

Analyze and Evaluate

(20 points total; 5 points each)

Answers will vary. Possible answers:

10. Bewilderment regarding weather; humans' lack of experience with nature

11. Fear of the risks of farming; humans' inability to control nature, yet understanding that "life goes on"

12. Anger at the men; frustration with nature's horror that is "better than it could have been"

13. Wonderment at the power of nature; love of nature, beauty of natural world, continuing coexistence of the human trying to control the natural world

BIG IDEA Connect (20 points)

14. Answers will vary. Possible answer: Margaret, Stephen, and Richard are white and are the owners of the farm. Apparently, the farm has belonged to Stephen for a long time. From the story, the reader concludes that all the farm workers are black and live in a compound on the farm. They seem to be cared for by the family, but there is no social interaction, and none of the workers' characters are developed.

The Train from Rhodesia

Selection Test (page 245)

Recall and Interpret

(40 points total; 8 points each)

1. c
2. b
3. d
4. c
5. a

Vocabulary Practice

(20 points total; 5 points each)

6. c
7. b
8. c
9. b

Analyze and Evaluate

(21 points total; 7 points each)

Answers will vary. Possible answers:

10. The people at the station are poor, black, undernourished, and hopeful that the train will bring some improvement in their fortunes, either through goods sold or charity received.

11. The train passengers are white and privileged, traveling in comfort and isolation through parts of a country with cultures that most have never experienced firsthand.

12. The train serves to symbolize the differences between the two groups: the whites protected and isolated by the glass and steel; the blacks exposed to the elements, seeking some sustenance from the sleek intruder into their domain. The train represents the power of the empire and the power of technology, both of which keep the races apart.

BIG IDEA Connect (20 points)

13. Answers will vary. Possible answer:

The woman may realize that what is just a diversion for her and her husband is more to the maker of the lion—it is his livelihood, his pride at stake. It may have taken this event for her to realize what her new husband is really like. She also may be considering the negative effect one culture (British) has had on another (native African).

Dead Men's Path

Selection Test (page 247)

Recall and Interpret

(40 points total; 10 points each)

1. a
2. c
3. c
4. d

Vocabulary Practice

(12 points total; 4 points each)

5. b
6. c
7. b

Answers

Analyze and Evaluate

(20 points total; 10 points each)

Answers will vary. Possible answers:

8. Important to Obi: progress

Supporting details: statements about getting rid of "superannuated" faculty, imposing higher new standards, and "improving" the school compound.

9. Important to villagers: tradition

Supporting details: village priest's explanation about the historical meaning of the sacred path, diviner's interpretation of the young woman's death, villagers' insistence on maintaining their old ways

BIG IDEA Connect (28 points)

10. Answers will vary. Possible answer:

Most students will agree that one culture or group does not have the right to force its values and ideas on another. They might cite current events or situations in their school or neighborhoods as support for their arguments. Students should also refer to the story.

Telephone Conversation

Open-Book Selection Test (page 249)

Recall and Interpret

(40 points total; 8 points each)

1. a
2. d
3. b
4. c
5. c

Vocabulary Practice

(20 points total; 5 points each)

6. c
7. a
8. a
9. b

Analyze and Evaluate

(20 points total; 5 points each)

10. The caller is a sensitive, intelligent, witty person.

11. He knows from the "silence" he hears when he says he's African that the landlady is taken aback. He knows his "self-confession" might pose a challenge to the woman, because he's probably had similar experiences in the past. When the woman asks about his degree of darkness, he can hardly believe the question is real but when he realizes it is, he becomes ironic, inventing a name for his shade and finally going on about the parts of his anatomy that are white. He defuses the woman's racism and maintains his dignity.

12. The woman is a prosperous, insensitive racist.

13. She reveals this by her questions about degrees of blackness, as though a person's skin color would reveal his character and reliability as a tenant.

BIG IDEA Connect (20 points)

14. The speaker has an ironic conversation with someone from whom he wants to rent a room. He "confesses" to being African, and she asks him point blank how dark he is, as if that had relevance to the issue of room rental. He answers her question, using vocabulary that she doesn't understand, and after she finally admits her ignorance, the comparison is developed in terms of chocolate. Further, he describes the varying colors of his body, finally saying, "Wouldn't you rather see for yourself?"

Two Sheep

Selection Test (page 251)

Recall and Interpret

(40 points total; 10 points each)

1. b
2. a
3. d
4. b

Vocabulary Practice

(15 points total; 5 points each)

5. c
6. a
7. b

Analyze and Evaluate

(20 points total; 10 points each)

Answers will vary. Possible answers:

8. First sheep:
- at the start of the story, accepts his mortality
- appreciates the beauty of life around him—the warm sun, the blue sky, and the natural grace of birds in flight
- when he accidentally escapes slaughter, becomes silent, timid, and fearful of life, like many humans who deprive themselves of the fullest experience

9. Second sheep:
- at the start, is unaware of his impending doom
- fusses over trivial things, like his physical comfort and the nature of his accommodations
- when he finally realizes that he's about to die, is able, like the first sheep at the start, to appreciate the beauty of life around him

BIG IDEA Connect (25 points)

10. Answers will vary. Possible answer:

The anthropomorphism used in the fable allows the writer to teach lessons about life in a way that will not offend people as a story with human characters might. Rather than expressing a single moral or lesson, this fable is complex and ambiguous. The first sheep and, later, the second sheep are happiest when they recognize their impending death, accept it, and try to enjoy their final moments. Yet when the first sheep escapes death, he becomes timid, silent, and fearful. The fable seems to be saying that we all accept our mortality in different ways, which leads us to different ways of living, none of which is perfect.

from **Tales of the Islands**

Open-Book Selection Test (page 253)

Recall and Interpret

(50 points total; 10 points each)

1. c

2. d

3. a

4. d

5. a

Vocabulary Practice

(10 points total; 5 points each)

6. b

7. a

Analyze and Evaluate

(20 points total; 10 points each)

Answers will vary. Possible answers:

8. "Folded in cloud"; touch and sight

9. "Silver glinting on the fuselage"; sight

BIG IDEA Connect (20 points)

10. Answers will vary but could include points similar to the following:
- The speaker feels affection for the island and apparently will miss it.
- He takes in every detail of the place and expresses love for those details, such as the mountains and sea.
- The place is very likely his home. He is probably heading to a place that is more cosmopolitan.
- The ending of the poem suggests that he will not get his wish that things will never change on the island.
- Although he prays for constancy, it has already rained or changed by the time he lands in Seawell, just a short distance away.
- He will probably be gone a long time; maybe he is going away to school.

Answers

B. Wordsworth

Selection Test (page 255)

Recall and Interpret

(36 points total; 6 points each)

1. c
2. b
3. d
4. b
5. c
6. c

Vocabulary Practice

(24 points total; 6 points each)

7. b
8. c
9. a
10. c

Analyze and Evaluate

(20 points total; 5 points each)

11. The narrator uses dialect to represent his speech as a young boy.

12. The mother speaks in dialect in contrast to the poet, who seems to be more educated. This may be parallel to her beating the little boy and her rudeness.

13. B. Wordsworth does not use dialect, nor does he correct the little boy; he is polite and seems to learn from everyone and every aspect of life.

14. The policeman's dialect seems to emphasize his lack of empathy for the poet and boy's "poetry."

BIG IDEA Connect (20 points)

15. B. Wordsworth says that his name is Black Wordsworth, in contrast to the white Wordsworth of British poetry. He takes the little boy into his world of nature and adventure, watching ants, eating mangoes, and telling him about his background. The poetry that he shares is poetry that can be enjoyed anywhere in the world. The stars are the same, although viewed from different perspectives, worldwide.

from *Imaginary Homelands*

Selection Test (page 257)

Recall and Interpret

(60 points total; 10 points each)

1. d
2. d
3. b
4. c
5. c
6. d

Analyze and Evaluate

(20 points total; 10 points each)

Answers will vary. Possible answers:

7. Rushdie notes that Indian British writers who are no longer in India or Pakistan or their places of origin face the challenge of sometimes feeling guilty for leaving and for not being involved in the day-to-day affairs of the countries they write about.

8. He says that the distance Indian British writers have can afford them fresh perspectives on their homelands and thus enrich the literature. He also points out that more and more writers are writing from places such as England, and are inevitably changing the Indo-British fiction.

BIG IDEA Connect (20 points)

9. Answers will vary but could include points similar to the following:

- He states that the English language must be embraced by British Indian writers.
- He acknowledges complexities in the issue, noting that Indian British writers must remake the language to suit their own needs. He points out that they cannot simply use the language the way the British did and do.
- He also points out that many writers feel a deep ambivalence about using English but that this ambivalence is productive, as it reflects other conflicts writers are portraying.
- He says that English has to be embraced, because it is the language of

future generations.
- He notes that in forging a new kind of English language, writers have much to lose and gain in the process of "translation."

Games at Twilight

Selection Test (page 259)

Recall and Interpret

(50 points total; 10 points each)

1. d
2. a
3. d
4. c
5. c

Vocabulary Practice

(10 points total; 2 points each)

6. c
7. a
8. c
9. b
10. b

Analyze and Evaluate

(20 points total; 10 points each)

Answers will vary. Possible answers:

11. Raghu: character traits / how revealed
- physically large and imposing / apparently older than the other children and possessed of "long, hefty, hairy footballer legs"
- hothead and bully / accusing Mira of cheating because he was "It"; kicking the smaller, younger Manu after Manu trip over a hose; shoving the much-smaller Ravi aside even at the end
- rough and insensitive / trampling on flowers as he stomps around looking for the children who are hiding

12. Mira: character traits / how revealed
- commands respect / is able to get the children organized into games when they are unruly
- "motherly" but can be bossy / deciding what games to play and what roles different children will play
- courageous / entering into the fights that occur among the younger boys and breaking them up
- not particularly sensitive to Ravi's situation and feelings / doesn't even notice he's missing

BIG IDEA Connect (20 points)

13. The story is an example of globalization in two primary ways. First the games that the children play are likely ones that were learned from the British when they occupied the country. Second, the story reveals the universality of human experience, as in the way that Ravi learns he did not win the game and that he has, in fact, been forgotten. The way the children pester their mother to go outside and the way they treat each other are both examples of the global human experience.

Elegy for the Giant Tortoises

Open-Book Selection Test (page 261)

Recall and Interpret

(48 points total; 12 points each)

1. d
2. b
3. d
4. c

Vocabulary Practice

(12 points total; 3 points each)

5. a
6. b
7. b
8. a

Analyze and Evaluate (20 points)

Answers will vary. Possible answers:

9. "subway stations"; has the effect of repeating *s* sounds, which convey a slithery, slippery feeling, reinforcing the idea that she cannot quite picture the tortoises when she wants to, because they are disappearing "plodding past"; has the effect of slowing the rhythm down by repeating *p* sounds reinforcing the sense of the tortoises' slowness

BIG IDEA Connect (20 points)

10. Answers will vary but could include points similar to the following:

- The disappearance of the giant tortoises from the earth is a global concern.
- The speaker also mourns the loss of other animals and peoples to extinction.
- The speaker meditates on humanity's indifference to the loss of so many species and concludes by saying we merely keep extinct creatures preserved in museums, as if that were enough.

Music Goes Global

Selection Test (page 263)

Recall and Interpret

(60 points total; 10 points each)

1. a
2. d
3. b
4. a
5. c
6. a

Analyze and Evaluate

(20 points total; 10 points each)

Answers will vary. Possible answers:

7. Asserting national cultures in the face of American domination; Britain, South Africa, Jamaica, and other places

8. Blending traditional and new genres of music; Tijuana, Colombia, Brazil, and elsewhere.

BIG IDEA Connect (20 points)

9. Answers will vary but could include points similar to the following:

- The author expresses an optimistic attitude toward the globalization of music.
- His tone throughout the article is celebratory and cheerful, reflecting his admiration for what musicians around the world are doing today.
- He describes how musicians around the world are drawing on different cultures, genres, and languages to create new forms of music, such as Ragga, Nortec, and a blend of samba and art-pop.
- He notes that musicians have always drawn on different musical traditions to good effect and that technology has simply made this happen at a much faster rate than before.
- Although he acknowledges that globalization has the power to threaten the individuality of local musical traditions, he concludes by saying that musicians are staying true to their roots even as they explore other forms of global music.

Unit 1: The Anglo-Saxon Period and the Middle Ages, 449–1485

Open-Book Unit Test (page 265)

Part A. (40 points total; 20 points each)

Answers will vary. Model answers follow.

1. Beowulf's major talent lies in his fighting skills. He is extraordinarily strong and skillful in hand-to-hand combat and sword fighting. These skills would be most useful in a warrior society.

Sir Gawain's major quality is that he is a good and perfect knight. He offers himself in place of Arthur to fight the Green Knight and then behaves impeccably—or almost impeccably—with the Green Knight's wife. His qualities would make him a welcome member of any society.

2. In *The Seafarer*, the speaker's heart and soul call him to set sail for far-off countries despite the fact that he is usually fearful and miserable while on board ship. In his view, this is his fate, or God's will, and he is at the mercy of fate and God because they are stronger than "any man's mind."

In *The Canterbury Tales*, Chaucer's pilgrims set out in a more lighthearted manner, motivated by the wanderlust brought on by the awakening of the earth at the end of winter. They set off for the shrine at Canterbury for a variety of reasons, but many demonstrate their love of God and describe the power of faith as they talk to each other and tell their stories.

3. The Wife of Bath thinks that women will find happiness if they have authority over their husbands; she also thinks that women cannot keep secrets. She has been married five times and finally gained dominance over her fifth husband before he died.

Like the Wife of Bath, the wife in "Get Up and Bar the Door" is engaged in a struggle to gain dominance over her husband. The two make a pact that the first person to say a word will get up and bar the door, and unlike Midas's wife in "The Wife of Bath's Tale," this wife proves highly capable of keeping her mouth shut. When two robbers threaten to cut off the old man's beard and kiss his wife, the old man finally breaks down and protests. The wife, ignoring the robbers, is concerned only about her victory over her husband.

Part B. (20 points total; 5 points each)
Model answer for "Sir Patrick Spens":

4. Who dies: Sir Patrick Spens

5. How: His ship goes down in a storm.

6. Effects: The mission Sir Patrick was on presumably fails. Sir Patrick's crew all die with him. The wives of his men will wait in vain for their husbands to return.

7. Message: This poem depicts a world in which nobles do what their king asks of them no matter what the cost. Although this trip costs Sir Patrick and his men their lives, their fame lives on through this ballad.

Part C. (20 points total; 10 points each)
Model answer for Margery Kempe:
Mistake: She let the devil convince her not to confess her sins, so they festered.
Consequences: She went mad until she was saved by her vision of Jesus.

Part D. (20 points)
Model answer for Sir John Graeme in "Bonny Barbara Allan":
Struggle: He struggles to win some sympathy from the woman he loves, Barbara Allan.
Win or lose: He loses.
Characteristics: Sir John is an example of the medieval chivalrous knight; he dies for love. There is also some indication that he spoke improperly about his love in toasts in the pub.

Unit 2: The English Renaissance, 1485–1650

Open-Book Unit Test (page 267)

Part A. (40 points total; 20 points each)

1. Model answer for "To His Coy Mistress" and "The Constant Lover":

In "To His Coy Mistress," the speaker argues that he and his beloved don't have all the time in the world, so they should get on with their lives and "seize the day." I found his argument effective mainly because he does an excellent job of moving my emotions. He convinces me that his beloved truly is worth the effort it would take to court her forever, if he had forever; that old age and death are creeping up on them; and that he is truly devoted to his beloved and wants far more from her than just a fling. These arguments not only provoke an emotional response but also make sense. The speaker also seems like the kind of person to whom a woman would not regret devoting herself: fun-loving, witty, confident, intelligent, and caring.

In "The Constant Lover," the speaker argues that there's never been a more loyal lover than he, but he appears to have his tongue in his cheek. The speaker is clearly a womanizer whose so-called devotion will last only until he lays eyes on some prettier face, since his devotion seems to be based entirely on his beloved's face. He is amazed at himself for devoting three whole days to one woman as opposed to his usual "dozen dozen." It is clear that he is used to being constantly—not constant—in love and that it is simply a matter of time before he returns to his former self.

Reason and logic were more important to writers in this period than to previous writers because of the humanist belief in the vast abilities of people to think and solve problems. People felt more in control of their fates and tried to improve their lives through reasoning.

2. Model answer for "On Monsieur's Departure" and "Sonnet 30":

These two poems, one written by the queen herself and the other by Edmund Spenser, who attended Elizabeth's court, transform painful subjects into little gems that courtiers could admire. Elizabeth's poem "On Monsieur's Departure" deals with the departure from court of a man whom Elizabeth admired and perhaps loved; she certainly responds negatively to his leaving, but she cannot show her feelings openly, writing, "I grieve and dare not show my discontent." This complaint in line 1 is followed by a series of clever oppositions that describe her divided state: She loves but must seem to hate; she is outwardly silent but inwardly turning the matter over and over; she cannot be herself. The poem's cleverness is also found in Elizabeth's control of the form, rhyme scheme, and rhythm of each line. She also uses literary devices such as personification and paradox. In this way she is able to wittily compliment the departed Monsieur to a public and approving court, yet keep the depth of her feelings to herself.

"Sonnet 30" deals with another painful subject, unrequited love. Surely everyone in court who heard or read the sonnet knew the pain of rejected love and understood the long, thoughtful series of contradictions around which the poem is constructed. Throughout the poem is imagery about the speaker's fiery love and his beloved's icy response. Spenser's mastery of the complicated problem-solution format is clear, with the first twelve lines presenting the problem and the couplet commenting on it. His ability to play by the rules of the sonnet is also clear. "Sonnet 30" is not just a lament that love can drive someone to these unpleasant sensations; it is also a display of poetic talent that the court would appreciate and that other courtiers would try to imitate.

3. Model answer for "On My First Son" and "To the Virgins, to Make Much of Time":

Ben Jonson's poem "On My First Son" expresses his deep sadness at the death of his son in his seventh year and makes the point that children are merely "lent" to their parents. The idea that one should "seize the day" is relevant to the speaker's situation and the feelings expressed because the speaker's time with his child was so brief.

In "To the Virgins, to Make Much of Time," Robert Herrick's tone is lighter, and his subject matter—how quickly beauty fades—is not as serious as the death of a child. He speaks with tongue in cheek to beautiful young women who reject the love of young men, scolding them lightly and warning them that someday they'll have no beauty to attract lovers. This is why they should "seize the day." Jonson comforts himself with the thought that his son has escaped the hard things of life. Herrick doesn't want to miss a day of life with its potential for pleasure.

Part B. (20 points)

Model answer for "Whoso List to Hunt":
Metaphor: "Whoso list to hunt, I know where is an hind"
Compares: the hunt to the lover's pursuit of the beloved; the hind, or female deer, to the beloved
Communicates the ideas that

- the relationship between a man and a woman is like that of hunter and hunted

and the man (the hunter) will be frustrated if he cannot win the woman (the hind)
- women are like a wild and shy animal, beautiful but hard to keep and tame

Part C. (20 points)
Model answer for "Sonnet 130":
Problem: The speaker's beloved is not as fair as the sun; her skin is not white as snow; her breath is not sweet as perfume. The poet can't use the traditional words of love to describe her and stay honest.
Solution: The speaker argues that false praise isn't what makes a woman beautiful. He loves this woman, and to him she is "rare," one of a kind, perfect as she is.
Opinion: I agree with this solution. Beauty is in the eye of the beholder. No one is perfect, but love makes an imperfect person seem beautiful.

Part D. (20 points)
Model answer:
MACBETH/Early:
- courageous in battle
- unsure of himself off the battlefield
- ambitious
- susceptible to manipulation
- troubled by conscience
- weaker than his wife

MACBETH/Late:
- courageous in battle
- confident in himself
- ambitious to hold on to power
- corrupt, evil, cruel
- a murderer
- not troubled by his conscience
- stronger than his wife

LADY MACBETH/Early:
- scheming and ambitious
- unlikable
- a murderer
- not troubled by her conscience
- stronger than her husband

LADY MACBETH/Late:
- deeply thoughtful
- miserably unhappy
- plagued by conscience
- going mad
- suicidal
- weaker than her husband

Unit 3: From Puritanism to the Enlightenment, 1640–1780

Open-Book Unit Test (page 269)

Part A. (40 points total; 20 points each)

1. Model answer for *A Modest Proposal*:

A Modest Proposal is a very effective work of criticism. Swift makes his indictment of British policy in Ireland both scathing and witty. His speaker's proposal to feed Irish children to the rich is surprisingly strong from a purely economic standpoint, which would have pleased readers of this period, to whom logic mattered. However, like British policy in Ireland, the proposal has one fatal flaw: It is fundamentally inhumane. By suggesting in a darkly comic way that cannibalism might be an improvement on British policy in Ireland, Swift does a masterly job of driving home the cruelty of British policies.

2. Model answer for *A Modest Proposal* and Lady Montagu's "Letter to Her Daughter":

A Modest Proposal is such a bitter indictment of British policy in Ireland that the reader is completely convinced of Swift's revulsion for his speaker and the heartless "powers that be" who crafted and supported such brutal policies.

In "Letter to Her Daughter," Lady Montagu's belief about the importance of raising a daughter for the station she is most likely to hold later in life comes across loud and clear. She explains to her daughter that she was raised to be a wife but that her own daughter is not likely to become a wife and so should be raised in a different manner. She gives sensible reasons for her beliefs and uses metaphors that clearly support her opinions. She obviously feels strongly about her subject and would like to convince her daughter to come to the same conclusions.

3. Model answer for Pope's epigrams and Dryden's *Essay of Dramatic Poesy*:

Pope's epigrams speak to modern readers. Like all good epigrams, these reflect an understanding of the human condition, which doesn't change much from century to century. The epigrams give advice as useful to us today as it was to the people of the time in which they were written.

Dryden's *Essay of Dramatic Poesy*, however, is outdated in a number of ways. Although Dryden's ideas are relatively simple, his old-fashioned style makes these ideas nearly impenetrable to modern readers. The essay is also outdated in that few modern readers have even heard of some of the playwrights he admires, such as Beaumont and Fletcher.

Part B. (20 points)

Model answer for Milton and Addison:

Milton's portrayal of the disaster that befell humankind in *Paradise Lost* has much to say about absolute obedience to an absolute authority. It is because Satan wants "to set himself in glory above his peers" that humans lose paradise and become subject to death. Satan cannot accept the order of things decreed by God, and his rebellion brings death to humans and damnation to himself. This text seems to argue that people must accept the wisdom of the social order led by the king, who rules by divine right, and not disturb it or disaster might follow.

Joseph Addison, in his essay "Country Manners," expresses a more liberal point of view. Of course, he is not discussing morals, as he is quick to make clear, but merely "behavior and good breeding." Still, he asserts that "a certain openness of behavior" is now the norm in the city, whereas country dwellers remain "encumbered with show and ceremony." Addison is happier in a fashionable world that prefers a more "free and easy" way of life, in which not so much attention is paid to rank and precedence.

Part C. (20 points)

Model answer for Samuel Pepys and the narrator of *A Journal of the Plague Year*:

Samuel Pepys is at first mildly entertained by the London fire and is then very much distressed by it. This is because it seems at first to be an ordinary fire that will not affect anyone he knows. His distress increases as the fire engulfs more and more of the city, including important monuments, public buildings, and the homes of his friends, and as it advances toward his own home. Pepys comes to feel more a part of the city as all its inhabitants suffer together.

The narrator of *A Journal of the Plague Year* is, depending on one's point of view, curious about, morbidly fascinated by, or obsessed with the plague epidemic. This is probably because the plague has killed so many people in his parish in such a horrible manner in such a short period of time. It would be a wonder if anyone in such a situation were capable of focusing on anything else.

Part D. (20 points total; 10 points each)

Model answer for the speaker in *A Modest Proposal*:

Description of attitude:

- feeling of superiority over others
- mask of false compassion for others
- logic without feeling of shared humanity
- smug belief that he knows what is best for others

Words or phrases that indicate attitude:

- calling Irish mother a "dam" and referring to birth as "dropped from its dam"
- references to "computation" and

"calculation" to show off supposed intelligence
- assuming that Irish women abort babies "more to avoid the expense than the shame"
- "I shall now therefore humbly propose my own thoughts," ironic because he is proud of his proposal

Unit 4: The Triumph of Romanticism, 1750–1837

Open-Book Unit Test (page 271)

Part A. (40 total points; 20 points each)

1. Model answer for "Lines Composed a Few Miles Above Tintern Abbey":

This poem displays many of the characteristics of Romantic poetry, such as valuing the individual over society, the natural over the artificial, and emotions over logic. The poem focuses on an individual's response to nature and clearly shows the speaker's preference for simple country life over "the din / Of towns and cities." The speaker remarks that his memories of the natural beauty around Tintern Abbey have given him "that blessed mood, / . . . In which the heavy and the weary weight / Of all this unintelligible world, / Is lightened." The speaker has a highly emotional response to the natural beauty he sees. The poem might be summed up in the lines "Nature never did betray / The heart that loved her"—a truly Romantic thought.

2. Model answer for Byron and Shelley:

The poets in this unit use similes to create vivid descriptions. For example, Byron, describing a beautiful woman, says, "She walks in beauty, like the night." This description conveys the sense of the dark, somewhat mysterious beauty of the woman. In "Ode to the West Wind," Shelley uses this simile: "The wingèd seeds, where they lie cold and low, / Each like a corpse within its grave." This simile lends a somber mood to the poem, reinforces the seasonal setting, and emphasizes the theme that winter is like death but spring will bring a resurrection.

3. Model answer for "Ozymandias":

In Shelley's "Ozymandias," the real event described in the poem is an encounter with an ancient Egyptian statue of a pharaoh who at one time ruled the known world. The sculptor celebrated this man and his power. Thousands of years after the creation of the statue, Shelly presents the irony of the situation: The statue is crumbled and the long-dead Ozymandias is no longer "king of kings" but a forgotten tyrant. This natural event—the slow weathering and decay over time of a man-made artifact by natural forces—takes on the meaning that all the trappings of human power and arrogance must inevitably fail and fade with the passage of time. Shelley has made an observed scene stand for much more, presenting his views on the nature and power of mortality.

Part B. (20 points)

Model answer for the excerpts from *A Vindication of the Rights of Woman* and *Pride and Prejudice*:

The excerpts from *A Vindication of the Rights of Woman* and *Pride and Prejudice* display the lives of one group of relatively powerless people in this time period: women, especially young women. Mary Wollstonecraft addresses the problems that women face as they attempt to live meaningful, virtuous lives. Without education, prospects for gainful employment, and respect for their mature understanding, Wollstonecraft argues, women cannot be good wives to their husbands or good mothers to their children. She complains that girls are taught to be pretty and sweet and graceful in order to get husbands who will then support them, when they should be taught to be rational instead. All the feminine graces prized at this time kept women in a state of perpetual childhood, dependent on men to make important decisions for them and to guide their morality. Until this situation is changed, Wollstonecraft says, women are nothing more than grown-up children to be used and abused however the men in their lives decide.

In *Pride and Prejudice*, Jane Austen tackles the same idea, using a very different approach. The gentle satire of her fictional story deals with the marriage question for five daughters who have been raised just as Wollstonecraft describes: to be ornaments to their husbands. For this reason, arranging good marriages for them is a critical task for their mother. The daughters can't exist in a socially acceptable fashion on their own and aren't trained or expected to make their own way in the world. They are prisoners of social norms and pawns in the marriage game. But Austen hints that things could be different by creating the character of Mr. Bennet, who shows a clear preference for his daughter Elizabeth, the smartest and most practical of his children. This is the kind of woman that Austen and Wollstonecraft admire—virtuous because she is intelligent and reasonable.

The question of self-determination, of the individual's right to determine his or her own life rather than to do what society dictates, is part of the Romantic emphasis on the individual over the group.

Part C. (20 points)

Model answer:

Fanny Burney's diary entries describe the life of a young woman who has just had a novel published anonymously to huge success. As a result, she is invited to the houses of important people to meet other stars of the literary world. She describes how she listens to people discuss her book, not being aware that they are in the presence of the author. She visits a bookstore and enjoys seeing her book on display. A young woman today would be less likely to have her book published anonymously, although anonymous publication still occurs and still provokes rumor and gossip. In any case, her experiences would probably be much the same. She would be invited to the houses of important people. She would visit bookstores to see her book and would be excited by knowing her words were on everyone's lips.

In *Pride and Prejudice*, the importance of social rank is clear. People's attention and time are valued according to their position in society and their wealth. Mr. Bennet may call on Mr. Bingley because Mr. Bennet is established in the community and is older; however, Mr. Bingley's wealth makes his schedule more important than the Bennets' schedule. The women can't visit on their own at all, as this would be very improper. Today such distinctions are less important and less rigid, although they haven't disappeared. People of many classes, careers, and backgrounds are more likely to mingle without regard for rules of behavior.

Part D. (20 points)

Model answer:

This individual: Mrs. Bennet

Feels: deep responsibility and an almost desperate desire

About: the successful marriages of her five daughters

Why: She feels this way because she lives in a world where women cannot safely or respectably be on their own, where unmarried women are a burden to their families and often scorned by the community because they have failed to make a successful match. She feels this way as well because she loves and is proud of her daughters.

Answers

Unit 5: The Victorian Age, 1837–1901

Open-Book Unit Test (page 273)

Part A. (40 points total; 20 points each)

1. Possible points for an answer based on Elizabeth Barrett Browning's "Sonnet 43" and Edna St. Vincent Millay's "Love Is Not All: It Is Not Meat nor Drink":

- Both emphasize the importance of romantic love.
- Both also make use of the sonnet, a traditional form for expressing courtship.
- Browning's poem catalogs the ways the speaker loves her lover and affirms that she will love him more after death, if that is possible. The tone of this poem is stately. The attitude is idealistic.
- Millay's tone is more casual, and she expresses more ambivalence about love than the speaker in "Sonnet 43." The attitude is realistic.

2. Possible points based on Alfred, Lord Tennyson's "Crossing the Bar" and Lewis Carroll's "Jabberwocky":

- Tennyson's poem seems the most traditional to me.
- Tennyson uses a traditional poetic structure, with regular stanzas and rhyme scheme.
- His subject and theme is also traditional, affirming Victorian values, and his tone is stately. For example, he uses a regular *abab* rhyme scheme in "Crossing the Bar," and he expresses a desire to see Christ after he dies.
- "Jabberwocky" strikes me as the most contemporary of the Victorian selections.
- Although Carroll uses a traditional rhyme scheme and regular stanzas in the poem, his subject—killing an imaginary creature—is unusual.
- Moreover, his exuberant tone and use of made-up words make his poem seem modern.

3. Possible points based on John Lennon and Paul McCartney's "In My Life" and Gerard Manley Hopkins's "Spring and Fall: To a Young Child":

- The speaker in Lennon and McCartney's song, pays tribute to his true love but also to the places he remembers from his earlier life.
- His reasons for paying tribute to his true love are the usual ones—she is more important to him than anything else—but in comparing her to places, lovers, and friends that are also important to him, he pays tribute to all of them. He may want to pay tribute to the places, lovers, and friends because he wants to remind himself not to forget them.
- The speaker in Hopkins's poem, pays tribute to a young girl's grief "Over Goldengrove unleaving," or over the departure of summer and the coming of winter. He enlarges this theme to pay tribute to sorrow itself.
- His reason for paying this tribute is to touch the heart of the reader as his heart is touched by the child's sadness. In articulating her reasons for mourning, he articulates his own and the reader's reasons for mourning and gives them voice.

Part B. (20 points total; 10 points each)

Answers will vary. Possible answers:

4. Selection: *Jane Eyre*

Character who embraces life: Jane Eyre

What makes you think this: Despite her circumstances, Jane is a curious, observant, loving child who would give the crumbs of her breakfast to a hungry robin. When asked how she should avoid falling into Hell, she answers,

"I must keep in good health, and not die." Her instincts are to defend herself against injustice rather than to give in to it.

5. Selection: "Dover Beach"
Character who fears life: the speaker
What makes you think this: The world as the speaker sees it "Hath really neither joy, nor love, nor light, / Nor certitude, nor peace, nor help for pain." The possibility of faith no longer exists. His only hope is that he and his love will be true to each other and so provide some comfort in an otherwise comfortless world.

Part C. (20 points total; 10 points each)
Answers will vary. Possible answers:

6. Selection: *Oliver Twist*
Societal problems: poverty; mistreatment of the poor by the rich, who exploit them as cheap labor; particular mistreatment of orphans
How author creates sympathy: Dickens portrays Oliver's experiences in the workhouse. He shows Oliver suffering repeatedly at the hands of greedy board members who starve the children and use them essentially as slaves. In addition, Dickens uses irony and exposition to elucidate the problems.

7. Selection: *Jane Eyre*
Societal problems: mistreatment of orphans; extreme differences in treatment according to class; sexist treatment of girls
How author creates sympathy: Brontë portrays Jane's plight while in the care of Mrs. Reed, who exploits Jane's vulnerable position by making her work as a servant in the household. She also shows Jane standing up for herself against Mrs. Reed's cruel treatment and makes it clear that Jane's options are limited, since she is not a rich girl.

Part D. (20 points total; 10 points each)
Answers will vary. Possible answers:

8. Selection: *Oliver Twist*
Example: "What a noble illustration of the tender laws of England! They let the paupers go to sleep!"
Type of irony: verbal
Effect: It satirically conveys how awful the conditions were for orphans and the poor in Victorian England. The narrator means the opposite of what he says.

9. Selection: "Ah, Are You Digging on My Grave?"
Example: The dog apologizes to his former owner for digging on her grave and explains that he was just trying to bury a bone there because he'd forgotten she was buried there.
Type of irony: situational
Effect: It heightens the impact of the message that the dead are soon forgotten. In the poem, even the dog—a model of loyalty—forgets his old mistress, and the irony creates an effect that is both humorous and chilling.

Unit 6: The Modern Age, 1901–1950

Open-Book Unit Test (page 275)

Part A. (40 points total; 20 points each)

1. Possible points for an answer based on "The Parable of Lazarus and the Rich Man" and George Orwell's "Shooting an Elephant":

- Both explore how class differences result in vastly different experiences.
- Both also imply that one's class is randomly assigned—in other words, whether one is rich or poor, British or Burmese, is a matter of luck, not entitlement.
- Both emphasize the misery that extreme class differences can cause for everyone.
- "The Parable of Lazarus" ascribes rewards in the afterlife to those who have suffered poverty on earth and punishment in the afterlife to those who have enjoyed earthly wealth.
- Orwell's essay describes his experiences as an official in the British colony of Burma. He shows how the idea of

colonial power is a myth in the day-to-day reality of colonial life.
- Orwell expresses the belief that all freedom is destroyed for both parties when rigid colonialism creates class differences.

2. Possible points based on Sigfried Sassoon's "Dreamers" and Wilfred Owen's "Dulce et Decorum Est":
- Both speakers are adversely affected by their experiences.
- The speaker in Sassoon's poem pictures soldiers suffering in "foul dugouts, gnawed by rats" while they dream of returning to the peace and banality of home.
- The speaker in Owen's poem is similarly haunted by the memory of a fellow soldier dying from gas poisoning.
- The speaker in Sassoon's poem seems sad and angry but self-possessed.
- The speaker in Owen's poem seems visibly scarred: He describes the nightmare of war in detail, and he is enraged by the idea that dying for one's country is considered sweet and honorable.

3. Possible points based on W. B. Yeats's "Sailing to Byzantium" and W. H. Auden's "Musée des Beaux Arts":
- Both poems emphasize the central importance of art in life.
- Both poems also imply that great art has a lasting impact.
- In "Sailing to Byzantium," the speaker expresses a desire to take the form of an art object such as "Grecian goldsmiths make" rather than a human body, which will decay over time.
- The speaker values the permanence of art and its function as a form of entertainment.
- Auden's poem expresses the idea that the Old Masters were right about suffering and how indifferent human beings are to each other's plights. The poem suggests that part of the function of art is to depict human experiences, such as suffering, in an unflinching, unsentimental way.
- Both poems suggest that art is consoling and that the function of art is to provide solace in the face of despair.

Part B. (20 points total; 10 points each)
Answers will vary. Possible answers:

4. Selection: "Preludes"
Speaker and subject: an unnamed speaker who describes the gritty world of working- or middle-class
Tone: bitter and melancholic
Ideas about modern life: The poem presents modern life as dreary and desolate.

5. Selection: "The Unknown Citizen"
Speaker and subject: an unnamed speaker describes the unknown citizen, a deceased man who lived a perfectly average life
Tone: ironic
Ideas about modern life: The poem satirizes the absurdity of modern life and shows how contemporary society erodes people's individuality and spirit.

Part C. (20 points)
Answers will vary. Points for possible answers:
Rupert Brooke's "The Soldier":
- Brooke's poem focuses on the possibility of dying while serving England during World War I.
- The speaker anticipates feeling a sense of peace should he die for England.
- The speaker's fervent patriotism and good memories of England make him feel that no matter what happens, he will be fine.

Paul Fussell's *The Great War and Modern Memory*:

- Fussell handles the subject of war in this excerpt by describing the trenches used during World War I.
- He expresses optimism in his tone of admiration for the ingenuity displayed by the soldiers who created the system of trenches.
- Rather than focusing on how grisly the war was, Fussell emphasizes the physical and psychological resourcefulness of the soldiers in combat and marvels at how intricate the trench system was.

Part D. (20 points)
Answers will vary. Points for possible answers Yeats's "The Second Coming":

- The main psychological characteristics of the speaker in Yeats's poem are fearfulness and a deep sense of dread.
- Yeats conveys these characteristics by having the speaker describe how he sees the world at present and his vision of an apocalyptic future.
- He uses symbolism to heighten the impact of his poem. For example, the "rough beast" symbolizes a force of evil.
- He also uses trochaic meter to emphasize the speaker's sense that things are not right.
- This poem gave me a sense of dread. Although the speaker could be dismissed as paranoid, he creates a powerful and frightening scenario.

Virginia Woolf's *Mrs. Dalloway*:

- The main psychological characteristics of Clarissa Dalloway are an intelligent self-awareness, a need to please others, and anxiety.
- Woolf conveys these characteristics by using stream of consciousness to show Clarissa's thoughts and feelings from moment to moment as she walks through London.
- This technique made me feel as if I were inside the character's head with all her worries and concerns.

Unit 7: An International Literature, 1950–Present

Open-Book Unit Test (page 277)

Part A. (40 points total; 20 points each)
Answers will vary.

1. Possible points for an answer based on Li-Young Lee's "Mnemonic" and Michael Ondaatje's "Photograph":

- Both works feature adult speakers who recall their parents with fondness.
- Both works also create a nostalgic mood.
- The mood of "Mnemonic" is also melancholy. The speaker recalls how he looked up to his father, who was both stern and loving.
- He remembers how his dad sometimes punished him and ruminates on how lonely he sometimes feels.
- The speaker chooses to focus on how his father showed him tenderness, although remembering his father is bittersweet.
- The mood of "Photograph" is more neutral or detached.
- The speaker looks for evidence of how well suited his parents were for each other. Although he finds this evidence, he expresses a bit of wistful sadness and implies that they didn't stay together long.
- The speaker in Ondaatje's work admires his parents' sense of fun and playfulness.

2. Possible points based on Stevie Smith's "Not Waving but Drowning" and Penelope Lively's "At the Pitt-Rivers":

- The speaker in Smith's poem describes the death of an unnamed man.
- The speaker's relationship to the dead man is not clear, but the speaker is able, in stanza 2, to report the comments of

the drowned man's acquaintances."

- The speaker expresses sadness and a sense of helplessness about the man and his death and suggests that he died from loneliness and despair rather than physical conditions.
- The narrator of Lively's story observes a couple he sees in a museum.
- Although he is at first repulsed by them because of the difference in their ages, he becomes curious about them and enjoys observing how in love they are.
- At the end of the story, the narrator is despondent because he has witnessed the couple's parting and the woman's great sadness.

3. Possible points based on Wole Soyinka's "Telephone Conversation" and Harold Pinter's "That's All":

- Both works use innovative techniques to portray modern life.
- Both works are also structured as conversations between two people. These conversations reveal important themes of contemporary life.
- Soyinka's poem focuses on a telephone conversation between a black man and a prospective white landlady.
- The conversation shows how racism plays out in day-to-day contemporary life.
- Soyinka uses free verse in the poem, breaking from traditional rhymed poetic forms.
- Pinter's play is very short, and he employs absurdism to make a point about how banal and meaningless everyday conversation often is in contemporary life.
- The play consists of a conversation between two women, in which one character, Mrs. B, mostly just says "yes" and "no."
- The conversation underscores how tenuous modern relationships are and how disconnected people can be from one another.

Part B. (20 points total; 10 points each)
Answers will vary. Possible answers:

4. Selection: "Follower"
Traditional themes: father-son relationship, how the son supplants the father when he becomes an adult, what we owe our ancestors
Traditional form: rhymed quatrains with *abab* rhyme scheme in each stanza
Why poet chose this form: Traditional form of rhymed quatrains suits traditional theme; movement of rhyme scheme, switching back and forth between *a* and *b* rhymes, mimics motion of plowing a field.

5. Selection: excerpt from *Tales of the Islands*
Traditional themes: longing for home, saying good-bye to one's homeland, nostalgia for the past
Traditional form: sonnet
Why poet chose this form: Sonnet is traditional for subjects of longing and mourning; he makes the form new by changing the rhyme scheme to create a hybrid of Italian and English sonnet forms.

Part C. (20 points)
Possible points based on excerpts from Derek Walcott's *Tales of the Islands* and Salman Rushdie's *Imaginary Homelands:*

- Walcott and Rushdie address the postcolonialist theme of longing for a home in a country that was once part of the British Empire.
- The speaker in Walcott's poem watches his home of St. Lucia literally recede from view as he flies to a destination that has presumably become his new home.
- He fears that the country he's leaving will change and thus implies that in

a postcolonial world old customs and traditions fade away.

- He also refers to French Creole customs in the poem, drawing on both his native land and the English literary tradition to express his views.
- The tone of the poem is nostalgic and sad, and Walcott's attitude is a bit rueful but resigned.
- Rushdie outlines the challenges Indian British writers face, especially as writers who live outside the Indian subcontinent.
- He describes longing for and writing about a home country that he has not lived in for many years.
- He notes that he and other postcolonial writers are changing the body of Indo-British fiction and that these writers hail from all over the world.
- His tone is challenging and informative, and his attitude toward the subject is observant and curious about how things are unfolding in the postcolonial world.

Part D. (20 points)

Possible points based on the excerpt from Salman Rushdie's *Imaginary Homelands* and Christopher John Farley's "Music Goes Global":

- Rushdie's attitude toward globalization seems to be one of resigned acceptance.
- In his essay, he focuses on how postcolonialism has affected him personally as an Indian British writer who was born in Bombay but grew up elsewhere and lives in London.
- Although Rushdie points out some of the complications of being an Indian British writer, such as the challenge of writing about India from a distance, he believes that writers in his position are changing Indo-British fiction.
- He also believes that Indian British writers need to embrace writing in English. He notes that English will continue to spread throughout the world and that the next generation will probably speak English as its first language.
- Farley is enthusiastic about the globalization of music, which is the subject he focuses on in his essay.
- He sees the cross-pollination of national musical genres as a very positive and exciting phenomenon.
- Although he acknowledges that some local culture may be lost in the process of globalization, he believes that musicians can both retain their roots and blend world cultures in their music.
- He notes that many contemporary musicians are recording albums in both English and other languages. He sees this bilingualism in music as a good thing.
- I agree more with Farley's ideas because I believe that the expansion of musical opportunities is a good thing for musicians and for listeners around the world.